G000243580

NEW CONCISE

PROJECT MATHS 3B

FOR LEAVING CERT ORDINARY LEVEL

GEORGE HUMPHREY, BRENDAN GUILDEA, GEOFFREY REEVES
LOUISE BOYLAN

 GILL EDUCATION

Gill Education
Hume Avenue
Park West
Dublin 12
www.gilleducation.ie

Gill Education is an imprint of M.H. Gill & Co.

© George Humphrey, Brendan Guildea, Geoffrey Reeves and
Louise Boylan 2012

978 07171 5359 6

Print origination by MPS Limited

All rights reserved.
No part of this publication may be copied, reproduced or transmitted in any
form or by any means without written permission of the publishers or else
under the terms of any licence permitting limited copying issued by the Irish
Copyright Licensing Agency.

Any links to external websites should not be construed as an endorsement
by Gill Education of the content or views of the linked materials.

For permission to reproduce photographs, the authors and publisher
gratefully acknowledge the following:

© Alamy: 29B, 40L; © Getty Images: 29T, 40R.

The authors and publisher have made every effort to trace all copyright
holders, but if any has been inadvertently overlooked we would be pleased to
make the necessary arrangement at the first opportunity.

Contents

Acknowledgments

The authors would like to thank Sorcha Forde, David Grimes, Elaine Guildea, Jessica Hayden, Colman Humphrey, Allison Lynch and Gráinne McKnight who helped with the proofreading, checked the answers and made many valuable suggestions that are included in the final text.

The authors also wish to express their thanks to the staff of Gill & Macmillan, and special thanks to Kristin Jensen, for her advice, guidance and untiring assistance in the preparation and presentation of the book.

Preface

New Concise Project Maths 3B is one of two books covering the new Leaving Certificate Ordinary Level course for students taking the 2014 exam and onwards. The second book is *New Concise Project Maths 3A*.

New Concise Project Maths 3B incorporates the approach to the teaching of mathematics envisaged in **Project Maths**. It reflects the greater emphasis on the understanding of mathematical concepts, developing problem-solving skills and relating mathematics to everyday events.

The authors strongly empathise with the main aims and objectives of the new Project Maths syllabus and examination. In the worked examples, a numbered, step-by-step approach is used throughout the book to help with problem solving. The constructions are demonstrated with excellent diagrams. There is a comprehensive range of carefully graded exercises to reflect the new exam. Exam-style in-context questions are included to enhance students' understanding of everyday practical applications of mathematics. The emphasis is on a clear and practical presentation of the material. Simple and concise language is used throughout, instead of technical language, which is not required in the exam.

Additional teachers' resources, including a **Digital Flipbook**, are provided online at www.gillmacmillan.ie.

An excellent resource for teachers and students is the dynamic software package **GeoGebra**. The package is of particular use for coordinate geometry, geometry and graphing functions. It can be accessed at www.geogebra.org.

George Humphrey
Brendan Guildea
Geoffrey Reeves
Louise Boylan
April 2012

CHAPTER 1

COMPLEX NUMBERS

Imaginary numbers, the symbol i

Consider the equations **(i)** $x^2 - 1 = 0$ and **(ii)** $x^2 + 1 = 0$.

(i) $x^2 - 1 = 0$
$$x^2 = 1$$
$$x = \pm\sqrt{1}$$
$$x = \pm 1$$

(ii) $x^2 + 1 = 0$
$$x^2 = -1$$
$$x = \pm\sqrt{-1}$$

The solution to the second equation, $x^2 + 1 = 0$, requires finding $\sqrt{-1}$. This is the problem. To overcome this problem, mathematicians invented a new number. They defined:

$$i = \sqrt{-1} \qquad \text{or} \qquad i^2 = -1$$

$$x^2 + 1 = 0$$
$$i^2 + 1 = 0 \qquad \text{(replace } x \text{ with } i)$$
$$-1 + 1 = 0 \qquad \text{(true, where } i^2 = -1)$$

The square root of a negative number is called an **imaginary** number, e.g. $\sqrt{-4}, \sqrt{-9}, \sqrt{-64}, \sqrt{-100}$ are imaginary numbers.

Imaginary numbers cannot be represented by a real number, as there is no real number whose square is a negative number.

All imaginary numbers can now be expressed in terms of i, for example:

$$\sqrt{-36} = \sqrt{36 \times -1} = \sqrt{36}\sqrt{-1} = 6i$$
$$\sqrt{-81} = \sqrt{81 \times -1} = \sqrt{81}\sqrt{-1} = 9i$$

Exercise 1.1
Express each of the following in the form ki, where $k \in \mathbb{N}$.

1. $\sqrt{-16}$ 2. $\sqrt{-9}$ 3. $\sqrt{-4}$ 4. $\sqrt{-25}$

5. $\sqrt{-64}$ 6. $\sqrt{-100}$ 7. $\sqrt{-49}$ 8. $\sqrt{-144}$

Complex numbers

A complex number has two parts, a **real** part and an **imaginary** part.

Some examples are $3 + 4i$, $2 - 5i$, $-6 + 0i$, $0 - i$.

Consider the complex number $4 + 3i$:

    4 is called the **real** part.

    3 is called the **imaginary** part.

Note: $3i$ is **not** the imaginary part.

> Complex number = (real part) + (imaginary part) i

The set of complex numbers is denoted by $\mathbb{C}$.

The letter z is usually used to represent a complex number. For example:

$$z_1 = 2 + 3i \qquad z_2 = -2 - i \qquad z_3 = -5i$$

If $z = a + bi$, then:

  (i) a is called the real part of z and is written $Re(z) = a$.

  (ii) b is called the imaginary part of z and is written $Im(z) = b$.

Note: u, v and w are also often used to denote complex numbers.

EXAMPLE

Write down the real and imaginary parts of each of the following complex numbers.

| **(i)** $3 + 2i$ | **(ii)** $-6 - 8i$ | **(iii)** 7 | **(iv)** $-5i$ |

Solution:

	Real part	Imaginary part
(i) $3 + 2i$	3	2
(ii) $-6 - 8i$	-6	-8
(iii) $7 = 7 + 0i$	7	0
(iv) $-5i = 0 - 5i$	0	-5

Note: i **never** appears in the imaginary part.

Exercise 1.2

Write down the real and imaginary parts of each of the following complex numbers.

1. $5 + 3i$
2. $2 + 5i$
3. $6 + 7i$
4. $5 + 4i$
5. $2 - 7i$
6. $-4 + 6i$
7. $-3 - 5i$
8. $-9 + 8i$
9. $2 + i$
10. $3 - i$
11. $-5 + i$
12. $-1 - i$
13. 6
14. $2i$
15. -2
16. $-5i$

Addition, subtraction and multiplication by a real number

To add or subtract complex numbers, do the following:

> Add or subtract the real and the imaginary parts separately.

Note: A real number is often called a scalar.

EXAMPLE

(i) If $u = 2 + 3i$ and $w = 1 - i$, express $2u + 3w$ in the form $a + bi$.

(ii) If $z_1 = 3 - 2i$ and $z_2 = 1 + i$, express $z_1 - 2z_2$ in the form $x + yi$.

Solution:

(i) $2u + 3w$

$= 2(2 + 3i) + 3(1 - i)$

$= 4 + 6i + 3 - 3i$

$= 4 + 3 + 6i - 3i$

$= 7 + 3i$

(ii) $z_1 - 2z_2$

$= (3 - 2i) - 2(1 + i)$

$= 3 - 2i - 2 - 2i$

$= 3 - 2 - 2i - 2i$

$= 1 - 4i$

Exercise 1.3

Write each of the following in questions 1–10 in the form $a + bi$, where $a, b \in \mathbb{R}$.

1. $2 + 3i + 4 + 2i$
2. $5 + 8i - 2 - 4i$
3. $11 + 3i - 5 + 4i$
4. $7 + 5i - 9 - 2i$
5. $-3 - 7i + 5 + 11i$
6. $5 + 2i + 4i - 8$
7. $2(4 + i) + 3(2 + i)$
8. $5(3 + 2i) + 2(1 + 3i)$
9. $2(2 - 3i) - 3(5 - i) + 11 + 6i$
10. $-2(-5 + 3i) + 5(1 + i) + i$

If $u = 2 + i$, $w = 3 - 2i$ and $z = 1 + i$, express questions 11–19 in the form $p + qi$, where $p, q \in \mathbb{R}$.

11. $u + w$ **12.** $u + z$ **13.** $w + z$

14. $u - i$ **15.** $w + 2i$ **16.** $w + 1$

17. $2u + z$ **18.** $w + 2z$ **19.** $3z - 2w + 3$

If $z_1 = 2 + 3i$, $z_2 = 1 - 5i$, $z_3 = 4$ and $z_4 = 2i$, express questions 20–25 in the form $x + yi$, where $x, y \in \mathbb{R}$.

20. $z_1 + z_2$ **21.** $z_2 + z_3$ **22.** $z_1 + z_4$

23. $2z_1 + z_2$ **24.** $2(z_3 + z_4)$ **25.** $z_3(z_2 - z_1)$

Multiplication of complex numbers

Multiplication of complex numbers is performed using the usual algebraic method, except:

> i^2 is replaced with -1.

EXAMPLE

(i) Simplify $4(2 - i) + i(3 + 5i)$ and write your answer in the form $x + yi$, where $x, y \in \mathbb{R}$.

(ii) If $u = 1 - 3i$ and $w = 2 + i$, express uw in the form $p + qi$, where $p, q \in \mathbb{R}$.

Solution:

(i) $4(2 - i) + i(3 + 5i)$

$= 8 - 4i + 3i + 5i^2$

$= 8 - 4i + 3i + 5(-1)$

(replace i^2 with -1)

$= 8 - 4i + 3i - 5$

$= 3 - i$

(ii) uw

$= (1 - 3i)(2 + i)$

$= 1(2 + i) - 3i(2 + i)$

$= 2 + i - 6i - 3i^2$

$= 2 + i - 6i - 3(-1)$

(replace i^2 with -1)

$= 2 + i - 6i + 3$

$= 5 - 5i$

Exercise 1.4

Express questions 1–15 in the form $a + bi$, where $a, b \in \mathbb{R}$ and $i^2 = -1$.

1. $2i(3 - 2i)$
2. $3i(4 + 2i)$
3. $i(-1 + 2i)$

4. $i(2 - 5i) + i - 1$
5. $2(3 - i) + i(4 + 5i)$
6. $4(2 - i) + i(3 + 5i)$

7. $(2 + 3i)(4 + i)$
8. $(3 + i)(2 + i)$
9. $(3 + 2i)(2 - 5i)$

10. $(6 - i)(4 - 3i)$
11. $(-3 - 4i)(2 - i)$
12. $(2 + 3i)(2 - 3i)$

13. $(2 + i)^2$
14. $(3 - 2i)^2$
15. $(5 + 2i)^2$

If $u = 2 + 3i$ and $w = 1 - i$, express questions 16–19 in the form $p + qi$, where $p, q \in \mathbb{R}$ and $i^2 = -1$.

16. uw
17. u^2
18. $2iu^2$
19. $w^2 - 2w$

If $z_1 = 1 + i$, $z_2 = -1 + 2i$ and $z_3 = 2 + 3i$, express questions 20–23 in the form $x + yi$, where $x, y \in \mathbb{R}$ and $i^2 = -1$.

20. $z_1 z_2$
21. $z_2 z_3$
22. $z_1 z_3$
23. $i \, z_1^2$

24. If $u = 2 + 3i$, where $i^2 = -1$, show that $u^2 - 4u + 13 = 0$.

Complex conjugate

Two complex numbers that differ only in the sign of their imaginary parts are called **complex conjugate numbers**, each being the conjugate of each other. For example, $-3 + 4i$ and $-3 - 4i$ are complex conjugates and each is called the conjugate of the other.

If z represents a complex number, the conjugate of z is denoted by $\bar{z}$ (pronounced 'z bar').

$$z = a + bi \qquad \Leftrightarrow \qquad \bar{z} = a - bi$$

To find the conjugate, simply **change the sign of the imaginary part only**. Do **not** change the sign of the real part.

For example, if $z = -2 - 5i$, then $\bar{z} = -2 + 5i$.

Note: If a complex number is added to or multiplied by its conjugate, the result will **always** be a real number. If complex conjugates are subtracted, the result is **always** an imaginary number.

EXAMPLE

If $z = -2 + 3i$, simplify the following.

(i) $z + \bar{z}$ (ii) $z - \bar{z}$ (iii) $z\bar{z}$

Solution:

If $z = -2 + 3i$, then $\bar{z} = -2 - 3i$ (change sign of imaginary part only).

(i) $z + \bar{z}$

$= (-2 + 3i) + (-2 - 3i)$

$= -2 + 3i - 2 - 3i$

$= -4$ (real number)

(ii) $z - \bar{z}$

$= (-2 + 3i) - (-2 - 3i)$

$= -2 + 3i + 2 + 3i$

$= 6i$ (imaginary number)

(iii) $z\bar{z}$

$= (-2 + 3i)(-2 - 3i)$

$= -2(-2 - 3i) + 3i(-2 - 3i)$

$= 4 + 6i - 6i - 9i^2$

$= 4 - 9(-1)$

$= 4 + 9$

$= 13$ (real number)

Exercise 1.5

Find $\bar{z}$ for each of the following in questions 1–8.

1. $z = 3 + 2i$ 2. $z = 4 - 3i$ 3. $z = -2 + 6i$ 4. $z = -3 - 7i$

5. $z = 1 - 5i$ 6. $z = -1 + 3i$ 7. $z = -4 - 5i$ 8. $z = -2 + 3i$

9. Let $u = (4 - 3i) - (-3 - 6i)$. Express $\bar{u}$ in the form $a + bi$, where $a, b \in \mathbb{R}$.

10. Let $w = (1 + i)(2 - i)$. Express $\bar{w}$ in the form $p + qi$, where $p, q \in \mathbb{R}$.

11. Let $z = (1 + 3i)^2$. Express $\bar{z}$ in the form $x + yi$, where $x, y \in \mathbb{R}$.

Find (i) $z + \bar{z}$ (ii) $z - \bar{z}$ (iii) $z\bar{z}$ for each of the following in questions 12–15.

12. $z = 4 + 5i$ 13. $z = 3 - 2i$ 14. $z = -4 + 2i$ 15. $z = -1 - i$

16. Let $z = 5 - 3i$. Find the real number k such that $k(z + \bar{z}) = 20$.

17. Let $u = 4 + i$. Find the real number p such that $p(z - \bar{z}) = 12i$.

18. $u = 2 + 3i$, where $i^2 = -1$. Evaluate $u + \bar{u} + u\bar{u}$.

19. If $w = 3 - 4i$, where $i^2 = -1$, show that $w^2 - 6w + w\bar{w} = 0$.

20. Let $u = 2 + i$ and $w = 3 - i$. Show that:

     (i) $u\bar{w} + \bar{u}w$ is a real number   (ii) $u\bar{w} - \bar{u}w$ is an imaginary number

21. If $u = 3 + 2i$, evaluate $\sqrt{u^2 + \bar{u}^2}$.

Division by a complex number

> Multiply the top and bottom by the conjugate of the bottom.

This will convert the complex number on the bottom into a real number. The division is then performed by dividing the real number on the bottom into each part on the top.

EXAMPLE

Express $\dfrac{1 + 7i}{4 + 3i}$ in the form $a + bi$, where $a, b \in \mathbb{R}$ and $i^2 = -1$.

Solution:

$\dfrac{1 + 7i}{4 + 3i} = \dfrac{1 + 7i}{4 + 3i} \times \dfrac{4 - 3i}{4 - 3i}$ (multiply top and bottom by the conjugate of the bottom)

Top by the top	Bottom by the bottom
$= (1 + 7i)(4 - 3i)$	$= (4 + 3i)(4 - 3i)$
$= 1(4 - 3i) + 7i(4 - 3i)$	$= 4(4 - 3i) + 3i(4 - 3i)$
$= 4 - 3i + 28i - 21i^2$	$= 16 - 12i + 12i - 9i^2$
$= 4 - 3i + 28i - 21(-1)$	$= 16 - 9(-1)$
$= 4 - 3i + 28i + 21$	$= 16 + 9$
$= 25 + 25i$	$= 25$

$\therefore \dfrac{1 + 7i}{4 + 3i} = \dfrac{25 + 25i}{25} = \dfrac{25}{25} + \dfrac{25}{25}i = 1 + i$

Exercise 1.6

Express questions 1–12 in the form $a + bi$, where $a, b \in \mathbb{R}$ and $i^2 = -1$.

1. $\dfrac{2 + 10i}{3 + 2i}$

2. $\dfrac{7 + 4i}{2 - i}$

3. $\dfrac{3 + 4i}{2 + i}$

4. $\dfrac{1 + 7i}{1 - 3i}$

5. $\dfrac{19 - 4i}{3 - 2i}$

6. $\dfrac{7 - i}{1 + i}$

7. $\dfrac{11 - 7i}{2 + i}$

8. $\dfrac{7 - 17i}{5 - i}$

9. $\dfrac{8 - 4i}{2 - i}$

10. $\dfrac{3 - 2i}{2 + 3i}$

11. $\dfrac{2 + i}{1 - i}$

12. $\dfrac{4 - 2i}{2 + i}$

13. $u = 9 + 7i$ and $w = 2 + i$. Express $\dfrac{u}{w}$ in the form $p + qi$, where $p, q \in \mathbb{R}$ and $i^2 = -1$.

14. $z_1 = 8 - 2i$ and $z_2 = 1 + i$. Express $\dfrac{z_1}{z_2}$ in the form $x + yi$, where $x, y \in \mathbb{R}$ and $i^2 = -1$.

15. $u = 3 + 2i$, $v = -1 + i$ and $w = u - v - 2$, where $i^2 = -1$.

Express the following in the form $a + bi$: **(i)** w　**(ii)** $\dfrac{2u + v}{w}$

16. Let $u = 2 - i$.

(i) Express $\left(u + \dfrac{5}{u} \right)$ in the form $a + bi$, where $a, b \in \mathbb{R}$ and $i^2 = -1$.

(ii) Hence, solve for k: $k\left(u + \dfrac{5}{u} \right) = 24$.

17. Let $z = \dfrac{1 + i}{1 - i}$. Evaluate z^2.

18. Let $u = 2 + i$, where $i^2 = -1$.

(i) Investigate if $\dfrac{5}{u} = \bar{u}$.

(ii) Express $\dfrac{u + 10i}{u}$ in the form $a + bi$, where $a, b \in \mathbb{R}$, and evaluate $\sqrt{a^2 + b^2}$.

(iii) Show that $iu + \dfrac{u}{i} = 0$.

19. Find the real part and the imaginary part of $\dfrac{-4 + 7i}{1 + 2i}$.

Equality of complex numbers

If two complex numbers are equal, then **their real parts are equal and their imaginary parts are also equal.**

For example, if $a + bi = c + di$, then $a = c$ and $b = d$.

This definition is useful when dealing with equations involving complex numbers.

Equations involving complex numbers are usually solved with the following steps.

---

1. Remove the brackets (if any).
2. Put an R under the real parts and an I under the imaginary parts to identify them.
3. Let the real parts equal the real parts and the imaginary parts equal the imaginary parts.
4. Solve these resultant equations (usually simultaneous equations).

Note: If one side of the equation does not contain a real part or an imaginary part, it should be replaced with 0 or $0i$, respectively.

EXAMPLE 1

(i) Let $w = 1 + i$. Express $\dfrac{6}{w}$ in the form $x + yi$, where $x, y \in \mathbb{Z}$ and $i^2 = -1$.

(ii) a and b are real numbers such that $a\left(\dfrac{6}{w}\right) - b(w + 1) = 3(w + i)$.

Find the value of a and the value of b.

Solution:

(i) $\dfrac{6}{w} = \dfrac{6}{1 + i}$ (multiply top and bottom by the conjugate of the bottom)

$= \dfrac{6}{1 + i} \times \dfrac{1 - i}{1 - i} = \dfrac{6 - 6i}{1 - i + i - i^2} = \dfrac{6 - 6i}{1 + 1} = \dfrac{6 - 6i}{2} = 3 - 3i$

(ii) $a\left(\dfrac{6}{w}\right) - b(w + 1) = 3(w + i)$

$a(3 - 3i) - b(1 + i + 1) = 3(1 + i + i)$ $\left(\text{put in } \dfrac{6}{w} = 3 - 3i \text{ and } w = 1 + i\right)$

$a(3 - 3i) - b(2 + i) = 3(1 + 2i)$

$3a - 3ai - 2b - bi = 3 + 6i$ (remove the brackets)

$\quad$ R $\quad$ I $\quad$ R $\quad$ I $\quad$ R $\quad$ I (identify real and imaginary parts)

Real parts $=$ **Real parts** $\qquad$ **Imaginary parts = Imaginary parts**

$3a - 2b \quad = \quad 3$ ① $\qquad\qquad\qquad -3a - b = 6$ ②

Now solve the simultaneous equations ① and ②.

$3a - 2b = 3$ ① $\qquad\qquad$ Put $b = -3$ into ① or ②.

$\underline{-3a - b = 6}$ ② $\qquad\qquad$ $3a - 2b = 3$ ①

$\qquad -3b = 9$ (add) $\qquad\qquad$ $3a - 2(-3) = 3$

$\qquad3b = -9$ $\qquad\qquad\qquad$ $3a + 6 = 3$

$\qquadb = -3$ $\qquad\qquad\qquad\qquad$ $3a = -3$

$\qquad\qquad\qquad\qquad\qquad\qquad\qquad$ $a = -1$

Thus, $a = -1$ and $b = -3$.

EXAMPLE 2

$z_1 = 4 - 2i$ and $z_2 = -2 - 6i$. If $z_2 - pz_1 = qi$, where $p, q \in \mathbb{R}$, find p and q.

Solution:

$$z_2 - pz_1 = qi$$

The right-hand side has no real part, hence a 0, representing the real part, should be placed on the right-hand side.

Now the equation is:

$$z_2 - pz_1 = 0 + qi \qquad \text{(put 0 in for real part)}$$

$$(-2 - 6i) - p(4 - 2i) = 0 + qi \qquad \text{(substitute for } z_1 \text{ and } z_2\text{)}$$
$$-2 - 6i - 4p + 2pi = 0 + qi \qquad \text{(remove the brackets)}$$
$$\text{R} \quad \text{I} \quad \text{R} \quad \text{I} \quad \text{R} \quad \text{I} \qquad \text{(identify real and imaginary parts)}$$

Real parts = Real parts   **Imaginary parts = Imaginary parts**

$$-2 - 4p = 0 \quad ① \qquad\qquad\qquad -6 + 2p = q \quad ②$$

Solve between the equations 1 and 2.

$$-2 - 4p = 0 \quad ①$$
$$-4p = 2$$
$$4p = -2$$
$$p = -\tfrac{2}{4} = -\tfrac{1}{2}$$

Substitute $p = -\tfrac{1}{2}$ into equation ②.
$$-6 + 2p = q$$
$$-6 + 2(-\tfrac{1}{2}) = q$$
$$-6 - 1 = q$$
$$-7 = q$$

Thus, $p = -\tfrac{1}{2}$, $q = -7$

Exercise 1.7

Solve questions 1–10 for x and y, where $i^2 = -1$ and $x, y \in \mathbb{R}$.

1. $2x + 3yi = 10 + 9i$
2. $5x - 4yi = 30 + 12i$
3. $4x - 5 + 3yi + 4i = 3 + 7i$
4. $x + y + xi + 2yi = 8 + 13i$
5. $(2x + y) + (3x - y)i = 7 + 3i$
6. $2(x + yi) + 2 - 5i = 4 + 3xi$
7. $(4x - 2) + i(x - 4) = 2(2 - y + yi)$
8. $x(3 + 4i) + 2y(2 + 3i) = 2i$
9. $x(2 + 3i) + y(4 + 5i) - 19i = 16$
10. $2x + 5yi = (1 - 3i)(4 + 2i)$

11. Find real k and l, such that $k(3 - 2i) + l(i - 2) = 5 - 4i$.

12. Find real p and q, such that $2p - q + i(7i + 3) = 2(2i - q) - i(p + 3q)$.

13. $z_1 = 4 - 3i$ and $z_2 = 5 + 5i$. Find real k and t such that $k(z_1 + z_2) = 18 + i(t + 2)$.

14. Let $z = 5 - 3i$. Find the real number k such that $ki + 4z = 20$.

15. Let $z = 1 - 2i$. Find the real numbers k and t such that $kz + t\bar{z} = 2z^2$.

16. Let $u = 2 - 3i$, where $i^2 = -1$. If $u + 3(p + 2qi) = 5 + 9i$, find p and q, where $p, q \in \mathbb{R}$.

17. (i) Let $w = -2 + i$. Express w^2 in the form $a + bi$, where $a, b \in \mathbb{R}$.

    (ii) Hence, solve for real k and t: $kw^2 = 2w + 1 + ti$.

18. (i) Let $z = 1 + i$. Show that $\dfrac{z}{\bar{z}} = i$.

    (ii) Hence, solve $k\left(\dfrac{z}{\bar{z}}\right) + tz = -3 - 4i$ for real k and t.

19. (i) Let $z_1 = 5 + 12i$ and $z_2 = 2 - 3i$. Show that $\dfrac{z_1}{z_2} = -z_2$.

    (ii) Hence, solve for real p and q: $\dfrac{z_1}{z_2} = p(q + i) + 1$.

20. (i) Let $w = 1 - i$. Express $\dfrac{4}{w}$ in the form $x + yi$, where $x, y \in \mathbb{R}$ and $i^2 = -1$.

    (ii) a and b are real numbers such that $a\left(\dfrac{4}{w}\right) - b(w + 1) = 2(w + 4)$. Find the value of a and the value of b.

21. Let $z = 6 - 4i$. Find the real numbers s and t such that $\dfrac{s + ti}{4 + 3i} = z$.

22. Solve $(x + 2yi)(1 - i) = 7 + 5i$ for real x and real y.

23. (i) Express $\dfrac{3 - 2i}{1 - 4i}$ in the form $x + yi$.

    (ii) Hence or otherwise, find the values of the real numbers p and q such that
    $$p + 2qi = \dfrac{17(3 - 2i)}{1 - 4i}.$$

24. Let $z = a + bi$, where $a, b \in \mathbb{R}$. Find the value of a and the value of b for which $3z - 10i = (2 - 3i)z$.

Quadratic equations with complex roots

When a quadratic equation cannot be solved by factorisation, the following formula can be used.

> The equation $ax^2 + bx + c = 0$ has roots given by:
> $$x = \frac{-b \pm \sqrt{b^2 - 4ac}}{2a}$$

Note: The whole of the top of the right-hand side, including $-b$, is divided by $2a$.
It is often called the **quadratic** or **$-b$ formula**.

If $b^2 - 4ac < 0$, then the number under the square root sign will be negative and so the solutions will be complex numbers.

EXAMPLE 1

Solve the equation   (i) $z^2 + 4z + 5 = 0$ (ii) $z^2 - 6z + 13 = 0$.
Write your answers in the form $x + yi$ where $x, y \in \mathbb{R}$.

Solution:

(i) $z^2 + 4z + 5 = 0$

$az^2 + bz + c = 0$

$a = 1, b = 4, c = 5$

$z = \dfrac{-b \pm \sqrt{b^2 - 4ac}}{2a}$

$z = \dfrac{-4 \pm \sqrt{(4)^2 - 4(1)(5)}}{2(1)}$

$z = \dfrac{-4 \pm \sqrt{16 - 20}}{2}$

$z = \dfrac{-4 \pm \sqrt{-4}}{2}$

$z = \dfrac{-4 \pm 2i}{2}$

$z = -2 \pm i$

(ii) $z^2 - 6z + 13 = 0$

$az^2 + bz + c = 0$

$a = 1, b = -6, c = 13$

$z = \dfrac{-b \pm \sqrt{b^2 - 4ac}}{2a}$

$z = \dfrac{6 \pm \sqrt{(-6)^2 - 4(1)(13)}}{2(1)}$

$z = \dfrac{6 \pm \sqrt{36 - 52}}{2}$

$z = \dfrac{6 \pm \sqrt{-16}}{2}$

$z = \dfrac{6 \pm 4i}{2}$

$z = 3 \pm 2i$

Note: Notice in both solutions the roots occur in conjugate pairs. If one root of a quadratic equation with real coefficients is a complex number, then the other root must also be complex and the conjugate of the first.

i.e. if $3 - 4i$ is a root, then $3 + 4i$ is also a root

if $-2 - 5i$ is a root, then $-2 + 5i$ is also a root

if $a + bi$ is a root, then $a - bi$ is also a root

EXAMPLE 2

Verify that $-2 + 5i$ is a root of the equation $z^2 + 4z + 29 = 0$ and find the other root.

Solution:

Method 1

If $-2 + 5i$ is a root, then when z is replaced by $-2 + 5i$ in the equation, the equation will be satisfied, i.e.

$$(-2 + 5i)^2 + 4(-2 + 5i) + 29 = 0$$

Check:

$$(-2 + 5i)^2 + 4(-2 + 5i) + 29$$
$$= (-2 + 5i)(-2 + 5i) + 4(-2 + 5i) + 29$$
$$= 4 - 10i - 10i - 25 - 8 + 20i + 29$$
$$= 33 - 33 + 20i - 20i$$
$$= 0$$

∴ $-2 + 5i$ is a root and

$-2 - 5i$ is the other root

(the conjugate of $-2 + 5i$)

Method 2

$$z^2 + 4z + 29 = 0$$

$a = 1, b = 4, c = 29$

$$z = \frac{-b \pm \sqrt{b^2 - 4ac}}{2a}$$

$$z = \frac{-4 \pm \sqrt{(4)^2 - 4(1)(29)}}{2(1)}$$

$$z = \frac{-4 \pm \sqrt{16 - 116}}{2}$$

$$z = \frac{-4 \pm \sqrt{-100}}{2}$$

$$z = \frac{-4 \pm 10i}{2}$$

$$z = -2 \pm 5i$$

∴ $-2 + 5i$ is a root and

$-2 - 5i$ is the other root

Sometimes we have to find unknown coefficients.

EXAMPLE 3

Let $z = 3 - 4i$ be one root of the equation $z^2 + pz + q = 0$, where $p, q \in \mathbb{R}$.
Find the value of p and the value of q.

Solution:
If $3 - 4i$ is a root, then $3 + 4i$ is also a root (roots occur in conjugate pairs).

Method: Form a quadratic equation with roots $3 - 4i$ and $3 + 4i$.

$$\text{Let } z = 3 - 4i \quad \text{and} \quad z = 3 + 4i$$

$\therefore \qquad\qquad z - 3 + 4i = 0 \qquad \text{and} \quad z - 3 - 4i = 0$

And $\qquad\qquad\qquad\qquad (z - 3 + 4i)(z - 3 - 4i) = 0 \qquad\qquad (0 \times 0 = 0)$

$$z(z - 3 - 4i) - 3(z - 3 - 4i) + 4i(z - 3 - 4i) = 0$$
$$z^2 - 3z - 4zi - 3z + 9 + 12i + 4zi - 12i - 16i^2 = 0$$
$$z^2 - 6z + 9 - 16(-1) = 0 \qquad\qquad (i^2 = -1)$$
$$z^2 - 6z + 25 = 0$$

By comparing $\qquad z^2 - 6z + 25 = 0 \quad \text{to} \quad z^2 + pz + q = 0$
$$p = -6 \quad \text{and} \quad q = 25$$

Note: An alternative method is to substitute $3 - 4i$ into the equation $z^2 + pz + q = 0$, equate the coefficients and solve these equations.

Exercise 1.8

Solve each of the following equations in questions 1–12.

1. $x^2 - 6x + 13 = 0$
2. $z^2 - 2z + 10 = 0$
3. $x^2 + 4x + 5 = 0$
4. $z^2 - 10z + 34 = 0$
5. $z^2 + 4z + 13 = 0$
6. $x^2 - 10x + 41 = 0$
7. $z^2 + 2z + 2 = 0$
8. $x^2 - 2x + 5 = 0$
9. $x^2 + 8x + 17 = 0$
10. $x^2 + 4 = 0$
11. $x^2 + 25 = 0$
12. $z^2 + 9 = 0$

Solve for x in questions 13–15.

13. $2x^2 - 2x + 1 = 0$
14. $2x^2 - 6x + 5 = 0$
15. $4x^2 - 8x + 5 = 0$
16. Verify that $1 - 2i$ is a root of $z^2 - 2z + 5 = 0$ and find the other root.
17. Verify that $2 - 5i$ is a root of $z^2 - 4z + 29 = 0$ and find the other root.
18. Verify that $4 - 3i$ is a root of $x^2 - 8x + 25 = 0$ and find the other root.

19. Verify that $-1 - 2i$ is a root of $x^2 + 2x + 5 = 0$ and find the other root.

20. Verify that $-6 - i$ is a root of $z^2 + 12z + 37 = 0$ and find the other root.

21. p and k are real numbers such that $p(2 + i) + 8 - ki = 5k - 3 - i$.

    (i) Find the value of p and the value of k.

    (ii) Investigate if $p + ki$ is a root of the equation $z^2 - 4z + 13 = 0$.

22. (i) Express $\dfrac{1 + 7i}{1 - 3i}$ in the form $p + qi$.

    (ii) Hence, show that $\dfrac{1 + 7i}{1 - 3i}$ is a root of the equation $z^2 + 4z + 5 = 0$ and write down the other root in the form $a + bi$, where $a, b \in \mathbb{R}$.

23. Show that $\dfrac{11 - 7i}{2 + i}$ is a root of the equation $z^2 - 6z + 34 = 0$ and write down the other root in the form $p + qi$, where $p, q \in \mathbb{R}$.

Form a quadratic equation with roots for questions 24–29.

24. $-2 \pm i$ 25. $1 \pm i$ 26. $-1 \pm 3i$

27. $3 \pm 5i$ 28. $\pm 4i$ 29. $\pm i$

30. If $3 + 5i$ is a root of $x^2 + px + q = 0$, where $p, q \in \mathbb{R}$, find the value of p and q.

31. If $7 - i$ is a root of $z^2 + az + b = 0$, where $a, b \in \mathbb{R}$, find the value of a and b.

32. If $-3 - 3i$ is a root of $x^2 + mx + n = 0$, where $m, n \in \mathbb{R}$, find the value of m and n.

33. If $1 + 5i$ is a root of $x^2 + 2x + k = 0$, where $k \in \mathbb{R}$, find the value of k.

Proving that a line and a curve do not meet

In Chapter 1 of *New Concise Project Maths 3A* on algebra we learned how to find the point(s) of intersection of a line and a curve. In this section we are going to show how to prove that a line and a curve do not meet.

To prove that a line and a curve do not intersect, do the following.

Write the quadratic equation in the form $ax^2 + bx + c = 0$.

Method 1

Using the formula $x = \dfrac{-b \pm \sqrt{b^2 - 4ac}}{2a}$, show that the quadratic equation $ax^2 + bx + c = 0$ has complex roots. Therefore, the line and curve do not intersect.

Method 2

Evaluate $b^2 - 4ac$.

If $b^2 - 4ac < 0$, then the quadratic equation $ax^2 + bx + c = 0$ has complex roots. Therefore, the line and the curve do not intersect.

EXAMPLE

Show that the line $x - y + 6 = 0$ does not meet the curve $x^2 + y^2 = 10$.

Solution:

$$x - y + 6 = 0 \text{ and } x^2 + y^2 = 10$$

1. $\qquad x - y + 6 = 0$ (get x or y on its own from the line)

$$-y = -x - 6$$

$$y = x + 6 \qquad (y \text{ on its own})$$

2. $\qquad x^2 + y^2 = 10$

$$x^2 + (x + 6)^2 = 10 \qquad (\text{put in } (x + 6) \text{ for } y)$$

$$x^2 + x^2 + 12x + 36 = 10 \qquad ((x + 6)^2 = x^2 + 12x + 36)$$

$$2x^2 + 12x + 36 = 10 \qquad (\text{simplify the left-hand side})$$

$$2x^2 + 12x + 26 = 0 \qquad (\text{subtract 10 from both sides})$$

$$x^2 + 6x + 13 = 0 \qquad (\text{divide both sides by 2 in the form } ax^2 + bx + c = 0)$$

Method 1: Using the formula $x = \dfrac{-b \pm \sqrt{b^2 - 4ac}}{2a}$

$$x = \frac{-6 \pm \sqrt{(6)^2 - 4(1)(13)}}{2(1)} \qquad (a = 1, b = 6, c = 13)$$

$$x = \frac{-6 \pm \sqrt{36 - 52}}{2(1)} = \frac{-6 \pm \sqrt{-16}}{2} = \frac{-6 \pm 4i}{2} = -3 \pm 2i$$

As the roots are complex, the line does not intersect the curve.

Method 2: Evaluate $b^2 - 4ac$

$$b^2 - 4ac = (6)^2 - 4(1)(13) = 36 - 52 = -16 < 0$$

As $b^2 - 4ac < 0$, the line does not intersect the curve.

Exercise 1.9

In questions 1–14, show that the line l and the curve c do not intersect.

1. $l : y = 2x - 5,$ $c : y = x^2 - 2x + 8$
2. $l : y = -x - 5,$ $c : y = x^2 + 5x + 20$
3. $l : y = x - 3,$ $c : y = x^2 + 3x + 2$
4. $l : y = 3x - 11,$ $c : y = x^2 - 5x + 30$
5. $l : y = 1,$ $c : y = x^2 + 10$
6. $l : y = 3x - 2,$ $c : y = x^2 + 3x + 2$
7. $l : x - y + 4 = 0,$ $c : xy + 29 = 0$
8. $l : x + y - 6 = 0,$ $c : xy - 34 = 0$
9. $l : x + y - 2 = 0,$ $c : xy = 2$
10. $l : x - y - 1 = 0,$ $c : xy + 2 = x - 15$
11. $l : y = x + 4,$ $c : x^2 + y^2 = 6$
12. $l : y = x + 6,$ $c : x^2 + y^2 = 16$
13. $l : y = 8 - x,$ $c : x^2 + y^2 = 30$
14. $l : y = 10 - x,$ $c : x^2 + y^2 = 42$

15. (i) Show that $(x + 3)^2 = x^2 + 6x + 9$.

    (ii) l is the line $x - y + 3 = 0$ and c is the curve $y^2 = 2(x - 10)$. Verify that l and c do not intersect.

16. (i) Show that $(2y + 15)^2 = 4y^2 + 60y + 225$.

    (ii) l is the line $x - 2y - 15 = 0$ and c is the circle $x^2 + y^2 = 25$. Show l and c on a coordinate diagram.

    (iii) Verify algebraically that l and c do not intersect.

17. The numbers x and y are such that when they are added the result is 4 and when they are multiplied the result is 13. Show that x and y are not real numbers.

18. The numbers a and b are such that when they are added the result is 10 and when they are multiplied the result is 29. Show that a and b are not real numbers.

Argand diagram

An Argand diagram is used to plot complex numbers. It is very similar to the x- and y-axes used in coordinate geometry, except that the **horizontal** axis is called the **real axis (Re)** and the **vertical** axis is called the imaginary axis **(Im)**. It is also called the **complex plane**.

Each complex number must be written in the form $a + bi$ and then plot the point (a, b).

For example, the complex number $5 - 4i$ is represented by the point $(5, -4)$.

EXAMPLE

$z = 2 + 3i$. Plot z, $z - 3$, iz, $-i\bar{z}$ and $\dfrac{13}{z}$ on an Argand diagram.

Solution:

First write each complex number in the form $a + bi$.

$$z = 2 + 3i = (2, 3)$$
$$z - 3 = 2 + 3i - 3 = -1 + 3i = (-1, 3)$$
$$iz = i(2 + 3i) = 2i + 3i^2 = 2i + 3(-1) = 2i - 3 = -3 + 2i = (-3, 2)$$
$$-i\bar{z} = -i(2 - 3i) = -2i + 3i^2 = -2i + 3(-1) = -2i - 3 = -3 - 2i = (-3, -2)$$
$$\frac{13}{z} = \frac{13}{2 + 3i} = \frac{13}{2 + 3i} \cdot \frac{2 - 3i}{2 - 3i} = \frac{26 - 39i}{4 - 6i + 6i - 9i^2} = \frac{26 - 39i}{13} = 2 - 3i = (2, -3)$$

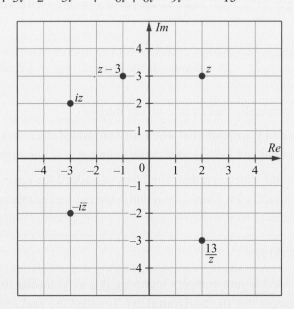

Exercise 1.10

1. Copy the Argand diagram on the following page and plot each of the following complex numbers.

   $z_1 = 5 + 2i$ $z_2 = -6 + 3i$ $z_3 = 3 - 4i$

   $z_4 = -4 - 2i$ $z_5 = -3i$ $z_6 = 4$

   $z_7 = 2(3 - i) + i(4 + 5i)$ $z_8 = 4(2 - i) + i(3 + 5i)$ $z_9 = 3(2 - 3i) + i(5 + 6i)$

   $z_{10} = (3 - i)(-1 + i)$ $z_{11} = \dfrac{5i}{1 + 2i}$ $z_{12} = \dfrac{-1 - 9i}{1 + i}$

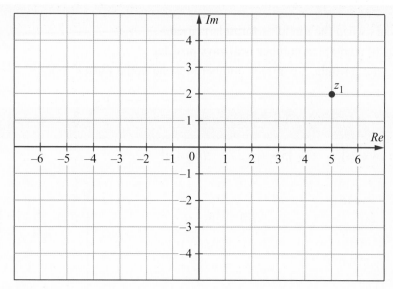

2. Two complex numbers are $u = 3 + 2i$ and $v = -1 + i$, where $i^2 = -1$.

   (i) Given that $w = u - v - 2$, show that $w = 2 + i$.

   (ii) Construct an Argand diagram with the range on the real axis from -5 to 7 and the range on the imaginary axis from -4 to 5. On this Argand diagram, plot each of the following complex numbers.

(a) u	**(b)** v	**(c)** w	**(d)** $2u$

   (e) $4v$ **(f)** $-u$

   (g) iw **(h)** w^2 **(i)** v^2 **(j)** $\dfrac{u + v + w}{4}$ **(k)** $\dfrac{13}{w + 2i}$ **(l)** $\dfrac{2u + v}{w}$

3. $u = 3 + 2i$, $v = 2 - 4i$ and $w = 4u + kv$. Find the real number k such that w lies on
   (i) the imaginary axis **(ii)** the real axis. In each case, plot w.

Modulus

The **modulus** of a complex number is the **distance** from the origin to the point representing the complex number on the Argand diagram.

If $z = a + bi$, then the modulus of z is written as $|z|$ or $|a + bi|$.

The point z represents the complex number $a + bi$.

The modulus of z is the distance from the origin, O, to the complex number $a + bi$.

Using Pythagoras' theorem, $|z| = \sqrt{a^2 + b^2}$.

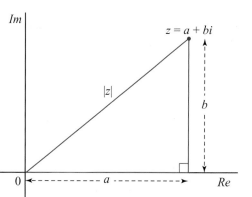

> If $z = a + bi$, then
> $$|z| = |a + bi| = \sqrt{a^2 + b^2}.$$

Notes:

1. *i* **never** appears when the modulus formula is used.
2. The modulus of a complex number is **always positive**.
3. Before using the formula, a complex number must be in the form $a + bi$.

EXAMPLE 1

Find: **(i)** $|4 + 3i|$ **(ii)** $|5 - i|$ **(iii)** $|2i|$

Solution:

(i) $|4 + 3i|$
$$= \sqrt{4^2 + 3^2}$$
$$= \sqrt{16 + 9}$$
$$= \sqrt{25} = 5$$

(ii) $|5 - i|$
$$= \sqrt{5^2 + 1^2}$$
$$= \sqrt{25 + 1}$$
$$= \sqrt{26}$$

(iii) $|2i| = |0 + 2i|$
$$= \sqrt{0^2 + 2^2}$$
$$= \sqrt{0 + 4}$$
$$= \sqrt{4} = 2$$

EXAMPLE 2

Let $u = 3 - 6i$ where $i^2 = -1$. Calculate $|u + 2i|$.

Solution:

$u = 3 - 6i$

$u + 2i = 3 - 6i + 2i$

$u + 2i = 3 - 4i$

$|u + 2i|$
$= |3 - 4i|$
$= \sqrt{3^2 + 4^2}$
$= \sqrt{9 + 16} = \sqrt{25} = 5$

EXAMPLE 3

Let $z_1 = 2 + 3i$ and $z_2 = 5 - i$.
Investigate whether $|z_1 + z_2| > |z_1 - z_2|$.

Solution:

$$z_1 = 2 + 3i \quad \text{and} \quad z_2 = 5 - i$$

$z_1 + z_2$
$= (2 + 3i) + (5 - i)$

$z_1 - z_2$
$= (2 + 3i) - (5 - i)$

$$= 2 + 3i + 5 - i$$
$$= 7 + 2i$$
$$\therefore \ |z_1 + z_2|$$
$$= |7 + 2i| = \sqrt{7^2 + 2^2} = \sqrt{49 + 4} = \sqrt{53}$$
$$= 7\cdot3 \text{ (correct to one decimal place)}$$

$$= 2 + 3i - 5 + i$$
$$= -3 + 4i$$
$$\therefore \ |z_1 - z_2|$$
$$= |-3 + 4i| = \sqrt{3^2 + 4^2} = \sqrt{9 + 16} = \sqrt{25} = 5$$

$$7\cdot3 > 5$$
$$\therefore \ |z_1 + z_2| > |z_1 - z_2|$$

EXAMPLE 4

For what values of k is $|11 + ki| = |10 - 5i|$, where $k \in \mathbb{Z}$?

Solution:

Given:
$$|11 + ki| = |10 - 5i|$$
$$\sqrt{11^2 + k^2} = \sqrt{10^2 + 5^2}$$
$$\sqrt{121 + k^2} = \sqrt{100 + 25}$$
$$\sqrt{121 + k^2} = \sqrt{125}$$
$$121 + k^2 = 125 \qquad \text{(square both sides)}$$
$$k^2 = 4$$
$$k = \pm\sqrt{4}$$
$$k = \pm 2$$

Exercise 1.11

Evaluate each of the following in questions 1–16.

1. $|3 + 4i|$
2. $|6 + 8i|$
3. $|5 - 12i|$
4. $|-8 - 15i|$
5. $|10 - 24i|$
6. $|-24 - 7i|$
7. $|-20 + 21i|$
8. $|-9 - 40i|$
9. $|3i|$
10. $|-2 + i|$
11. $|-5 - 6i|$
12. $|(3 - 2i)^2|$
13. $\left|\dfrac{-14 - 2i}{1 + i}\right|$
14. $\left|\dfrac{2 + i}{1 + 2i}\right|$
15. $\left|\dfrac{3 + i}{2 - i}\right|$
16. $\left|\dfrac{5 + i}{1 - i}\right|$

17. Let $u = 5 + 8i$ and $w = 3 + 7i$. Show that $|u + w| = 17$.
18. Evaluate $|4(2 - i) + i(3 + 5i)|$.
19. $u = 5 - 3i$ and $w = 3 - 6i$ are two complex numbers. Verify that $|u - 1| = |w + 2i|$.

20. Let $z_1 = 1 + 7i$ and $z_2 = 4 + 3i$.

Express $\dfrac{z_1}{z_2}$ in the form $a + bi$, where $a, b \in \mathbb{R}$. Calculate $\left| \dfrac{z_1}{z_2} \right|$.

21. Let $u = 3 + 4i$ and $w = 12 - 5i$. Investigate whether $|u| + |w| = |u + w|$.

22. Let $z_1 = 2 + 3i$ and $z_2 = 5 - i$. Plot z_1, z_2 and $z_1 - z_2$ on an Argand diagram.
   Investigate whether $|z_1 + z_2| > |z_1 - z_2|$.

23. Let $w = 1 + 3i$. Investigate whether $|iw + w| = |iw| + |w|$.

24. (i) Let $u = (1 - 3i)(2 + i)$. Express u in the form $p + qi$, where $p, q \in \mathbb{Z}$.
    (ii) Verify that $|u + \bar{u}| = |u - \bar{u}|$.

25. Let $w = 2 + 5i$.
    (i) Express w^2 in the form $x + yi$, where $x, y \in \mathbb{R}$.
    (ii) Verify that $|w^2| = |w|^2$.

26. Let $z_1 = 1 + 7i$ and $z_2 = 1 - 3i$.

    (i) Express $z_1 z_2$ and $\dfrac{z_1}{z_2}$ in the form $a + bi$.

    (ii) Show that (a) $|z_1|.|z_2| = |z_1 z_2|$ (b) $\dfrac{|z_1|}{|z_2|} = \left| \dfrac{z_1}{z_2} \right|$.

27. $u = 6 + 8i$ and $w = -5 + 12i$ are two complex numbers. Find the value of the real number k such that $k|u| = |w|$.

28. Let $z = 3 - 4i$.
    (i) Calculate $|z|$.
    (ii) Find the real numbers p and q such that $|z|(p + qi) + (q - pi) = 17 + 7i$.
    (iii) Find the real numbers s and t such that $|z|(s + ti) = \dfrac{5}{z}$.

29. $u = -5 + 12i$ and $w = 8 + 10i$ are two complex numbers. Which complex number is nearer to the origin? Justify your answer.

30. (i) Find the values of the real numbers x and y such that $3x + i(7 - 2y) = xi + 2(y + 3) - yi$.
    (ii) Explain why the complex numbers $x + yi$ and $y + xi$ are the same distance from the origin.

31. (i) Let $z = 1 + 7i$ and $w = -1 + i$. Express $\dfrac{z}{w}$ in the form $a + bi$, $a, b \in \mathbb{R}$ and $i^2 = -1$.

    (ii) Verify that $\dfrac{|z|}{|w|} = \left| \dfrac{z}{w} \right|$.

    (iii) Solve for real h and k: $hz = \left| \dfrac{z}{w} \right| kw + 16i$.

32. Let $u = 1 + 2i$. Solve for real a and b: $(1 + 2i)(a + bi) = |u|^2$.

33. Let $u = \dfrac{2 - i}{1 - 2i}$. Show that (i) $u = \dfrac{4}{5} + \dfrac{3}{5}i$ (ii) $|u| = 1$.

34. (i) If $x^2 = 9$, verify that $x = \pm 3$.
    (ii) If $|a + 3i| = 5$, $a \in \mathbb{R}$, find two possible values of a.

35. If $|8 + ki| = 10$, $k \in \mathbb{R}$, find two possible values of k.

36. If $|4 + qi| = |2 - 4i|$, $q \in \mathbb{R}$, find two possible values of q.
37. If $|a + ai| = |1 - 7i|$, $a \in \mathbb{R}$, find two possible values of a.
38. Let $z_1 = 8 + i$ and $z_2 = k + 7i$, $k \in \mathbb{R}$.
    If $|z_2| = |z_1|$, find two possible values of k.

Higher powers of i

Every integer (positive or negative whole number) power of i is a number of the set $\{1, -1, i, -i\}$.

$i = \sqrt{-1}$

$i^2 = -1$

$i^3 = i^2 \times i = (-1)i = -i$

$i^4 = i^2 \times i^2 = (-1)(-1) = 1$

$$\boxed{\begin{array}{l} i = \sqrt{-1} \\ i^2 = -1 \\ i^3 = -i \\ i^4 = 1 \end{array}}$$

$$\boxed{\begin{array}{ll} i^{4n} = 1 & \text{(n is a multiple of 4)} \\ i^{4n+1} = i & \text{(n is one more than a multiple of 4)} \\ i^{4n+2} = -1 & \text{(n is two more than a multiple of 4)} \\ i^{4n+3} = -i & \text{(n is three more than a multiple of 4)} \end{array}}$$

EXAMPLE

Simplify the following.

(i) i^8 (ii) i^7 (iii) $-i(i^4 + i^5 + i^6)$ (iv) $(2i)^3$

Solution:

(i) $i^8 = i^4 \times i^4 = 1 \times 1 = 1$

(ii) $i^7 = i^4 \times i^3 = 1 \times -i = -i$

(iii) $\quad -i(i^4 + i^5 + i^6)$

$\quad = -i(1 + i - 1)$

$\quad = -i(i)$

$\quad = -i^2 = -(-1) = 1$

$$\boxed{\begin{array}{l} i^4 = 1 \\ i^5 = i^4 \times i^1 = 1 \times i = i \\ i^6 = i^4 \times i^2 = 1 \times -1 = -1 \end{array}}$$

(iv) $(2i)^3 = 2i \times 2i \times 2i = 8i^3 = 8(-i) = -8i$

Exercise 1.12

Express questions 1–12 without indices.

1. i^2 2. i^3 3. i^4 4. i^5 5. i^6 6. i^7

7. i^8 8. i^{10} 9. i^{13} 10. i^{16} 11. i^{22} 12. i^{23}

Simplify questions 13–14.

13. $-2i(i^4 + i^5 + i^6)$ 14. $3i(i^5 + i^6 + i^7)$

15. Express each of the following in the form $a + bi$.

    (i) $i^2 + 5i^3$ (ii) $2i^6 + 3i^5$ (iii) $2i^7 - 6i^{10}$

16. If $u = 2i$, verify that $u^3 + u^2 + 4u + 4 = 0$.

17. If $w = 3i$, verify that $w^3 - w^2 + 9w - 9 = 0$.

18. $z = \dfrac{1 + i}{1 - i}$. Calculate: (i) z^2 (ii) z^3 (iii) z^4 (iv) $-z(z^2 + z^3 + z^4)$

19. Let $u = \dfrac{3 + 4i}{4 - 3i}$. Evaluate: (i) u^2 (ii) u^3 (iii) u^4 (iv) $u(u^6 + u^7 + u^8)$

Further geometrical properties of complex numbers

Rotations

> A **rotation** turns a point through an angle about a fixed point.

An **anticlockwise** turn is described as a **positive rotation**	A **clockwise** turn is described as a **negative rotation**
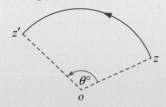	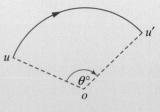
Written R_θ	Written $R_{-\theta}$

Successive multiplication by i on an Argand diagram

> Multiplication by i rotates a complex number by $90°$ ($R_{90°}$).
>
> Multiplication by i^2 rotates a complex number by $180°$ ($R_{180°}$).
>
> Multiplication by i^3 rotates a complex number by $270°$ ($R_{270°}$).
>
> Multiplication by i^4 rotates a complex number by $360°$ ($R_{360°}$).

Note: Multiplication by $-i$, $-i^2$, $-i^3$ and $-i^4$ reverses the direction of the rotation.

If you multiply a complex number by a scalar (a number), then its modulus (distance from the origin) will be multiplied by this scalar. In other words, if you multiply a complex number by 3, then its distance from the origin will be three times as far from the origin as the original complex number. If you multiply a complex number by $\frac{1}{2}$, then its distance from the origin will be half as far from the origin as the original complex number.

> If z is a complex number, then $|kz| = k|z|$, where k is a real number.

If you multiply a complex number by $2i$, its modulus will be doubled and it will also be rotated by $90°$.

EXAMPLE

(i) $z = 3 + 2i$. Represent z, iz, i^2z and i^3z on an Argand diagram.

(ii) $u = 2 + i$. Represent $2u$ on an Argand diagram. Verify that $|2u| = 2|u|$.

Solution:

(i) $i^2 = -1$ and $i^3 = -i$

$z = 3 + 2i \qquad (3, 2)$

$iz = i(3 + 2i) = 3i + 2i^2 = 3i + 2(-1) = 3i - 2 = -2 + 3i \qquad (-2, 3)$

$i^2z = -1(3 + 2i) = -3 - 2i \qquad (-3, -2)$

$i^3z = -i(3 + 2i) = -3i - 2i^2 = -3i - 2(-1) = -3i + 2 = 2 - 3i \qquad (2, -3)$

(ii) $u = 2 + i$

$2u = 2(2 + i) = 4 + 2i \qquad (4, 2)$

(i)

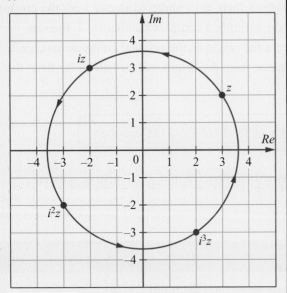

(ii)

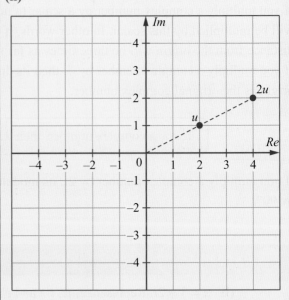

$|z| = |3 + 2i| = \sqrt{3^2 + 2^2} = \sqrt{9 + 4} = \sqrt{13}$

$|z| = |iz| = |i^2z| = |i^3z|$

In other words, they are all the same distance from the origin. This can be seen on the diagram as all four complex numbers lie on the same circle of centre O and radius $\sqrt{13}$.

$|u| = |2 + i| = \sqrt{2^2 + 1^2} = \sqrt{4 + 1} = \sqrt{5}$

$|2u| = |4 + 2i| = \sqrt{4^2 + 2^2} = \sqrt{16 + 4} = \sqrt{20}$

$\sqrt{20} = \sqrt{4 \times 5} = \sqrt{4}\,\sqrt{5} = 2\sqrt{5}$

$\therefore |2u| = 2|u|$

In other words, $2u$ is twice as far from the origin as u. This can be seen on the diagram. A line from the origin passes through u and $2u$.

Exercise 1.13

1. $z = 3 + 4i$. Investigate whether $|z| = |iz|$. Give a geometrical interpretation for your answer.

2. $z = 2 + i$ and $u = -4 + 3i$.

   (i) On the Argand diagram, plot:

   (a) z, iz, i^2z and i^3z

   (b) u, iu, i^2u and i^3z

   (ii) Describe the position of i^4z.

   (iii) Describe a transformation, which is not a rotation, that maps iz onto i^3z.

   (iv) Name the image of u under a central symmetry in iz.

   (v) Explain why iz and i^5z can be represented by the same point on the Argand diagram.

   (vi) $w = 2iu$. Give a geometrical interpretation of how to find the position of w on the Argand diagram.

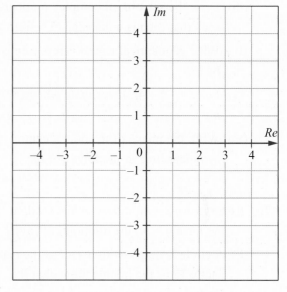

   (vii) Using the diagram, explain why $|u| > |z|$.

3. (i) Let $z = 7 + i$, $w = 3 - i$, $u = z - w$ and $v = \dfrac{z}{w}$.

   Express u and v in the form $a + bi$ and plot u and v on an Argand diagram.

   (ii) $u = kv$, where $k \in N$. Find the value of k.

   (iii) $v = lu$, where $l \in Q$. Find the value of l.

   (iv) On your Argand diagram, plot $2i^3v$ and $-iv$. Comment on the position of $2i^3v$ and $-iv$.

4. (i) $w = 3 - 2i$. On an Argand diagram, plot w, $-iw$, $-i^2w$, $-i^3w$ and $-i^4w$.

   (ii) Explain why w and i^4w have the same position on the Argand diagram.

   (iii) Is $i^2w = -i^2w$? Justify your answer.

   (iv) $u = 3iw$. Give a geometrical interpretation of u.

5. (i) Construct an Argand diagram with the real and imaginary axis from -4 to 4. Let $z_1 = 2 + 4i$. Verify that z_1 is a solution of the equation $z^2 - 4z + 20 = 0$ and write down z_2, the other solution.

   (ii) Plot z_1 and z_2 on the Argand diagram.

   (iii) Is $iz_1 = z_2$? Justify your answer.

   (iv) Describe the transformation that maps z_1 onto z_2.

   (v) Investigate whether the image of z_2 under an axial symmetry in the imaginary axis has the same position as i^2z_1 on the Argand diagram.

6. **(i)** Let $z = 2 + i$ and $w = -1 - 3i$.

Plot z and w on the Argand diagram.

(ii) Verify that $|w - z| = 5$.

(iii) Draw the set k of all complex numbers such that each is a distance of 5 from z.

(iv) What geometrical figure is represented by k?

(v) Let $u = -2 + 4i$. Investigate whether $u \in k$.

(vi) Write the image of w under a central symmetry in z in the form $a + bi$.

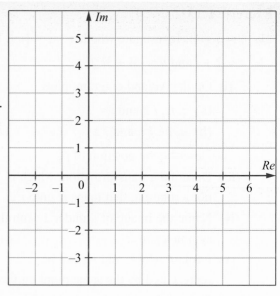

7. **(i)** Let $u = -2 + 3i$ and $v = 4 + i$. Find, in the form $a + bi$, the midpoint of $[uv]$.

(ii) A circle is drawn with $a + bi$ as the centre and $\sqrt{10}$ as the radius. Show that the circle passes through u and v.

8. Four complex numbers, z_1, z_2, z_3 and z_4, are shown on the Argand diagram. They satisfy the following conditions:

$z_2 = iz_1$

$z_3 = kz_1$, where $k \in \mathbb{R}$

$z_4 = z_2 + z_3$

The same scale is used on both axes.

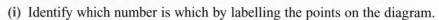

(i) Identify which number is which by labelling the points on the diagram.

(ii) Write down the value of k.

9. **(i)** z is the complex number $1 + i$, where $i^2 = -1$. Find z^2 and z^3.

(ii) Verify that $z^4 = -4$. **(iii)** Show z, z^2, z^3 and z^4 on the Argand diagram.

(iv) Make one observation about the pattern of points on the diagram.

(v) Using the value of z^4 or otherwise, find the values of z^8, z^{12} and z^{16}.

(vi) Based on the pattern of values in part **(v)** or otherwise, state whether z^{40} is positive or negative. Explain how you got your answer.

(vii) Write z^{40} as a power of 2. **(viii)** Find z^{41}.

(ix) On an Argand diagram, how far from the origin is z^{41}?

Proportion

A proportion of an object is usually given as a fraction comparing a part of the object with the complete object. For example, if a basket of 20 flowers contains eight roses, then the proportion of the roses in the basket is $\frac{8}{20}$ or $\frac{2}{5}$. Comparing the top with the bottom, we can say that 2 out of every 5 flowers are roses.

A proportion can be given as a percentage. We could say that $\frac{2}{5} = 40\%$ of the flowers are roses.

Note: It is sometimes easier to compare proportions if they are converted to percentages.

EXAMPLE 1

  (i)   A class of 30 students contains 25 who own a mobile phone.

       What proportion do not own a mobile phone?

  (ii)   In an election, the proportion of voters who supported the Happy Party was 55%. There were 12,000 voters in total.

      (a) Express the proportion as a fraction.

      (b) Find the number of Happy Party supporters.

Solution:

(i)   There are $30 - 25 = 5$ students who do not own a mobile phone.

    The proportion is $\frac{5}{30}$ or $\frac{1}{6}$.

(ii) **(a)** $55\% = \frac{55}{100} = \frac{11}{20}$

     (b) $\frac{11}{20}$ of $12{,}000 = \frac{11}{20} \times 12{,}000$

             $= 6{,}600$ supporters

EXAMPLE 2

A packet of 12 sweets contains three flavours: strawberry, lemon and orange. There are four strawberry and six lemon sweets. The rest are orange flavoured.

(i) How many are orange?

(ii) Find the proportions of each flavour.

(iii) Show that the total of the proportions add up to 1.

(iv) If the flavours are supposed to be equal, what proportion should there be of each flavour?

Solution:

(i) The are 12 sweets in the packet, so:

Orange = 12 − (Strawberry + Lemon) = 12 − (4 + 6) = 2

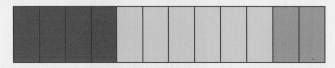

(ii) Strawberry: $\frac{4}{12} = \frac{1}{3}$; Lemon: $\frac{6}{12} = \frac{1}{2}$; Orange: $\frac{2}{12} = \frac{1}{6}$.

(iii) Using the unsimplified fractions: $\frac{4}{12} + \frac{6}{12} + \frac{2}{12} = \frac{12}{12} = 1$.

(iv) 12 sweets, three flavours, so ideally 12 ÷ 3 = 4 sweets per flavour.

Proportion: $\frac{4}{12} = \frac{1}{3}$.

OR

Three flavours, so $\frac{1}{3}$ per flavour would be expected.

Exercise 2.1

1. There are two rotten apples at the bottom of a barrel containing 12 apples. Express the proportion of rotten apples as a (simplified) fraction and as an exact percentage.

2. A prize fund of €1,200 is distributed as follows: $\frac{1}{2}$ for first prize, $\frac{2}{5}$ for second prize and the remainder for third prize.

   (i) Calculate the proportion of the third prize.

   (ii) How much is the third prize worth?

3. In English text, the proportions of the most frequent letters are **e** 13%, **a** 8% and **t** 9%.
    (i) Rene Descrates once said:

    I think; therefore I am.

    (a) Ignoring punctuation and spaces, write down the proportions of the letters **e**, **a** and **t** in the above quote.
    (b) For each letter, indicate whether it is more or less frequent than usual.

    (ii) Isaac Newton once said:

    If I have seen further than others, it is by standing upon the shoulders of giants.

    (a) Ignoring punctuation and spaces, write down the proportions of the letters **e**, **a** and **t** in the above quote.
    (b) For each letter, indicate whether it is more or less frequent than usual.

    (iii) Why would the proportions be so different?

4. In a survey, the proportion of people who watched a football match on television was $\frac{3}{8}$.
    (i) What proportion did not watch the match?
    (ii) If 240,000 people did not watch the match, how many did?

5. €400 is $\frac{8}{11}$ of a prize fund. Find the total prize fund.

6. When a cyclist had travelled a distance of 17 km, she had completed $\frac{5}{8}$ of her journey. What was the length of the journey?

Dividing quantities in a given ratio

Ratios can be used to divide, or share, quantities.

To divide, or share, a quantity in a given ratio, do the following.

> 1. Add the ratios to get the total number of parts.
> 2. Divide the quantity by the total of the parts (this gives one part).
> 3. Multiply this separately by each ratio to find the shares.

Check your answers by confirming that the shares add up to the original total.

EXAMPLE 1

(i) Divide €450 in the ratio 5 : 3 : 7.   (ii) Divide 64 kg in the ratio $1 : \frac{1}{3} : 4$.

Solution:

(i)   Number of parts = $5 + 3 + 7 = 15$

$$1 \text{ part} = \frac{\text{€}450}{15} = \text{€}30$$

$$5 \text{ parts} = \text{€}30 \times 5 = \text{€}150$$

$$3 \text{ parts} = \text{€}30 \times 3 = \text{€}90$$

$$7 \text{ parts} = \text{€}30 \times 7 = \text{€}210$$

∴ €450 in the ratio 5 : 3 : 7

$= \text{€}150, \text{€}90, \text{€}210$

Check:

$$\text{€}150 + \text{€}90 + \text{€}210 = \text{€}450 \checkmark$$

(ii) $1 : \frac{1}{3} : 4 = 3 : 1 : 12$

(multiply each part by 3)

Number of parts = $3 + 1 + 12 = 16$

$$1 \text{ part} = \frac{64 \text{ kg}}{16} = 4 \text{ kg}$$

$$3 \text{ parts} = 4 \text{ kg} \times 3 = 12 \text{ kg}$$

$$12 \text{ parts} = 4 \text{ kg} \times 12 = 48 \text{ kg}$$

∴ 64 kg in the ratio $1 : \frac{1}{3} : 4$

$= 12 \text{ kg}, 4 \text{ kg}, 48 \text{ kg}$

Check:

$$12 \text{ kg} + 4 \text{ kg} + 48 \text{ kg} = 64 \text{ kg} \checkmark$$

Sometimes we are given an equation in disguise.

 EXAMPLE 2

Amy and Beatrice share a prize in the ratio 7 : 5.
Beatrice gets €45. How much should Amy get?

Solution:

Equation given in disguise:

$$5 \text{ parts} = \text{€}45 \qquad \text{(Beatrice's share} = 5 \text{ parts)}$$

$$1 \text{ part} = \frac{\text{€}45}{5} = \text{€}9 \qquad \text{(divide both sides by 5)}$$

Amy's share = 7 parts = $7 \times \text{€}9 = \text{€}63$.

Exercise 2.2

1. Divide: **(i)** €80 in the ratio 7 : 3   **(ii)** 450 g in the ratio 5 : 4

2. Divide: **(i)** €480 in the ratio 3 : 4 : 5   **(ii)** €4,000 in the ratio 5 : 8 : 7

3. Divide: **(i)** 238 g in the ratio 7 : 2 : 5   **(ii)** 162 cm in the ratio 4 : 3 : 2

4. Divide: **(i)** €504 in the ratio 3 : 4 : 5   **(ii)** 336 cm in the ratio 2 : 5 : 7

5. Divide: **(i)** €374 in the ratio 6 : 7 : 9   **(ii)** 1,560 g in the ratio 8 : 1 : 4

In questions 6–9, write the given ratio as a ratio of whole numbers, in its simplest form.

6. $1\frac{1}{2} : 2$ 7. $\frac{1}{3} : 1$ 8. $\frac{1}{2} : \frac{1}{4} : 1$ 9. $\frac{3}{4} : \frac{1}{2} : 1$

10. Divide: **(i)** €42 in the ratio $1 : \frac{1}{2}$ **(ii)** 280 g in the ratio $\frac{1}{2} : 2$

11. Divide: **(i)** €210 in the ratio $1 : 2 : \frac{1}{2}$ **(ii)** 585 cm in the ratio $\frac{1}{2} : 2 : 5$

12. Divide: **(i)** 546 g in the ratio $1 : \frac{2}{3} : \frac{1}{2}$ **(ii)** €920 in the ratio $\frac{1}{2} : \frac{2}{3} : \frac{3}{4}$

13. In a competition, team A scored $22\frac{1}{2}$ points and team B scored $17\frac{1}{2}$ points. The two teams share a prize of €28,000 in proportion to the number of points they scored. How much money does each team receive?

14. One town, A, has a population of 4,800 and a second town, B, has a population of 6,720. The two towns share a grant of €429,120 in proportion to their populations. How much does town A receive?

15. **(i)** David, Eric and Fred decide to buy a lottery ticket for €2. David pays 50c, Eric pays 90c and Fred pays the remainder. In what ratio should a prize be shared?

     (ii) If their ticket wins a prize of €500, how much should each get?

16. A and B share a sum of money in the ratio 2 : 3. If A's share is €80, calculate B's share.

17. Two lengths are in the ratio 7 : 5. If the larger length is 140 cm, calculate the other length.

18. The lengths of the sides of a triangle are in the ratio 4 : 3 : 2. If the shortest side is of length 36 cm, calculate the perimeter of the triangle.

19. P, Q and R share a sum of money in the ratio 2 : 4 : 5, respectively. If Q's share is €60, find: **(i)** P's share **(ii)** the total sum of money shared.

20. The profits of a business owned by A, B and C are shared in the ratio of their investments, €32,000, €16,000 and €20,000, respectively. If C received €6,350, how much did A receive?

21. A glass rod falls and breaks into three pieces whose lengths are in the ratio 8 : 9 : 5. If the sum of the lengths of the two larger pieces is 119 cm, find the length of the third piece.

22. A woman gave some money to her four children in the ratio 2 : 3 : 5 : 9. If the difference between the largest and the smallest share is €3,500, how much money did she give altogether?

23. €360 is divided between A and B in the ratio 3 : k. If A received €135, find the value of k.

24. Roy and Sam share €440 in the ratio 8 : 3.

    (i) How much does each get?

    (ii) If Roy gives €45 of his share to Sam, what ratio is the money in now?

Percentages

In many questions dealing with percentages, we will not be given the original amount. The best way to tackle this type of problem is to treat it as an equation given in disguise. From this we can find 1% and, hence, any percentage we like.

EXAMPLE 1

An auctioneer's fee for the sale of a house is $1\frac{1}{2}$% of the selling price.

If the fee is €4,200, calculate the selling price.

Solution:
Given: auctioneer's fee is €4,200.

$1\frac{1}{2}$% = €4,200	(equation given in disguise)
3% = €8,400	(multiply both sides by 2)
1% = €2,800	(divide both sides by 3)
100% = €280,000	(multiply both sides by 100)

∴ The selling price of the house was €280,000.

EXAMPLE 2

A bill for €102·85 includes VAT at 21%. Calculate the amount of the bill before VAT is added.

Solution:
Think of the bill before VAT is added on as 100%. After 21% VAT, this becomes 121%.

Given:	121% = €102·85	(equation given in disguise)
	1% = €0·85	(divide both sides by 121)
	100% = €85	(multiply both sides by 100)

∴ The bill before VAT is added is €85.

EXAMPLE 3

A shopkeeper buys an armchair for €410. He adds a mark-up of 40% to find his basic sale price. VAT must be added at a rate of 21%. Suggest a suitable retail price point.

Solution:
To add 40%, we find 140% of the amount.

As $140\% = \dfrac{140}{100} = 1\cdot4$, a simple way to do this is to multiply by $1\cdot4$.

€410	(base price)
€410 × 1·4 = €574	(add 40% mark-up)
€574 × 1·21 = €694.54	(add 21% VAT)

A suitable price point might be €695, €699 or €699·99.

Exercise 2.3

1. Calculate: **(i)** 8% of €120 **(ii)** 12% of €216 **(iii)** 21% of €124

2. A musical store owner pays €2,800 for a set of drums and marks it up so that he makes a profit of 35%. Then 21% VAT is added on. Calculate the selling price.

3. **(i)** A shopkeeper pays €240 for a bicycle and marks it up so that she makes a profit of 20%. Find the selling price.
   (ii) During a sale, the price of the bicycle is reduced by 15%.
   Calculate: **(a)** the sale price **(b)** the percentage profit on the bicycle during the sale.

4. One litre of water is added to four litres of milk in a container. Calculate the percentage of water in the container.

5. A tank contains 320 litres of petrol. 128 litres are removed. What percentage of the petrol remains in the tank?

6. A bill for €96·76 includes VAT at 18%. Calculate the amount of the bill before VAT is added.

7. A bill for €58·08 includes VAT at 21%. Calculate the amount of VAT in the bill.

8. When a woman bought a television set in a shop, VAT at 21% was added on.
   (i) If the VAT on the cost of the set was €252, what was the price of the television set before VAT was added?
   (ii) What was the price including VAT?

9. A boy bought a calculator for €74·75, which included VAT at 15%. Find the price of the calculator if VAT was reduced to 12%.

10. When the rate of VAT was increased from 18% to 21%, the price of a guitar increased by €81. Calculate the price of the guitar, inclusive of the VAT at 21%.

11. When 9% of the pupils in a school are absent, 637 are present. How many pupils are on the school roll?

12. 15% of a number is 96. Calculate 25% of the number.

13. A salesperson's commission for selling a car is $2\frac{1}{2}\%$ of the selling price. If the commission for selling a car was €350, calculate the selling price.

14. A solicitor's fee for the sale of a house is $1\frac{1}{2}\%$ of the selling price. If the fee is €3,480, calculate the selling price.

15. In a sale, the price of a piece of furniture was reduced by 20%. The sale price was €1,248. What was the price before the sale?

16. A salesperson's income for a year was €59,000. This was made up of basic pay of €45,000 plus a commission of 4% of sales. Calculate the amount of the sales for the year.

17. A fuel mixture consists of 93% petrol and 7% oil. If the mixture contains 37·2 litres of petrol, calculate the volume of oil.

18. A book of raffle tickets sells for €10. The prizes in euro are 2,000, 1,000, 500 and 250. If printing costs amount to €250, calculate the smallest number of books which must be sold to: (i) cover costs (ii) make a profit of €3,000.

19. A lottery had a first prize of 70% of the prize fund and a consolation prize of 30%. Six people shared the first prize and each received €3,500. If the consolation prize was divided between 450 people, how much did each receive?

20. (i) A tanker delivered heating oil to a school. Before the delivery, the meter reading showed 11,360 litres of oil in the tanker. After the delivery, the meter reading was 7,160 litres. Calculate the cost of the oil delivered if 1 litre of oil cost 36·5c.

    (ii) When VAT was added to the cost of the oil delivered, the bill to the school amounted to €1,808·94. Calculate the rate of VAT added.

21. (i) An antiques dealer bought three chairs at an auction. He sold them later for €301·60, making a profit of 16% on their total cost. Calculate the total cost of the chairs.

    (ii) The first chair cost €72 and it was sold at a profit of 15%. Calculate its selling price.

    (iii) The second chair cost €98 and it was sold for €91. Find the percentage profit made on the sale of the third chair.

22. A retailer buys an item for €299. Can she add on a 40% mark-up and still sell it for under €500 including 21% VAT?

23. To match a competitor's price of €14,950 (including 21% VAT), a car dealer has to recalculate his potential profit. He purchased the car for €9,200.

    The dealer usually applies a mark-up of between 30% and 35% – can he match the price or make an even better offer to the customer?

24. A shopkeeper want to sell toys at three prices: €9·99, €12·99 and €24·99, including 21% VAT. What is the maximum price that the shopkeeper must pay for each item and still include a minimum of a 30% mark-up? Round your answers down to the nearest cent.

25. During 1874, the population of a small town rose by 4%. The following year, the population declined by 4%. Would the population at the start of 1876 be less than, equal to or greater than the population two years earlier? Explain your answer.

Relative error and percentage error

When calculations are being made, errors can occur, especially calculations which involve rounding. It is important to have a measure of the error.

Definitions

> Error = | true value – estimate value | and is always considered positive.

> Relative error = $\dfrac{\text{Error}}{\text{True value}}$

> Percentage error = $\dfrac{\text{Error}}{\text{True value}} \times 100\%$

● EXAMPLE 1

A distance of 190 km was estimated to be 200 km. Calculate:

(i) The error (ii) The relative error (iii) The percentage error, correct to one decimal place

Solution:

True value = 190 km.   Estimated value = 200 km.

(i) Error = |true value – estimated value| = |190 – 200| = |–10| = 10 km (positive value)

(ii) Relative error = $\dfrac{\text{Error}}{\text{True value}} = \dfrac{10}{190} = \dfrac{1}{19}$

(iii) Percentage error = $\dfrac{\text{Error}}{\text{True value}} \times 100\% = \dfrac{10}{190} \times 100\% = 5{\cdot}3\%$ (correct to one decimal place)

● EXAMPLE 2

The answer to 5·6 + 7·1 was given as 12·5.

What was the percentage error, correct to two decimal places?

Solution:

True value = 5·6 + 7·1 = 12·7.   Estimated value = 12·5.

Error = |true value – estimated value| = |12·7 – 12·5| = |0·2| = 0·2

Percentage error = $\dfrac{\text{Error}}{\text{True value}} \times 100\% = \dfrac{0{\cdot}2}{12{\cdot}7} \times 100\% = 1{\cdot}57\%$ (correct to two decimal places)

Exercise 2.4

Complete the following table.

	True value	Estimated value	Error	Relative error (as a fraction)	Percentage error (correct to one decimal place)
1.	12	10			
2.	43	40			
3.	136	140			
4.	4·8	5			
5.	5·7	6			
6.	390	400			

7. The depth of a swimming pool was estimated to be 1·5 m. The true depth was 1·65 m.
   Find: **(i)** The error **(ii)** The percentage error, correct to one decimal place

8. The mass of a rock is estimated to be 65 kg. Its true mass is 67·5 kg.
   Find: **(i)** The error **(ii)** The percentage error, correct to one decimal place

9. A distance of 105 km was estimated to be 100 km. Calculate:
   (i) The error **(ii)** The relative error **(iii)** The percentage error, correct to one decimal place

10. The estimate for building a wall was €3,325. The actual cost was €3,500.
    Calculate the percentage error.

11. The number of people estimated to be at a meeting was 400. The actual number who attended the meeting was 423. Calculate the percentage error, correct to two decimal places.

12. The value of $\dfrac{48 \cdot 27 + 12 \cdot 146}{14 \cdot 82 - 3 \cdot 02}$ was estimated to be 5.

    Calculate the percentage error, correct to one decimal place.

13. The value of $\dfrac{30 \cdot 317}{\sqrt{24 \cdot 7009}}$ was estimated to be 6.

    Calculate: **(i)** The error **(ii)** The percentage error, correct to two decimal places

14. **(i)** Calculate the volume of a solid cylinder of radius 6 cm and height 14 cm $\left(\text{assume } \pi = \frac{22}{7}\right)$.

    (ii) When doing this calculation, a student used $\pi = 3$. Calculate the student's percentage error in the calculation, assuming that $\pi = \frac{22}{7}$ is the exact value, correct to one decimal place.

15. Calculate the percentage error in calculating the total of $324 + 432 + 234$ if the digit 4 is replaced by a 5 each time. Give your answer correct to one decimal place.

16. Four items in a shop cost €7·70, €14·90, €16·80 and €23·10.
    (i) Frank estimates the total cost of the four items by ignoring the cent part in the cost of each item. Calculate the percentage error in his estimate.
    (ii) Fiona estimates the total cost of the four items by rounding the cost of each item to the nearest euro. Calculate the percentage error in her estimate.

17. A food manufacturer sells carrots in 500 g tins. For two hours, a faulty machine filled 12,500 tins with only 495 g of carrots.
    (i) Calculate the percentage error.
    (ii) How many kg of carrots were used during the two hours?
    (iii) How many tins would usually be filled with the quantity used?
    (iv) If the tins had been sold at the usual price of 50c, how much profit would the manufacturer have made because of the fault?

Tolerance

Modern machines are manufactured from hundreds of components which need to fit together accurately. For that reason, the various parts must be made to exact measurements, although the level of exactness can vary. For example, the parts which make up a cruise ship might not need to be manufactured as accurately as parts of a watch.

Objects which must be made very accurately (such as a watch) would have a very low tolerance value. For example, a small circular cog for a watch might need to be 8 mm in diameter. If it was 10 mm in diameter, it would be unlikely to fit. The watchmaker could describe the part as needing a diameter of 8 mm ± 0·5 mm.

This would mean that the smallest acceptable diameter is 8 − 0·5 mm = 7·5 mm and the largest acceptable diameter is 8 + 0·5 mm = 8·5 mm.

EXAMPLE

A shipbuilder needs sheets of metal to be 2 m long by 1 m wide but will accept sheets which are 2 m ± 3 mm by 1 m ± 2 mm.

(i)   What are the dimensions (in mm) of the largest sheets and the smallest within the given tolerances?

(ii) Calculate, in m^2, the difference between the area of the largest and the smallest sheets.

Solution:

Draw a sketch:

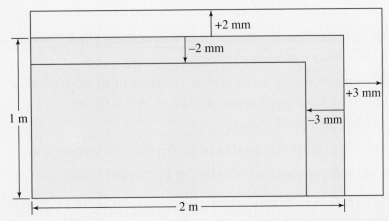

The shaded part shows the desired sheet. The larger outline shows the maximum sheet, while the smaller outline shows the minimum.

(i)   Maximum length: 2 m + 3 mm = 2,000 mm + 3 mm = 2,003 mm

  Maximum width: 1 m + 2 mm = 1,000 mm + 4 mm = 1,002 mm

  Maximum dimensions: 2,003 mm × 1,002 mm

  Minimum length: 2 m − 3 mm = 2,000 mm − 3 mm = 1,997 mm

  Minimum width: 1 m − 2 mm = 1,000 mm − 4 mm = 998 mm

  Minimum dimensions: 1,997 mm × 998 mm

(ii) Convert: 2,003 mm = 2·003 m;   1,002 mm = 1·002 m

  Maximum area: 2·003 m × 1·002 m = 2·007 006 m^2

  Convert: 1,997 mm = 1·997 m;   998 mm = 0·998 m

  Maximum area: 1·997 m × 0·998 m = 1·993 006 m^2

∴ The difference in the areas = (2·007 006 − 1·993 006) m^2 = 0·014 m^2

Exercise 2.5

In questions 1–6, calculate the minimum and maximum values, using appropriate units.

	Measurement	Tolerance	Minimum value	Maximum value
1.	12	±2		
2.	120	±5		
3.	80%	±5%		
4.	4 m	±5 mm		
5.	€3,200	±€450		
6.	3	±5		

7. A packet of sweets describes the contents as containing $150 \pm 2\%$ sweets.
   What is the tolerance in terms of sweets?

8. A bridge over a motorway needs to span a distance of 40 m. After some consultation, the
   specification for the bridge requires a width of $39{\cdot}9 \pm 0{\cdot}1$ m.

   (i) By how much can the bridge vary?

   (ii) Why would the bridge need to be shorter than the distance it needs to span?

9. A sheet of metal is manufactured to be 3 m by 1 m and 1 cm thick.

   (i) What is its volume in cm^3?

   (ii) The manufacturing process means that the thickness is highly accurate but the length
   and width are only accurate to ± 1 cm. What are the minimum and maximum volumes?

   (iii) The sheet is made of steel, which weighs 8 g per cm^3. What is the difference in weight
   between the smallest and the largest sheet?

   (iv) Given the difference in volume and also in weight, discuss the consequences of this
   tolerance.

Foreign exchange

Currency is another name for money. In many European countries the unit of currency is called the
euro (€). The method of direct proportion is used to convert one currency into another currency.

Note: Write down the equation given in disguise, putting the currency we want to find on the
right-hand side.

EXAMPLE 1

A book cost €8·60 in Dublin and US$10·08 in New York. If €1 = US$1·20, in which city is the book cheaper and by how many European cent?

Solution:
Express the price of the book in New York in euro and compare to the price in Dublin.

$$US\$1·20 = €1 \qquad (€ \text{ on the right because we want our answer in } €)$$

$$US\$1 = €\frac{1}{1·20} \qquad (\text{divide both sides by } 1·20)$$

$$\$10·08 = €\frac{1}{1·20} \times 10·08 \qquad (\text{multiply both sides by } 10·08)$$

$$\$10.08 = €8·40 \qquad (\text{simplify the right-hand side})$$

Difference = €8·60 − €8·40 = 20c

∴ The book is cheaper in New York by 20c.

EXAMPLE 2

A person changes €500 into Japanese yen (¥). A charge is made for this transaction. The exchange rate is €1 = ¥320. If the person receives ¥156,000, calculate the percentage charge.

Solution:
Express €500 in ¥.

$$€1 = ¥320 \qquad (¥ \text{ on the right because we want our answer in } ¥)$$

$$€500 = ¥500 \times 320 \qquad (\text{multiply both sides by } 500)$$

$$€500 = ¥160,000 \qquad (\text{full amount due})$$

Amount received = ¥156,000

∴ Charge = ¥160,000 − ¥156,000 = ¥4,000

$$\text{Percentage charge} = \frac{\text{Charge}}{\text{Full amount}} \times 100\% = \frac{4,000}{160,000} \times 100\% = 2·5\%.$$

Exercise 2.6

1. If €1 = $1·03, find the value of: **(i)** €250 in dollars **(ii)** $618 in euro

2. A train ticket costs $54. If €1 = $1·08, calculate the cost of the ticket in euro.

3. €1 = ¥304 (Japanese yen).

   (i) How many yen would you receive for €240?

   (ii) How many euro would you receive for ¥115,520?

4. A part for a tractor costs €600 in France and the same part costs R1,368 in South Africa. If €1 = R2·4, in which country is it cheaper and by how much (in euro)?

5. **(i)** A tourist changed €5,000 on board a ship into South African rand at a rate of €1 = R2·2. How many rand did she receive?

   (ii) When she came ashore she found that the rate was €1 = R2·35. How much did she lose, in rand, by not changing her money ashore?

6. **(i)** A person buys ¥167,400 when the exchange rate is €1 = ¥310. A charge is made for this. How much, in euro, is this charge if the person pays €548·10?

   (ii) Calculate the percentage commission on the transaction.

7. When the exchange rate is €1 = $0·98, a person buys $3,430 from a bank. If the bank charges a commission of $2\frac{1}{2}\%$, calculate the total cost in euro.

8. **(i)** A person buys 5,160 Canadian dollars when the exchange rate is €1 = $2·15. A charge (commission) is made for this service. How much, in euro, is this charge if the person pays €2,448?

   (ii) Calculate the percentage commission on the transaction.

9. Dollars were bought for €8,000 when the exchange rate was €1 = $1·02. A commission was charged for this service. If the person received $7,956, calculate the percentage commission charged.

10. If €1 = $1·10 and €1 = R2·64, how many dollars can be exchanged for 2,112 rand?

11. An importer buys goods for $1,286·40 when the exchange rate is €1 = $1·34. If he sells them for €1,100, find his profit in euro.

12. A supplier agrees to buy 100 computers for $600 each. She plans to sell them for a total of €62,400.

    (i) Calculate the percentage profit, on the cost price, she will make if the exchange rate is €1 = $1·25.

    (ii) Calculate the percentage profit, on the cost price, if the exchange rate changes to €1 = $1·20.

Interest

Interest is the sum of money that you pay for borrowing money or that is paid to you for lending money.

When dealing with interest, we use the following symbols.

P = the **principal**, the sum of money borrowed or invested at the beginning of the period.

t = the **time**, the number of weeks/months/years for which the sum of money is borrowed or invested.

i = the **interest rate**, the percentage rate per week/month/year expressed as a fraction or a decimal at which interest is charged.

A = the **amount** of money, including interest, at the end of a week/month/year.

F = the **final amount**, i.e. the final sum of money, including interest, at the end of the period.

Note: per annum = per year.

Compound interest

When a sum of money earns interest, this interest is often added to the principal to form a new principal. This new principal earns interest in the next year and so on. This is called **compound interest**.

When calculating compound interest, do the following.

Method 1:

Calculate the interest for the **first** year and add this to the principal to form the new principal for the next year. Calculate the interest for **one** year on this new principal and add it on to form the principal for the next year, and so on. The easiest way to calculate each stage is to multiply the principal at the beginning of each year by the factor:

$$(1 + i)$$

This will give the principal for the next year, and so on.

Method 2:

If the number of years is greater than three, then using a formula and a calculator will be much quicker.

Use the formula: $F = P(1 + i)^t$

Note: The formula does not work if:

> the interest rate, i, is changed during the period
> **or**
> money is added or subtracted during the period.

EXAMPLE 1

Calculate the compound interest on €10,000 for three years at 4% per annum.

Solution:

$$1 + i = 1 + \frac{4}{100} = 1 + 0{\cdot}04 = 1{\cdot}04$$

Method 1:

$P_1 = 10{,}000$	(principal for the first year)
$A_1 = 10{,}000 \times 1{\cdot}04 = 10{,}400$	(amount at the end of the first year)
$P_2 = 10{,}400$	(principal for the second year)
$A_2 = 10{,}400 \times 1{\cdot}04 = 10{,}816$	(amount at the end of the second year)
$P_3 = 10{,}816$	(principal for the third year)
$A_3 = 10{,}816 \times 1{\cdot}04 = 11{,}248{\cdot}64$	(amount at the end of the third year)

Compound interest $= A_3 - P_1 = €11{,}248{\cdot}64 - €10{,}000 = €1{,}248{\cdot}64$.

The working can also be shown using a table:

Year	Principal	Amount
1	10,000	$10{,}000 \times 1{\cdot}04 = 10{,}400$
2	10,400	$10{,}400 \times 1{\cdot}04 = 10{,}816$
3	10,816	$10{,}816 \times 1{\cdot}04 = 11{,}248{\cdot}64$

Compound interest $= A_3 - P_1 = €11{,}248{\cdot}64 - €10{,}000 = €1{,}248{\cdot}64$.

Method 2:

Given: $P = 10{,}000$, $\quad i = \dfrac{4}{100} = 0{\cdot}04$, $\quad t = 3$. Find F.

$$F = P(1 + i)^t$$
$$= 10{,}000(1{\cdot}04)^3$$
$$F = 11{,}248{\cdot}64$$

Compound interest $= F - P = €11{,}248{\cdot}64 - €10{,}000 = €1{,}248{\cdot}64$.

EXAMPLE 2

€8,500 was invested for three years at compound interest. The rate for the first year was 6%, the rate for the second year was 8% and the rate for the third year was 5%.

Calculate: **(i)** the amount   **(ii)** the compound interest at the end of the third year.

Solution:

As the rate changes each year, we cannot use the formula.

Year	Principal	Amount	$(1 + i)$
1	8,500	$8,500 \times 1.06 = 9,010$	$\left(1 + \frac{6}{100} = 1.06\right)$
2	9,010	$9,010 \times 1.08 = 9,730.80$	$\left(1 + \frac{8}{100} = 1.08\right)$
3	9,730.80	$9,730.80 \times 1.05 = 10,217.34$	$\left(1 + \frac{5}{100} = 1.05\right)$

(i) The amount at the end of the third year is €10,217.34.

Alternatively, in one calculation: $A_3 =$ €8,500 × 1.06 × 1.08 × 1.05 = €10,217.34.

(ii) Compound interest $= A_3 - P_1 =$ €10,217.34 − €8,500 = €1,717.34.

Exercise 2.7 ~~Find the amount~~

In questions 1–8, ~~calculate the compound interest~~.

1. €12,000 for 2 years at 8% per annum
2. €15,000 for 2 years at 7% per annum
3. €18,000 for 3 years at 5% per annum
4. €25,000 for 3 years at 8% per annum
5. €750 for 3 years at 10% per annum
6. €5,000 for 3 years at 2% per annum
7. €12,400 for 2 years at 6·5% per annum
8. €80,000 for 3 years at 2·5% per annum
9. €4,000 was invested for two years at compound interest. The interest rate for the first year was 4% and for the second was 5%. Calculate the total interest earned.
10. €6,500 was invested for three years at compound interest. The interest rate for the first year was 5%, for the second year 8% and for the third year 12%. Calculate the total interest earned.
11. €7,500 was invested for three years at compound interest. The rate for the first year was 4%, the rate for the second year was 3% and the rate for the third year was $2\frac{1}{2}$%. Calculate the amount after three years.

Repayments/further investments

In some questions, money is repaid at the end of a year or a further investment is made at the beginning of the next year. It is important to remember that in these cases, the **formula does not work**. In the next example, F_1 = further investment at the beginning of the second year and $F_2 = a$ further investment at the beginning of the third year.

EXAMPLE 1

(i) A person invested €40,000 in a building society. The rate of interest for the first year was $3\frac{1}{2}\%$. At the end of the first year the person invested a further €6,000. The rate of interest for the second year was 4%. Calculate the value of the investment at the end of the second year.

(ii) At the end of the second year a further sum of €4,704 was invested. At the end of the third year the total value of the investment was €55,350. Calculate the rate of interest for the third year.

Solution:

(i) $P_1 = 40,000$

$A_1 = 40,000 \times 1{\cdot}035$ (amount at the end of the first year)

$\quad = 41,400$

$F_1 = 6,000$ (further investment of €6,000)

_____

$P_2 = 47,400$ ($A_1 + F_1 = P_2$ = principal for the second year)

$A_2 = 47,400 \times 1{\cdot}04$

$A_2 = 49,296$ (amount at the end of the second year)

Therefore, the value of the investment at the end of the second year = €49,296.

(ii) $F_2 = 4,704$ (further investment of €4,704)

$P_3 = A_2 + F_2$ ($A_2 + F_2 = P_3$ = principal for the third year)

$P_3 = 49,296 + 4,704 = 54,000$

Given $A_3 = 55,350$ (amount at the end of the third year)

Interest for the third year $= A_3 - P_3 = 55,350 - 54,000 = 1,350$

$$\text{Interest rate for the third year} = \frac{\text{Interest for the third year}}{\text{Principal for the third year}} \times 100\%$$

$$= \frac{1,350}{54,000} \times 100\%$$

$$= 2\tfrac{1}{2}\%$$

EXAMPLE 2

(i) A person invested €20,000 for three years at 6% per annum compound interest. Calculate the amount after two years.

(ii) After two years, a sum of money was withdrawn. The money which remained amounted to €22,260 at the end of the third year. Calculate the amount of money withdrawn after two years.

Solution:

(i) $P_1 = 20,000$ (principal for the first year)

           $A_1 = 20,000 \times 1 \cdot 06 = 21,200$ (amount at the end of the first year)

           $P_2 = 21,200$ (principal for the second year)

           $A_2 = 21,200 \times 1 \cdot 06 = 22,472$ (amount at the end of the second year)

    ∴ The amount after two years = €22,472.

(ii) At this point, a sum of money was withdrawn.

    What we do is **work backwards** from the end of the third year.

           $A_3 = 22,260$ (amount at the end of the third year)

           ∴ 106% = 22,260   (increased by 6% during the year)

           1% = 210   (divide both sides by 106)

           100% = 21,000   (multiply both sides by 100)

    ∴ The principal for the third year, P_3, was €21,000.

    But the amount at the end of the second year, A_3, was €22,472.

    ∴ The sum of money withdrawn at the end of the second year

    $= A_2 - P_3 = €22,472 - €21,000 = €1,472$.

Exercise 2.8

1. A woman borrowed €30,000 at 6% per annum compound interest. She agreed to repay €5,000 at the end of the first year, €5,000 at the end of the second year and to clear the debt at the end of the third year. How much was paid to clear the debt?

2. A man borrowed €40,000 at 4% per annum compound interest. He agreed to repay €8,000 at the end of the first year, €9,000 at the end of the second year and to clear the debt at the end of the third year. How much was paid to clear the debt?

3. A man borrowed €15,000. He agreed to repay €2,000 after one year, €3,000 after two years and the balance at the end of the third year. If interest was charged at 8% in the first year,

5% in the second year and 6% in the third year, how much was paid at the end of the third year to clear the debt?

4. €4,000 was invested for one year. The interest earned was €120. Calculate the rate of interest.

5. €2,500 amounts to €2,600 after one year. Calculate the rate of interest.

6. €8,400 amounts to €8,694 after one year. Calculate the rate of interest.

7. €6,500 amounts to €6,662·50 after one year. Calculate the rate of interest.

8. €12,000 was invested for two years at compound interest.

   (i) The interest at the end of the first year was €600. Calculate the rate of interest for the first year.

   (ii) At the end of the second year the investment was worth €13,167. Calculate the rate of interest for the second year.

9. €60,000 is borrowed for two years. Interest for the first year is charged at 4% per annum.

   (i) Calculate the amount owed at the end of the first year.

   (ii) €7,400 is then repaid. Interest is charged at r% per annum for the second year. The amount owed at the end of the second year is €56,650. Calculate the value of r.

10. €40,000 was invested for three years at compound interest. The rate of interest was 4% per annum for the first year and $3\frac{1}{2}$% per annum for the second year.

   (i) Calculate the amount of the investment after two years.

   (ii) A further €2,444 was invested. If the investment amounted to €46,637·50 at the end of the third year, calculate the rate of interest for the third year.

11. (i) A person invested €20,000 in a building society. The rate of interest for the first year was $2\frac{1}{2}$%. At the end of the first year the person invested a further €2,000. The rate of interest for the second year was 2%. Calculate the value of the investment at the end of the second year.

   (ii) At the end of the second year a further sum of €1,050 was invested. At the end of the third year the total value of the investment was €24,720. Calculate the rate of interest for the third year.

12. €10,000 was invested for three years at compound interest. The rate for the first year was 4%. The rate for the second year was $4\frac{1}{2}$%.

   (i) Find the amount of the investment at the end of the second year.

   (ii) At the beginning of the third year a further €8,000 was invested. The rate for the third year was r%. The total investment at the end of the third year was €19,434·04. Calculate the value of r.

13. €75,000 was invested for three years at compound interest. The rate for the first year was 3%. The rate for the second year was $2\frac{1}{2}\%$. At the end of the second year, €10,681·25 was withdrawn.

   (i) Find the principal for the third year.
   (ii) The rate for the third year was $r\%$. The total investment at the end of the third year was €70,897·50. Calculate the value of r.

In questions 14–17, it may make the working easier to calculate the amount after two years, then work backwards from the end of the third year to find the sum of money withdrawn.

14. A person invested €30,000 for three years at 5% per annum compound interest.

   (i) Calculate the amount after two years.
   (ii) After two years a sum of money was withdrawn. The money which remained amounted to €26,250 at the end of the third year. Calculate the amount of money withdrawn after two years.

15. A person invested €50,000 for three years at 4% per annum compound interest. At the end of the first year, €11,500 was withdrawn. At the end of the second year, another sum of money was withdrawn. At the end of the third year, the person's investment was worth €36,400. Calculate the amount of money withdrawn after two years.

16. €45,000 was invested for three years at compound interest. The interest rate for the first year was 6% per annum, the interest rate for the second year was 4% per annum and the interest rate for the third year was 3% per annum. At the end of the first year €7,700 was withdrawn. At the end of the second year €w was withdrawn. At the end of the third year the investment was worth €37,080. Find the value of w.

17. €60,000 was invested for three years at compound interest. The interest rate for the first year was $3\frac{1}{2}\%$ per annum, the interest rate for the second year was $2\frac{1}{2}\%$ per annum and the interest rate for the third year was 2% per annum. At the end of the first year €4,100 was withdrawn. At the end of the second year €w was withdrawn. At the end of the third year the investment was worth €56,100. Find the value of w.

Depreciation

For depreciation we multiply by the factor $(1 - i)$ for each year.

The formula for depreciation is:

$$F = P(1 - i)^t$$

P is the original value at the beginning of the period and F is the final amount at the end of the period.

EXAMPLE

A machine depreciates at 15% per annum. It was bought for €40,000.
How much is it worth after four years?

Solution:

Given: $P = 40,000,$ $i = \dfrac{15}{100} = 0{\cdot}15,$ $t = 4.$ Find F.

$$F = P(1 - i)^t$$
$$= 40,000(1 - 0{\cdot}15)^4$$
$$F = 20,880{\cdot}25$$

Thus, after four years, the machine is worth €20,880·25.

Exercise 2.9

1. A car depreciates at 15% per annum. It was bought for €30,000.
   How much is it worth after three years?
2. A machine depreciates at 10% per annum. It was bought for €55,000.
   How much is it worth after four years?

3. A machine cost €100,000 when new. In the first year it depreciates by 15%. In the second year it depreciates by 8% of its value at the end of the first year. In the third year it depreciates by 5% of its value at the end of the second year.

New price	€100,000
Value after 1 year	
Value after 2 years	
Value after 3 years	

   (i) By completing the table, calculate its value after three years.

   (ii) Calculate its total depreciation after three years.

4. A luxury car costs €50,000 when bought new. Each year it depreciates by 20%.

   (i) Copy and complete the following table.

Years after purchase	0	1	2	3	4
Value of car (€)	50,000	40,000			

   (ii) Plot the results on graph paper, putting the value of the car on the vertical axis.

   (iii) The graph is not linear. Why is this a good representation of the way cars depreciate?

5. A car was bought for €25,000. After one year, it had depreciated in value to €23,000.

   (i) What was the annual percentage rate of depreciation?

   (ii) If the car depreciated at this rate for a further three years, what was it worth at the end of the fourth year? Give your answer correct to the nearest euro.

Annual equivalent rate (AER) and annual percentage rate (APR)

Nowadays, if you put your money into a savings account or into an investment, you should be given the annual equivalent rate (AER). You may have invested your money for any period of time, but the AER tells you how much your money would earn in **exactly one year**. For example, suppose a bank offers you a five-year deal: 4% interest for the first six months followed by 2% for the remainder of the time. It will be much simpler to compare this deal with others if you can compare them on some common standard. The AER would, in this case, give you one simple annual percentage to use for comparison.

When borrowing money, there are often other costs involved, such as a set-up fee. Because these other costs can be significant, lenders are expected to tell the borrower the annual percentage rate (APR). This again allows a potential borrower to compare different loans and see which is more expensive.

Two of the most common loans are mortgages (a loan to purchase a home) and credit cards.

Note: An APR for a five-year loan is likely to be different to that for a three-year loan, even from the same lender. This can occur because there may be a set-up fee or an introductory reduced interest rate. A set-up fee will have little effect on the APR if it is spread over more years.

EXAMPLE 1

Calculate the value of an investment of €20,000 for 12 years at an annual equivalent rate (AER) of 3%, correct to the nearest cent.

Solution:

As $t > 3$, it is easier to use the formula.

Given: $P = 20,000,$ $i = \dfrac{3}{100} = 0.03,$ $t = 12.$ Find F.

$$F = P(1 + i)^t$$
$$= 20,000\,(1.03)^{12}$$
$$= 28,515.21774$$
$$= 28,515.22 \qquad \text{(correct to the nearest cent)}$$

The value of the investment = €28,515·22.

EXAMPLE 2

An investment of €50,000 will earn 15% interest after six years.
Calculate the annual equivalent rate (AER), correct to two decimal places.

Solution:

The final amount = €50,000 × 1·15 = €57,500.
Given: $P = 50,000,$ $F = 57,500,$ $t = 6.$ Find i.
Rewrite the formula so that the unknown is on the left.

$$P(1 + i)^t = F \qquad \text{(rewrite formula)}$$

$$50,000(1 + i)^6 = 57,500$$

$$(1 + i)^6 = \frac{57,500}{50,000} \qquad \text{(divide both sides by 50,000)}$$

$$(1 + i) = \sqrt[6]{\frac{57,500}{50,000}} \qquad \text{(get the sixth root of both sides)}$$

$$= 1.023567073$$

$$= 1.02 \qquad \text{(correct to two decimal places)}$$

The annual equivalent rate (AER) = 1·02%.

Depending on the model of your calculator and noting some functions need $\boxed{\text{SHIFT}}$ or $\boxed{\text{2nd F}}$, one of the following might work. Check the manual for your calculator.

(older) 6 $\boxed{\sqrt[x]{}}$ $\boxed{(}$ 57,500 $\boxed{\div}$ 50,000 $\boxed{)}$ $\boxed{=}$

(newer) $\boxed{\sqrt[x]{}}$ 6 $\boxed{\text{RIGHT}}$ $\boxed{\text{FRACTION}}$ 57,500 $\boxed{\text{DOWN}}$ 50,000 $\boxed{\text{RIGHT}}$ $\boxed{=}$

Exercise 2.10

In questions 1–4, calculate the value of the investment to the nearest cent after the given period.

1. €20,000 for eight years with an AER of 5%
2. €15,000 for four years with an AER of 7%
3. €36,000 for six years with an AER of 4%
4. €24,000 for 10 years with an AER of 2%

In questions 5–8, calculate the amount owing to the nearest cent after the given period.

5. €5,000 for three years with an APR of 6%
6. €12,000 for five years with an APR of 5%
7. €6,000 for six years with an APR of 4·5%
8. €4,000 for four years with an APR of $2\frac{1}{2}$%

9.   (i) Calculate the interest gained by investing €200 for one year:
  - (a) With 10% added at the end of the year
  - (b) With 5% added after each six months
  - (ii) What is the AER of each?
  - (iii) How would the interest compare if the investment had $2\frac{1}{2}$% added every three months?

10. Calculate the value of investing €100 for each of the following. Where appropriate, give answers correct to two decimal places.
  - (i) One year with 10% interest paid at the end of the year
  - (ii) One year with 6% interest paid after each six months
  - (iii) 12 months with 2% paid after every two months
  - (iv) Deduce the annual equivalent rate (AER) for each.

11.   (i) A credit card charges $1\frac{1}{2}$% interest on unpaid monthly balances. If €1,000 is borrowed at the beginning of a month and not paid for a year, how much will be owed?
  - (ii) What should the credit card company declare as the APR for this card? Give your answer correct to one decimal place.

12.   (i) If $F = P(1 + i)^t$, express P in terms of F, i and t.
  - (ii) Hence or otherwise, find what sum of money will amount to €88,578·05 in six years with an AER of 10%.

13. What sum of money will amount to €243,101·25 in four years with an AER of 5%?

14. An investment of €20,000 will earn you 25% interest over five years.
  - (i) Calculate the annual equivalent rate (AER), correct to three decimal places.
  - (ii) How much interest will you earn in the first two years? Answer to the nearest euro.
  - (iii) Why is 25% over five years not the same as 5% annually?

15. Two people invest money for eight years with a return of 20% when the investment matures. Shane invests €200 while Aoife invests €300. Show that the annual equivalent rate for each investor is the same.

16. An investor is offered a return of 16% after seven years. Calculate the AER, correct to two decimal places.
  (Hint: Use a simple amount as the investment, such as €100 or €1,000.)

Distance, speed and time

There are three formulas to remember when dealing with problems involving distance (*D*), speed (*S*) and time (*T*). It can be difficult to remember these formulas; however, the work can be made easier using a triangle and the memory aid Dad's Silly Triangle.

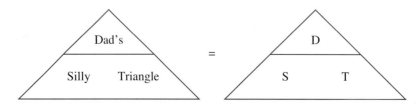

1. Speed = $\dfrac{\text{Distance}}{\text{Time}}$ 2. Time = $\dfrac{\text{Distance}}{\text{Speed}}$ 3. Distance = Speed × Time

Consider the triangle on the right. By covering the quantity required, *D*, *S* or *T*, any of the three formulas above can be found by inspection.

Note: Speed here means average speed.

Common units of speed

1. Kilometres per hour, written as km/h.

2. Metres per second, written as m/s.

Note: 'Per' means divided by.

Converting fractions or decimals of an hour to minutes
To convert fractions or decimals of an hour to minutes, **multiply by 60**.
For example:

$\frac{1}{3}$ hour = $\frac{1}{3}$ × 60 minutes = 20 minutes   0·7 hour = 0·7 × 60 minutes = 42 minutes

Converting minutes to hours
To convert minutes to hours, **divide by 60**.
For example:

15 minutes = $\frac{15}{60}$ hour = $\frac{1}{4}$ hour or 0·25 hour

48 minutes = $\frac{48}{60}$ hour = $\frac{4}{5}$ hour or 0·8 hour

EXAMPLE

(i) A train takes 3 hours 30 minutes to travel 280 km. Calculate the average speed in km/h.

(ii) How long, in hours and minutes, does it take a bus to travel 168 km at an average speed of 96 km/h?

(iii) A car travelled at an average speed of 120 km/h between 12:55 and 14:10. What distance did it travel?

Solution:

(i) Time has to be expressed in hours.

3 hours 30 minutes = $3\frac{1}{2}$ hours

$$\text{Speed} = \frac{\text{Distance}}{\text{Time}}$$

$$= \frac{280}{3\frac{1}{2}}$$

$$= 80 \text{ km/h}$$

(iii) 14 hrs 10 mins − 12 hrs 55 mins

$= 1$ hr 15 mins

$= 1\frac{1}{4}$ hrs

(ii) $\text{Time} = \dfrac{\text{Distance}}{\text{Speed}}$

$$= \frac{168}{96}$$

$$= 1 \cdot 75 \text{ hours}$$

$$= 1 \text{ hour } 45 \text{ minutes}$$

$(0 \cdot 75 \text{ hour} = 45 \text{ minutes})$

$\text{Distance} = \text{Speed} \times \text{Time}$

$$= 120 \times 1\frac{1}{4}$$

$$= 150 \text{ km}$$

Two-part problems

Two-part questions on distance, speed and time involve two separate journeys. In these questions we need the total distance travelled for both journeys and the total time for both journeys. We then use the formula:

$$\text{Overall average speed for both journeys} = \frac{\text{Total distance for both journeys}}{\text{Total time for both journeys}}$$

EXAMPLE

A train travelled 168 km at an average speed of 112 km/h. It then travelled for 45 minutes at an average speed of 100 km/h. Calculate:

(i) The total distance travelled

(ii) The total time taken

(iii) The average speed for the whole journey

Solution:

In the first journey, the time is required.

$$\text{Time} = \frac{\text{Distance}}{\text{Speed}}$$

$$= \frac{168}{112}$$

$$= 1\tfrac{1}{2} \text{ hours}$$

In the second journey, the distance is required.

$$\text{Distance} = \text{Speed} \times \text{Time}$$

$$= 100 \times \tfrac{3}{4}$$

$$= 75 \text{ km}$$

(**Note:** 45 minutes $= \tfrac{3}{4}$ hour)

(i) Total distance travelled $= 168 + 75 = 243$ km

(ii) Total time $= 1\tfrac{1}{2} + \tfrac{3}{4} = 2\tfrac{1}{4}$ hours

(iii) Average speed for the whole journey $= \dfrac{\text{Total distance travelled}}{\text{Total time taken}}$

$$= \frac{243}{2\tfrac{1}{4}} = 108 \text{ km/h}$$

Exercise 2.11

1. Express each of the following in minutes.

   (i) 0·5 hr   (ii) 0·6 hr   (iii) 0·1 hr   (iv) 0·7 hr   (v) 0·4 hr

2. Express each of the following in hours and minutes.

   (i) 1·2 hrs   (ii) $2\tfrac{3}{4}$ hrs   (iii) 3·35 hrs   (iv) $1\tfrac{1}{3}$ hrs   (v) 2·45 hrs

3. Express each of the following in hours.

   (i) 15 mins   (ii) 20 mins   (iii) 1 hr 30 mins   (iv) 2 hrs 45 mins   (v) 3 hrs 24 mins

4. A train takes 3 hours 30 minutes to travel 280 km. Calculate the average speed in km/h.

5. How long, in hours and minutes, does it take a bus to travel 168 km at an average speed of 96 km/h?

6. A car travelled at an average speed of 120 km/h between 12:55 and 14:10. What distance did it travel?

7. The distance, by rail, between Galway and Dublin is 240 km. On Tuesday, a train left Galway at 13:05 and travelled to Dublin. The average speed for this journey of 240 km was 100 km/h. At what time did the train arrive in Dublin?

8. Cormac went by car from Limerick to Cork, a journey of 100 km. He travelled at an average speed of 80 km/h.

   (i) How many hours and minutes did it take Cormac to complete the journey?

  (ii) Cormac left Limerick at 11:15. At what time did he arrive in Cork?

 (iii) Cormac's car used 1 litre of petrol for every 16 km travelled. On that day petrol cost €1·24 per litre. Find the cost of the petrol used on Cormac's journey from Limerick to Cork.

9. Find the average speed of a car that completes a journey of 208 km in 3 hours 15 minutes.

10. A girl ran a distance of 3,600 m in 15 minutes. Calculate her average speed in m/s.

11. A motorcyclist begins a journey of 280 km at 15:00. If the average speed is 80 km/h, find the time at which the journey is completed.

12. (i) Express 4 hours 15 minutes in hours.

  (ii) A train starts a journey of 255 km at 09:40 and completes the journey at 13:55. What was the average speed of the train?

13. A car travels 54 km in 45 minutes. Calculate its average speed in km/h.

14. A train travels 52 km in 40 minutes. How far will it travel in 1 hour 10 minutes at the same average speed?

15. Anne walks a distance of 1·7 km to school from home. She walks at an average speed of 5·1 km/h. What is the latest time she can leave home to be in school at 08:55?

16. A train travels 180 m in 10 seconds. What is its speed in (i) m/s   (ii) km/h?

17. A car travels 28 km at an average speed of 80 km/h. How long does the journey take?

18. A cyclist travels for 45 minutes at an average speed of 19 km/h. What distance does the cyclist travel?

19. Mary leaves her home at 06:40. She drives 87 km to work and she travelled at an average speed of 36 km/h. At what time did she arrive at work?

20. In a athletics match, the 100 m race was won in a time of 9·92 s and the 200 m race was won in a time of 19·92 s. Which race was won with the slowest average speed? Justify your answer.

21. A cyclist and a bus leave the same place at the same time to the same destination. However, the cyclist and the bus take two different routes. The cyclist's route takes 15 minutes at an average speed of 20 km/h. The route for the bus is 3 km longer. Calculate the average speed of the bus if it is to arrive at the destination at the same time.

22. When a cyclist had travelled a distance of 12·6 km, he had completed $\frac{3}{7}$ of his journey. What was the length of the journey?

23. In a 4 × 400 m relay race, the split times of the runners for each leg of a team are shown in the table.
Calculate, correct to two decimal places, in m/s:
   (i) The average speed of each runner
   (ii) The average speed of the relay team

First leg	46·15
Second leg	45·36
Third leg	45·04
Fourth leg	44·82

24. Frank drove from his home to his friend's house. He drove the first 3 hours at an average speed of 60 km/h. He then drove the remaining 90 km at an average speed of 45 km/h. Calculate Frank's average speed for the whole journey.

25. A car travels 100 km at an average speed of 50 km/h and then 180 km at an average speed of 60 km/h. Calculate: **(i)** the total distance travelled **(ii)** the total time taken **(iii)** the overall average speed.

26. A bus travels for 300 km at an average speed of 75 km/h and then 162 km at an average speed of 81 km/h. Calculate: **(i)** the total time taken **(ii)** the total distance travelled **(iii)** the overall average speed.

27. A woman drove her car for 200 km at an average speed of 80 km/h and then for 60 km at an average speed of 40 km/h. Find: **(i)** the total time taken **(ii)** the total distance travelled **(iii)** the overall average speed.

28. On an outward journey of 280 km, a driver takes $3\frac{1}{2}$ hours. On the return journey she takes a shortcut, driving at an average speed of 104 km/h, and this takes one hour less than the outward journey. Calculate the overall average speed.

29. A lorry travels 189 km in $3\frac{1}{2}$ hours. It then travels for $4\frac{1}{2}$ hours at an average speed of 70 km/h.
   (i) How far has it travelled altogether?
   (ii) What is the total time taken?
   (iii) What is the overall average speed?

30. On an outward journey of 330 km, a driver takes 6 hours, and on the return journey he takes one hour less. Calculate:
   (i) The average speed of the outward journey
   (ii) The average speed of the return journey
   (iii) The total time and the total distance
   (iv) The overall average speed

Universal Social Charge (USC)

A new tax, the Universal Social Charge (USC), was introduced in 2011 to be applied to gross income. Initially, the rates were:

0% if total annual income is €4,004 or under.

However, once over €4,004, the **full** annual income is taxed as:

2% for the first €10,036

4% for the next €5,980

7% on the balance

EXAMPLE

A woman earns €36,000 and is required to pay the Universal Social Charge (USC) as follows:

2% for the first €10,036

4% for the next €5,980

7% on the balance

What amount must she pay?

Solution:

Her income is over €10,036, so €36,000 − €10,036 = €25,964 must be paid at a higher rate. This is more than €5,980, so €25,964 − €5,980 = €19,984 must be paid at the highest rate. Her income must be split into three separate amounts:

Income (€)	Rate	Calculation	USC (€)
10,036	2%	10,036 × 0·02	200·72
5,980	4%	5,980 × 0·04	239·20
19,984	7%	19,984 × 0·07	1,398·88
36,000			1,838·80

She must pay €1,838·80.

Exercise 2.12

In questions 1–8, calculate the Universal Social Charge on the given salary if the rates are:

> 0% if under €5,000
>
> 2% for the first €10,000 of the full salary
>
> 3% for the next €6,000
>
> 6% on the balance

1. €8,000	2. €15,000	3. €25,000	4. €12,000
5. €20,000	6. €4,000	7. €160,000	8. €100,000

In questions 9–16, calculate the Universal Social Charge on the given salary if the rates are:

> 0% if €4,004 or under
>
> 2% for the first €10,036 of the full salary
>
> 4% for the next €5,980
>
> 7% on the balance

9. €9,500	10. €7,500	11. €14,000	12. €28,000
13. €40,000	14. €90,000	15. €240,000	16. €4,010

17. Two students work during their summer break, earning €100 per weekday and €150 on Saturdays. Alex works for eight weeks but does not work on Saturdays. Bruce works for seven weeks including Saturdays.

    (i) What is the gross earnings of each student?

    (ii) A Universal Social Charge (0% if €4,004 or under but 2% for the first €10,036 of the full salary if over €4,004) is applied. What is the Universal Social Charge for each student?

    (iii) Alex had considered working for one extra day on the Monday of the ninth week. Why might she have decided not to work?

    (iv) How much extra would she have earned for that day's work?

Income tax

The following is called the income tax equation:

> Gross tax − tax credit = tax payable

Gross tax is calculated as follows:

> Standard rate on all income up to the standard rate cut-off point
> +
> A higher rate on all income above the standard rate cut-off point

EXAMPLE 1

A woman has a gross yearly income of €48,000. She has a standard rate cut-off point of €27,500 and a tax credit of €3,852. The standard rate of tax is 18% of income up to the standard rate cut-off point and 37% on all income above the standard rate cut-off point. Calculate:

(i) The amount of gross tax for the year

(ii) The amount of tax paid for the year

Solution:

(i) Gross tax = 18% of €27,500 + 37% of €20,500

$\qquad$ = €27,500 × 0.18 × €20,500 + 0·37

$\qquad$ = €4,950 + €7,585

$\qquad$ = €12,535

> Income above the standard rate cut-off point
> = €48,000 − €27,500
> = €20,500

(ii) Income tax equation:

Gross tax − tax credit = tax payable

€12,535 − €3,852 = €8,683

Therefore, she paid €8,683 in tax.

Note: If a person earns less than their standard rate cut-off point, then they pay tax only at the standard rate on all their income.

EXAMPLE 2

A man paid €10,160 in tax for the year. He had a tax credit of €3,980 and a standard rate cut-off point of €26,000. The standard rate of tax is 17% of income up to the standard rate cut-off point and 36% on all income above the standard rate cut-off point. Calculate:

(i) The amount of income taxed at the rate of 36%

(ii) The man's gross income for the year

Solution:

(i) Income tax equation:

$$\text{Gross tax} - \text{tax credit} = \text{tax payable}$$

$$17\% \text{ of } €26{,}000 + 36\% \text{ of (income above cut-off point)} - €3{,}980 = €10{,}160$$

$$€4{,}420 + 36\% \text{ of (income above cut-off point)} - €3{,}980 = €10{,}160$$

$$36\% \text{ of (income above cut-off point)} + €440 = €10{,}160$$

$$36\% \text{ of (income above cut-off point)} = €9{,}720$$

$$1\% \text{ of (income above cut-off point)} = €270$$

(divide both sides by 36)

$$100\% \text{ of (income above cut-off point)} = €27{,}000$$

(multiply both sides by 100)

Therefore, the amount of income taxed at the higher rate of 36% was €27,000.

(ii) Gross income = standard rate cut-off point + income above the standard rate cut-off point

$$= €26{,}000 + €27{,}000 = €53{,}000$$

Exercise 2.13

In questions 1–4, make out a tax table similar to the following:

Gross pay	
Tax @ %	
Tax @ %	
Gross tax	
Tax credit	
Tax payable	
Take-home pay	

1. A woman has a gross yearly income of €39,000. She has a standard rate cut-off point of €24,000 and a tax credit of €3,800. The standard rate of tax is 20% of income up to the standard rate cut-off point and 42% on all income above the standard rate cut-off point. Calculate:

   (i) The amount of gross tax for the year

   (ii) The amount of tax paid for the year

2. A man has a gross yearly income of €37,000. He has a standard rate cut-off point of €20,500 and a tax credit of €2,490. The standard rate of tax is 18% of income up to the standard rate cut-off point and 38% on all income above the standard rate cut-off point. Calculate:

   (i) The amount of gross tax for the year

   (ii) The amount of tax paid for the year

3. A man has a gross yearly income of €43,000. He has a standard rate cut-off point of €28,400 and a tax credit of €3,240. The standard rate of tax is 15% of income up to the standard rate cut-off point and 35% on all income above the standard rate cut-off point. Calculate:

   (i) The amount of gross tax for the year

   (ii) The amount of tax paid for the year

4. A woman has a gross yearly income of €48,700. She has a standard rate cut-off point of €29,250 and a tax credit of €3,150. The standard rate of tax is 16% of income up to the standard rate cut-off point and 37% on all income above the standard rate cut-off point. Calculate:

   (i) The amount of gross tax for the year

   (ii) The amount of tax paid for the year

5. A man has a gross yearly income of €26,000. He has a standard rate cut-off point of €28,000 and a tax credit of €1,800. If he pays tax of €3,400, calculate the standard rate of tax.

6. A woman has a gross yearly income of €27,500. She has a standard rate cut-off point of €29,300 and a tax credit of €2,115. If she pays tax of €2,835, calculate the standard rate of tax.

7. A woman paid €10,280 in tax for the year. She had a tax credit of €2,540 and a standard rate cut-off point of €29,000. The standard rate of tax is 18% of income up to the standard rate cut-off point and 40% on all income above the standard rate cut-off point. Calculate:

   (i) The amount of income taxed at the rate of 40%

   (ii) The gross income for the year

8. A man paid €10,775 in tax for the year. He had a tax credit of €1,960 and a standard rate cut-off point of €28,500. The standard rate of tax is 15% of income up to the standard rate cut-off point and 36% on all income above the standard rate cut-off point. Calculate:

   (i) The amount of income taxed at the rate of 36%

   (ii) The gross income for the year

The USC and income tax

Both taxes are applied to the **gross salary** and could be applied in either order. We will calculate the USC first followed by the income tax payable.

EXAMPLE

Enda earns €200,000 in basic pay. The Universal Social Charge (USC) is as follows:

   2% for the first €10,036

   4% for the next €5,980

   7% on the balance

The standard rate of tax is 20% of income up to the standard rate cut-off point of €35,000 and 41% on all income above the standard rate cut-off point. Tax credits amount to €4,500.

Calculate Enda's take-home pay.

Solution:
Calculate the USC as before:

Income (€)	Rate	Calculation	USC (€)
10,036	2%	$10,036 \times 0.02$	200·72
5,980	4%	$5,980 \times 0.04$	239·20
183,984	7%	$183,984 \times 0.07$	12,878·88
200,000			13,318·80

Then calculate the income tax and include the USC.

Gross pay		200,000·00	
Tax @ 20% on €35,000	7,000		
Tax @ 41% on €165,000	67,650		
Gross tax	74,650		(add the two tax amounts)
Tax credit	4,500		
Tax payable		70,150·00	(subtract the tax credit)
USC		13,318·80	(from above)
Total payable		83,468·80	(add the two taxes)
Take-home pay		116,531·20	(subtract taxes from gross pay)

Exercise 2.14

In questions 1–4, calculate the take-home pay for the given gross annual salary and tax credit. The Universal Social Charge is calculated as follows:

0% if under €5,000

2% for the first €10,000 of the full salary

3% for the next €6,000

6% on the balance

The standard rate of tax is 20% of income up to the standard rate cut-off point of €32,000 and 40% on all income above the standard rate cut-off point.

1. Salary: €10,000; tax credit: €1,500
2. Salary: €45,000; tax credit: €4,200
3. Salary: €80,000; tax credit: €5,200
4. Salary: €120,000; tax credit: €4,800

In questions 5–8, calculate the take-home pay for the given gross annual salary. The Universal Social Charge is calculated as follows:

0% if €4,004 or under

2% for the first €10,036 of the full salary

4% for the next €5,980

7% on the balance

The standard rate of tax is 21% of income up to the standard rate cut-off point of €28,000 and 41% on all income above the standard rate cut-off point.

5. Salary: €15,000; tax credit: €3,600
6. Salary: €38,000; tax credit: €5,000
7. Salary: €150,000; tax credit: €6,100
8. Salary: €300,000; tax credit: €7,500

Index notation

Index notation is a shorthand way of writing very large or very small numbers. For example, try this multiplication on your calculator: 8,000,000 × 7,000,000.

The answer is 56,000,000,000,000.

It has 14 digits, which is too many to show on most calculator displays.

Your calculator will display your answer as $\boxed{5.6 \text{ E } 13}$ or $\boxed{5.6 \times 10^{13}}$ or $\boxed{5.6^{13}}$
This tells you that the 5·6 is multiplied by 10^{13}.
This is written as:

$$5.6 \times 10^{13}$$

This part is a number between 1 and 10 (but not including 10).

This part is written as a power of 10 (the power is always a whole number).

Another example to try on your calculator is 0·000 000 23 × 0·000 000 04.
The answer is 0·000 000 000 000 009 2.

Your calculator will display your answer as $\boxed{9.2 \text{ E} -15}$ or $\boxed{9.2 \times 10^{-15}}$ or $\boxed{9.2^{-15}}$

This tells you that the 9·2 is multiplied by 10^{-15}.
This is written as:
$$9.2 \times 10^{-15}$$

This way of writing a number is called **index notation** or **exponential notation**, or sometimes **standard form**. (It was formerly called **scientific notation**.)

Index notation gives a number in two parts

| Number between 1 and 10 (but not 10) | × | Power of 10 |

This is often written as $a \times 10^n$, where $1 \le a < 10$ and $n \in \mathbb{Z}$.

EXAMPLE 1

Express 3,700,000 in the form $a \times 10^n$, where $1 \leq a < 10$, $n \in \mathbb{Z}$.

Solution:

$$3,700,000 \cdot \text{ (put in the decimal point)}$$

$$3 \cdot 700\ 000 \text{ (move the decimal point six places to the \textbf{left}}$$

$$\text{to give a number between 1 and 10)}$$

$$\therefore 3,700,000 = 3 \cdot 7 \times 10^6$$

EXAMPLE 2

Express the number $0 \cdot 000846$ in the form $a \times 10^n$, where $1 \leq a < 10$, $n \in \mathbb{Z}$.

Solution:

$$0 \cdot 000846 \text{ (decimal point already there)}$$

$$8 \cdot 46 \text{ (move the decimal point four places to the \textbf{right}}$$

$$\text{to give a number between 1 and 10)}$$

$$\therefore 0 \cdot 000846 = 8 \cdot 46 \times 10^{-4}$$

EXAMPLE 3

(i) Express $\dfrac{1,456}{0.28}$ in the form $a \times 10^n$, where $1 \leq a < 10$, $n \in \mathbb{Z}$.

(ii) Find n if $\dfrac{441}{0 \cdot 007} = 6 \cdot 3 \times 10^n$.

Solution:

(i) $\dfrac{1,456}{0 \cdot 28} = 5,200 = 5 \cdot 2 \times 10^3$

(ii) $\dfrac{441}{0 \cdot 007} = 63,000 = 6 \cdot 3 \times 10^4$

By comparing $6 \cdot 3 \times 10^n$ to $6 \cdot 3 \times 10^4$,

$n = 4$.

Exercise 2.15

In questions 1–16, evaluate and express the result in the form $a \times 10^n$, where $1 \leq a < 10$ and $n \in \mathbb{Z}$.

1.	8,000	2.	54,000	3.	347,000	4.	470
5.	2,900	6.	3,400,000	7.	394	8.	39
9.	0·006	10.	0·0009	11.	0·052	12.	0·000432

13. $\dfrac{1,512}{0·36}$

14. $\dfrac{624}{0·008}$

15. $\dfrac{0·0048}{0·15}$

16. $\dfrac{0·0099}{2·2}$

In questions 17–19, calculate the value of n.

17. $\dfrac{2,856}{0·42} = 6·8 \times 10^n$

18. $\dfrac{73,080}{1·74} = 4·2 \times 10^n$

19. $\dfrac{0·0624}{2·6} = 2·4 \times 10^n$

Using a calculator

Most scientific calculators can be set to **display all answers** in index (scientific) notation. The procedure varies with different models and different manufacturers, so you are advised to read your calculator's manual. Furthermore, you will need to be able to return your calculator to its normal display settings.

Calculators that have a $\boxed{\text{SET UP}}$ button (which may need to be preceded with $\boxed{\text{SHIFT}}$) may offer you either an **FSE** option or take you to a list of display options. Selecting the **FSE** option may also take you to a list of display options.

The usual display options include **FIX**ed decimal place, **SCI**entific notation and **NORM**al. Using the **SCI** option will cause all answers to be displayed in index notation and the calculator screen should show **SCI** to confirm the display mode. You may continue to enter numbers in the usual manner.

To return your display to its usual state, you will need to go through the procedure again, this time choosing **NORM**al display. Most calculators have two versions of **NORM**al, so you may have to select **1** or **2**. The calculator screen will no longer show the **SCI** indicator.

Calculators that do not have a $\boxed{\text{SET UP}}$ button should have a MODE button, which if pressed repeatedly will provide display options.

Notes: 1. The display modes only refer to how the **answer** is displayed. You may enter numbers in any format at all times.

2. Very large and very small numbers are always displayed in index notation.

3. Remember to set your calculator back to **NORM**al display mode.

Addition and subtraction

Numbers given in index notation can be keyed into your calculator by using the **exponent key**. It is marked $\boxed{\text{EXP}}$ or $\boxed{\text{EE}}$ or $\boxed{\times 10^x}$.

To key in a number in index notation, do the following.

> 1. Key in 'a', the 'number part', first.
> 2. Press the exponent key next.
> 3. Key in the index of the power of 10.

To enter $3 \cdot 4 \times 10^6$, for example, key in $3 \cdot 4$ $\boxed{\text{EXP}}$ 6.

To enter negative powers, you need to find the **negative** button on your calculator. It is usually marked $\boxed{(-)}$ or $\boxed{+/-}$ and is used to enter negative numbers.

To enter $7 \cdot 1 \times 10^{-3}$, for example, key in $7 \cdot 1$ $\boxed{\text{EXP}}$ $\boxed{(-)}$ 3.

Note: If you press $\boxed{=}$ at the end, the calculator will write the number as a decimal number, provided the index of the power of 10 is not too large.

To add or subtract two numbers in index notation, do the following.

> 1. Write each number as a simple number.
> 2. Add or subtract these numbers.
> 3. Write your answer in index notation.
>
> Alternatively, you can use your calculator by keying in the numbers in index notation and adding or subtracting as required.

⬤ EXAMPLE 1

Express $2 \cdot 54 \times 10^4 - 3 \cdot 8 \times 10^3$ in the form $a \times 10^n$, where $1 \leq a < 10$ and $n \in \mathbb{Z}$.

Solution:

$$2 \cdot 54 \times 10^4 = 25{,}400$$
$$3 \cdot 8 \times 10^3 = \underline{\quad 3{,}800}$$
$$= 21{,}600 \qquad \text{(subtract)}$$
$$= 2 \cdot 16 \times 10^4$$

▦ $2 \cdot 54$ $\boxed{\text{EXP}}$ 4 $\boxed{-}$ $3 \cdot 8$ $\boxed{\text{EXP}}$ 3 $\boxed{=}$ $= 21{,}600$ (on the display) $= 2 \cdot 16 \times 10^4$

EXAMPLE 2

Express $2.68 \times 10^{-2} + 1.2 \times 10^{-3}$ in the form $a \times 10^n$, where $1 \leq a < 10$ and $n \in \mathbb{Z}$.

Solution:

$$2.68 \times 10^{-2} = 0.0268$$
$$1.2 \times 10^{-3} = \underline{0.0012}$$
$$= 0.0280 \qquad \text{(add)}$$
$$= 2.8 \times 10^{-2}$$

 2.68 [EXP] [(−)] 2 [+] 1.2 [EXP] [(−)] 3 [=] $= 0.028$ (on the display) $= 2.8 \times 10^{-2}$

Multiplication and division

To multiply or divide two numbers in index notation, do the following.

1. Multiply or divide the 'a' parts (the number parts).
2. Multiply or divide the powers of 10 (add or subtract the indices).
3. Write your answer in index notation.

Alternatively, you can use your calculator by keying in the numbers in index notation and multiplying or dividing as required.

EXAMPLE

Express **(i)** $(3.5 \times 10^2) \times (4.8 \times 10^3)$ **(ii)** $(4.86 \times 10^4) \div (1.8 \times 10^7)$ in the form $a \times 10^n$, where $1 \leq a < 10$ and $n \in \mathbb{Z}$.

Solution:

(i)
$$(3.5 \times 10^2) \times (4.8 \times 10^3)$$
$$= 3.5 \times 10^2 \times 4.8 \times 10^3$$
$$= 3.5 \times 4.8 \times 10^2 \times 10^3$$
$$= 16.8 \times 10^{2+3} \quad \text{(add the indices)}$$
$$= 16.8 \times 10^5$$
$$= 1,680,000$$
$$= 1.68 \times 10^6$$

 3.5 [EXP] 2 [×] 4.8 [EXP] 3 [=]
$= 1,680,000$ (on the display)
$= 1.68 \times 10^6$

(ii)
$$(4.86 \times 10^4) \div (1.8 \times 10^7)$$
$$= \frac{4.86 \times 10^4}{1.8 \times 10^7}$$
$$= \frac{4.86}{1.8} \times \frac{10^4}{10^7}$$
$$= 2.7 \times 10^{4-7} \quad \text{(subtract the indices)}$$
$$= 2.7 \times 10^{-3}$$

 4.86 [EXP] 2 [÷] 1.8 [EXP] 7 [=]
$= 0.0027$ (on the display)
$= 2.7 \times 10^3$

Exercise 2.16

In questions 1–22, simplify and express your answer in the form $a \times 10^n$, where $1 \leq a < 10$ and $n \in \mathbb{Z}$.

1. $2 \cdot 4 \times 10^3 + 8 \times 10^2$

2. $2 \cdot 52 \times 10^6 + 2 \cdot 8 \times 10^5$

3. $5 \cdot 48 \times 10^5 - 2 \cdot 8 \times 10^4$

4. $48 \cdot 2 \times 10^3 - 2 \cdot 52 \times 10^4$

5. $8 \cdot 45 \times 10^{-3} - 6 \cdot 5 \times 10^{-4}$

6. $3 \cdot 48 \times 10^{-4} - 5 \cdot 4 \times 10^{-5}$

7. $(1 \cdot 8 \times 10^3) \times (4 \times 10^4)$

8. $(2 \cdot 25 \times 10^4) \times (1 \cdot 6 \times 10^3)$

9. $(2 \cdot 2 \times 10^3) \times (3 \cdot 4 \times 10^2)$

10. $(5 \cdot 3 \times 10^2) \times (1.8 \times 10^4)$

11. $(3 \cdot 91 \times 10^5) \div (1 \cdot 7 \times 10^2)$

12. $(5 \cdot 04 \times 10^7) \div (3 \cdot 6 \times 10^2)$

13. $(8 \cdot 64 \times 10^5) \div (3 \cdot 6 \times 10^2)$

14. $(9 \cdot 86 \times 10^5) \div (1 \cdot 7 \times 10^2)$

15. $(3 \times 10^3) \div (2 \times 10^{-2})$

16. $(12 \cdot 6 \times 10^3) \div (4 \cdot 5 \times 10^7)$

17. $(5 \cdot 4 \times 10^2) \times (6 \cdot 5 \times 10^3)$

18. $(1 \cdot 35 \times 10^7) \div (2 \cdot 5 \times 10^3)$

19. $\dfrac{(2 \cdot 4 \times 10^4) \times (1 \cdot 5 \times 10^2)}{1 \cdot 2 \times 10^3}$

20. $\dfrac{(3 \cdot 2 \times 10^5) + (8 \cdot 5 \times 10^4)}{8 \cdot 1 \times 10^2}$

21. $\dfrac{2 \cdot 45 \times 10^5 - 1 \cdot 8 \times 10^3}{1 \cdot 6 \times 10^3}$

22. $\dfrac{1 \cdot 4 \times 10^3 + 5 \cdot 6 \times 10^2}{7 \times 10^{-1}}$

23. Calculate the value of $8 \cdot 45 \times 10^{-2} - 6 \cdot 5 \times 10^{-3}$.

    Write your answer as a decimal number.

    Say whether this number is greater than or less than $0 \cdot 08$.

24. Calculate the value of $\dfrac{2 \cdot 8 \times 10^4 + 4 \cdot 2 \times 10^5}{2 \cdot 24 \times 10^6}$.

    Write your answer as a decimal number.

    Say whether this number is greater than or less than $0 \cdot 19$.

25. $\sqrt{\dfrac{3 \cdot 64 \times 10^5 - 1 \cdot 7 \times 10^3}{9 \cdot 0575 \times 10^2}} = k$. Find the value of k.

Miscellaneous

Exercise 2.17

1. The owner of a small business agrees to give her staff an annual pay increase of 4% for the next three years.

   (i) If Paul is currently earning €23,000, what will his salary be (to the nearest euro) in three years' time?

(ii) Peter began employment just over 10 years ago. He began with a salary of €14,000 with a 3% increase per year. What is Peter's current salary to the nearest euro?

2. The population of a colony of rabbits in 2010 was 450. Allowing for births and deaths, it is estimated that the colony will grow by 12% annually. What is the expected population by 2020, to the nearest integer?

3. I invest €100,000 at an APR of 6%.

   (i) What will my investment be worth after 30 years (to the nearest cent)?

   (ii) What will my investment be worth after 35 years (to the nearest cent)?

   (iii) How long will it take to become €1 million?

4. Show that an APR of 10% is equivalent to 21% over two years.

5. A gift of €100 is invested for 21 years at an AER of 3%. What will it be worth (to the nearest euro) when it matures?

6. Harry invests €1,000 in a savings account with an AER of 4%.

   (i) Harry thinks it will double in value in 25 years. Explain why he is wrong.

   (ii) How much will it be worth in 25 years' time?

   (iii) At what rate would Harry's investment double in 25 years? Give your answer correct to one decimal place.

7. Jim is paid €7·50 an hour. The table shows the hours he worked during one week.

Day	Start	Finish
Monday	09:30	12:30
Tuesday	14:00	17:30
Friday	17:00	22:00

   (i) How many hours did Jim work?

   (ii) How much did he earn?

8. Holiday-makers who book with Sunny Travel and who cancel a holiday have to pay a charge. The cancellation charge depends on the number of days before the departure date when the customer cancels the holiday.

Number of days before departure date	Charge as a percentage of cost of holiday
29–55	40%
22–28	60%
15–21	80%
4–14	90%
3 or less	100%

   The cancellation charge is a percentage of the cost of the holiday, as shown in the table.

   (i) Bertie's holiday cost €650. He cancelled his holiday 26 days before the departure date. Calculate Bertie's cancellation charge.

   (ii) Joan's holiday cost €1,200. She had to pay a charge of €960. Estimate when she cancelled her holiday.

(iii) Ronald cancelled his holiday 30 days before the departure date. He had to pay a cancellation charge of €504. Calculate the cost of his holiday.

9. Alison pays a fixed monthly charge of €16 for her mobile phone. This charge includes 200 free text messages and 50 minutes of free call time each month. Further call time costs 28 cent per minute and additional text messages cost 11 cent each. In one month Alison sends 240 text messages and her call time is $2\frac{1}{2}$ hours.

   (i) Find the total cost of her fixed charge, text messages and call time.

   (ii) VAT is added to this cost at the rate of 21%. Find the amount paid, including VAT, to the nearest cent.

10. A supermarket has a special offer on three different brands of packets of soap. The following table gives details of the offer. Which brand has the cheapest price per gram?

Brand	No. of bars per packet	Weight of each bar	Price of packet
A	3	100 g	€1·35
B	6	100 g	€2·40
C	4	125 g	€2·38

In questions 11–27, express your answer in the form $a \times 10^n$, where $1 \leq a < 10$ and $n \in \mathbb{Z}$, unless otherwise instructed.

11. The base of a microchip is in the shape of a rectangle. Its length is 2×10^{-3} mm and its width is $1 \cdot 4 \times 10^{-3}$ mm. Find the area of the base of the microchip.

12. (i) Express 1·5 cm in m.

    (ii) Light travels at 3×10^8 m/s. Calculate the time it takes to travel 1·5 cm.

13. Given that $x = 2 \times 10^{-3}$ and $y = 7 \times 10^{-4}$, evaluate $x + 8y$.

14. (i) A floppy disk can store 1,440,000 bytes of data. Write the number 1,440,000 in the form $a \times 10^n$, where $1 \leq a < 10$ and $n \in \mathbb{Z}$.

    (ii) A hard disk can store $5 \cdot 112 \times 10^9$ bytes of data. Calculate the number of floppy disks needed to take a full copy of the hard disk.

15. (i) Light travels at a speed of approximately 3×10^8 m/s. How many kilometres will light travel in 8 minutes?

    (ii) The Andromeda galaxy is 21,900,000,000,000,000,000 km from Earth.

    Write this distance in the form $a \times 10^n$, where $1 \leq a < 10$ and $n \in \mathbb{Z}$, correct to two significant figures.

(iii) Calculate the number of years light takes to travel from the Andromeda galaxy to Earth, using 1 year = 365·25 days. Express your answer in the form $a \times 10^n$, where $1 \leq a < 10$ and $n \in \mathbb{Z}$, correct to two significant figures.

16. New York City produces more waste per person than any other city in the world. Each person produces an average of 1·6 kg of waste per day. The population of New York is about $1·5 \times 10^7$. Calculate, correct to two significant figures, the number of tonnes of waste produced in a year for New York City. (Note: 1 tonne = 10^3 kg. 1 year = 365 days.)

17. If $f = 5 \times 10^{-6}$, express $\frac{1}{f}$ in the form $a \times 10^n$, where $1 \leq a < 10$ and $n \in \mathbb{N}$.

18. The population density of a country is the average number of people per square kilometre. Sudan has a population of $2·75 \times 10^7$ and an area of $2·5 \times 10^6$ square kilometres. Calculate the population density of Sudan.

19. (i) A packet of A4 paper contains 5×10^2 sheets of paper. The packet is 6 cm in height. Calculate the thickness of one sheet of paper.

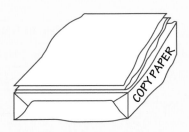

(ii) A magazine is made from 54 sheets of these A4 sheets of paper. The number of magazines printed is $6·48 \times 10^7$. Calculate the number of sheets of paper needed to print these magazines.

(iii) If all the magazines were piled up on top of each other, how high would the pile be? Give your answer to the nearest kilometre.

20. Express 2^{24} in the form $a \times 10^n$, where $1 \leq a < 10$ and $n \in \mathbb{N}$, correct to three significant figures.

21. The mass of Jupiter is $1·91 \times 10^{27}$ kg and the mass of Earth is $5·97 \times 10^{24}$ kg. How many times greater is the mass of Jupiter than the mass of Earth? Give your answer to an appropriate level of accuracy.

22. The circumference of the Earth at the equator is about 4×10^4 km. Calculate the length of the radius at the equator. Express your answer in the form $a \times 10^n$, where $1 \leq a < 10$ and $n \in \mathbb{Z}$, correct to three significant figures.

23. In 1981 the population of Peru was approximately $1·8 \times 10^7$. By 1988 the population had increased by 2·5 million. What would be the approximate population of Peru in 1988?

24. A postage stamp weighs $3·2 \times 10^{-5}$ kg. A speck of dust weighs $1·6 \times 10^{-7}$ kg. How many specks of dust weigh the same as a stamp?

25. The weight of an oxygen atom is $2 \cdot 7 \times 10^{-23}$ g and the weight of an electron is 9×10^{-28} g.

   If $k = \dfrac{\text{weight of an oxygen atom}}{\text{weight of an electron}}$, calculate the value of k.

26. The surface area of the Earth is approximately $5 \cdot 2 \times 10^{14}$ m^2. Approximately 30% of the surface area is land. What is the approximate area of the Earth that is covered by water?

27. Calculate h, the length of the hypotenuse of the right-angled triangle shown.

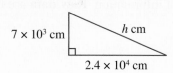

7×10^3 cm h cm

2.4×10^4 cm

Data

Data are pieces of information. **Raw data** are the data as they were collected before any processing has been done.

Primary data

Primary data (first-hand data) are data that you collect yourself or are collected by someone under your direct supervision.

Secondary data

Secondary data (second-hand data) are data that have already been collected and made available from an external source such as newspapers, government departments, organisations or the Internet.

Primary and secondary data have advantages and disadvantages.

Data	Advantages	Disadvantages
Primary	• Know how it was obtained. • Accuracy is also known.	• Time consuming. • Can be expensive.
Secondary	• Easy and cheap to obtain.	• Could be out of date. • May have mistakes and be biased. • Unknown source of collection.

Note: 'Data' is a plural word, so we should really say 'data are', not 'data is'. However, in everyday speech, most people use 'data' as a singular word. In this book we use data as a plural word.

Univariate data

When **one piece** of information is collected from each member of the sample, the data are called **univariate data**. Examples of univariate data are height, blood group or eye colour.

Bivariate data

When **two pieces** of information are collected from each member of the sample, the data are called **bivariate data**. Examples of bivariate data are age and height, number of hours spent studying and grades obtained in examinations, engine size and fuel consumption.

Types of data

Quantitative data

Quantitative data are data that are counted or measured. Numerical data are subdivided into **discrete** or **continuous** data.

<table>
<tr>
<td>

Discrete data
can only take particular values.

For example, shoe sizes:

| 5 | 5½ | 6 | 6½ | 7 | 7½ |

These values are discrete (separate). There are no values in between them. Discrete data have an **exact** value. (Fractions can be included.) Examples include goal scores, numbers on a die and number of children in a family.

</td>
<td>

Continuous data
can take any value within a range.

For example, your height, in cm:

These values can have any value in between, such as 164·3129 cm. Continuous data cannot be measured exactly, they are always rounded off. (Accuracy depends on the measuring device.) Examples include weight, temperature, pressure, time elapsed and area.

</td>
</tr>
</table>

Qualitative data

Qualitative data are data that **cannot be measured**. On our course we will meet two types of qualitative data: categorical and ordinal.

Categorical data

Categorical data are data that can only be described in words. The data are organised into categories, e.g. the colours red, blue and green. Other examples are place names, make of car and hobbies.

Ordinal data

Ordinal data are data organised in a logical order (ranking), such as examination grades: A, B, C, D, E, F, NG. Other examples are house numbers, numbers on a sports jersey or position in a race. It can be counted and ordered but not measured.

Exercise 3.1

Classify each of the following data as discrete, continuous, categorical or ordinal in questions 1–24.

1. Number of rooms in a school
2. Gender (male or female)
3. Height of a plant
4. Position in a race
5. Number of texts received today
6. Mass of a bar of soap

7. Number of goals scored in a match

8. Shoe colour

9. Number of coins in your pocket

10. Volume of a box

11. Speed of a car passing a house

12. Age correct to the nearest year

13. Distance from Cork to Galway

14. Football divisions

15. Leaving Certificate grades

16. Length of a road

17. Tyre pressure

18. Midday temperature

19. Country of birth

20. Favourite sport

21. Blood group

22. Types of trees in a forest

23. Area of a field

24. Length of your hair

25. The shirt sizes in a shop are 15, $15\frac{1}{2}$, 16, $16\frac{1}{2}$, 17, $17\frac{1}{2}$, 18 and $18\frac{1}{2}$. Are the shirt sizes discrete or continuous data? Justify your answer.

26. John says that he is 17 years of age. Is this continuous or discrete data? Discuss.

27. The waiter service at a restaurant is rated as follows:

    1 – Very poor   2 – Poor   3 – Fair

    4 – Good   5 – Very good   6 – Excellent

    Explain why this data is not numerical. What type of data is it?

28. Give one example of each of the following different types of data.

    (i) Discrete   (ii) Continuous

    (iii) Categorical   (iv) Ordinal

Collecting data

Census

The **population** is the complete set of data under consideration. For example, a population may be all the females in Ireland between the ages of 12 and 18, all the sixth year students in your school or the number of red cars in Ireland. A **census** is a collection of data relating to a population. A list of every item in a population is called a **sampling frame**.

Sample

A **sample** is a small part of the population selected. A **random sample** is a sample in which every member of the population has an equal chance of being selected. Data gathered from a sample are called **statistics**. Conclusions drawn from a sample can then be applied to the whole population (this is called **statistical inference**). However, it is very important that the sample chosen is representative of that population to avoid bias.

Bias

Bias (unfairness) is anything that distorts the data so that they will not give a representative sample. Bias can occur in sampling due to:

1. Failing to identify the correct population.
2. A sample size that is too small or using a sample that is not representative.
3. Careless or dishonest answers to questions.
4. Using questions that are misleading or ambiguous.
5. Failure to respond to a survey.
6. Errors in recording the data, for example recording 23 as 32.
7. The data can go out of date, for example conclusions drawn from an opinion poll can change over a period of time.

Reasons for using samples:

1. They are quick and cheap.
2. It is essential when the sampling units are destroyed (called destructive sampling). For example, we cannot test the lifetimes of every light bulb manufactured until they fail.
3. Quality of information gained is more manageable and better controlled, leading to better accuracy. (More time and money can be spent on the sample.)
4. It is often very difficult to gather data on a whole population.

Sample survey

A survey collects data (information). A **sample survey** is a survey that collects data from a sample of the population, usually using a questionnaire. Questionnaires are well-designed forms that are used to conduct sample surveys.

The main survey methods are:

- **Personal interview:** People are asked questions directly. This is regularly used in market research.
- **Telephone survey:** Often used for a personal interview.
- **Postal survey:** A survey is sent to someone's address.
- **Online questionnaires:** People fill out the questionnaire online.

Advantages and disadvantages of surveys are as follows.

Method	Advantages	Disadvantages
Personal interview (face to face)	• High response rate. • Can ask many questions. • Can ask more personal questions.	• Can be expensive. • Interviewer can influence response.
Telephone survey	• High response rate. • Can ask many questions. • Can ask more personal questions.	• Can be expensive. • Interviewer can influence response. • Easier to tell lies.
Postal survey	• Relatively cheap. • Can ask many questions. • Can ask more personal questions.	• Poor response rate. • Partly completed. • Limited in the type of data collected. • No way of clarifying any questions.
Online questionnaires	• Cheap and fast to collect large volumes of data. • More flexible design. • Ease of editing. • Can be sent directly to a database such as Microsoft Excel. • No interviewer bias. • Anonymity. • No geographical problems.	• Limited to those with access to an online computer. This leads to sample bias. • Technical problems (crashes, freezes). • Protecting privacy is an ethical issue.

Other methods for collecting data

Experiment

An **experiment** is a **controlled study** in which the researcher understands cause-and-effect relationships. The study is controlled. This method of collecting data is very popular with drug companies testing a new drug.

Observational studies

Data obtained by making observations are called **observational studies**. The data are collected by counting, measuring or noting things that happen. For example, a traffic survey might be done in this way to reveal the number of vehicles passing over a bridge. Important factors are place, time of day and the amount of time spent collecting the data. Observational studies can be laborious and time consuming.

Designed experiments

Data obtained by an experiment are called **designed experiments**. The data are collected by counting or measuring, e.g. throwing a die or tossing two coins a number of times and recording the results. The key things to remember are that the experiment must be repeated a number of times and that the experiment must be capable of being repeated by other people. **Data capture** is the process by which data are transferred from a paper copy, for example a questionnaire, to an electronic file, usually on a computer. Also, in an experiment, we can measure the effects, if any, that result from changes in the situation.

Surveys

Designing a questionnaire

Always have a clear aim for your survey and ask questions in a logical order.

A **questionnaire** is a set of questions used to obtain data from a population. Anyone who answers a questionnaire is called a **respondent**.

The questionnaire should:

Be clear about who is to complete it.	Be as brief as possible.
Start with simple questions.	Be able to be answered quickly.
Be clear how the answers are to be recorded.	Be clear where the answers are to be recorded.

The questions should:

Be short and use simple language.	Not be leading in any way, as this can influence the answer.
Provide tick boxes.	Not cause embarrassment or offend.
Be clear about what is asked.	Be relevant to the survey.
Allow a 'yes' or 'no' answer, a number or a response from a choice of answers.	Not be open-ended, which might produce long or rambling answers that are difficult to analyse.

Question	Comment
Gender: Male ☐ Female ☐	Good clear question.
How old are you?	Personal question, as people may be embarrassed to give their age. No indication of accuracy.
A better question would be: Which is your age group, in years? Under 18 18–40 41–60 Over 60 ☐ ☐ ☐ ☐	Only one response required. No gaps and no overlapping of boxes.

Question	Comment
You prefer to go out on Saturdays, don't you?	A leading question. It forces an opinion on the person being surveyed.
A better question is: On which day do you prefer to go out? Mon ☐ Tue ☐ Wed ☐ Thu ☐ Fri ☐ Sat ☐ Sun ☐	A much better question. Respondents have a choice. Better accuracy for the survey.
How much TV do you watch on a school weeknight? A lot ☐ A bit ☐ Very little ☐	This question is too vague.
A better question is: How many hours of TV, to the nearest hour, do you watch on a school weeknight? 0 ☐ 1 ☐ 2 ☐ 3 ☐ 4 or more ☐	This is more precise. Better accuracy for the survey.

Exercise 3.2

Comment critically on questions 1–7. If necessary, suggest how the question could be improved, either by rewriting the question and/or by giving a choice of answers.

1. Do you have a computer at home?   Yes ☐   No ☐

2. Saturday is the best day to have a disco, wouldn't you agree?

3. How many emails did you send today?   0–5 ☐   0–10 ☐   10 or more ☐

4. The waiter service in this restaurant is: Excellent ☐   Very good ☐

5. What do you think of our new and improved apple juice?

6. Sweets are bad for your teeth. Do you eat many sweets?

7. The new supermarket seems to be a great success. Do you agree?

8. Frank wants to find out how much time people spend playing computer games each week. Design a question he could use. Include tick boxes for a response.

9. Design a questionnaire with five questions you might include in a survey on school uniforms.

10. Draw up a short questionnaire to find out how students spend their leisure time. Briefly describe how you collect the data.

11. Brian wants to use a questionnaire to find out what kind of music the students at his school like. He also wants to find out if the boys and girls in his school like the same type of music and if there is a difference between year groups. Write down four questions that Brian might include in his questionnaire.

12. A company that makes toothpaste says the new brand is better than the old brand. A dentist wants to investigate this claim. He chooses 40 boys and 40 girls at random from his patients. The boys are given the new brand and the girls are given the old brand. After four months the dentist compares the boys' and girls' teeth.

   (i) Write down two reasons why this is not a reliable experiment.

   (ii) Give two ways in which this experiment could be improved.

13. Anne and Brendan carried out a sample survey of householders to see if they prefer to shop locally or in an out-of-town supermarket. They recorded their results in the following two-way table.

	Local shop	Out-of-town supermarket	Total
Men aged 25 or younger	18	12	30
Men older than 25	23	7	30
Women aged 25 or younger	6	24	30
Women older than 25	13	17	30
Total	60	60	120

Anne says, 'Sixty people prefer the local shop and 60 people prefer the out-of-town supermarket, so there is no difference in people's preferences.' Brendan says, 'I don't agree with you.' Explain why Brendan does not agree with Anne.

14. A company wants to find out what the public thinks of their products and services. To collect the data, they intend to use a questionnaire.

   (i) Write down three important points that should be remembered when designing the questionnaire.

   (ii) The company is going to post the questionnaire to people's homes. Give one
       (a) advantage and (b) disadvantage of using the postal system.

15. Prepare a data capture sheet for surveys to find out the following by observation.

   (i) The colours of cars at a road intersection

   (ii) The gender and approximate age of people entering a supermarket

16. Mary goes to an all-girls school. She decided to do a sample survey to find out the time students spent studying per week in her area. Mary chose 40 students randomly from her own school register and asked each of these students the time, to the nearest hour, they spent studying per week. The raw data were recorded as follows.

7 9 14   6   1 10   2   6   7 11 10   1 10   2   6   3   5   3   0   5

11 7 13 10   1   9   5   2 15   6   6 11   6   4   0 12   9 13   4   8

Complete the following grouped frequency table.

Time spent studying, in hours	0–3	4–7	8–11	12–15
Tally				
Number of students				

(i) Is this primary or secondary data? Give a reason for your answer.

(ii) Is the data discrete or continuous? Explain your answer.

(iii) Give two reasons why this may be a biased sample.

(iv) Suggest two ways Mary could improve her sample to make it more representative.

17. John carried out a survey to find out people's opinion on attending sports events in his local area. He stood outside the local sport stadium and asked a random sample of people their opinions on attending sport events as they entered the stadium.

(i) Is the data that John collects primary or secondary? Justify your answer.

(ii) Give two reasons why this sample may be biased.

(iii) Make two suggestions to John to improve the accuracy of his survey.

18. A soccer club with 300 members has 10 tickets to give to its members to attend an international soccer match. All 300 members want a ticket for the international match. Describe two fair methods that the club could use in choosing the 10 members at random to receive these international match tickets.

Averages

There are many types of averages. Three that we meet initially are called the **mean**, the **mode** and the **median**. They are also known as measures of central tendency.

Mean

The **mean** is the proper name for what most people call the average.

> The **mean** of a set of values is defined as the sum of all the values divided by the number of values.

That is:

$$\text{Mean} = \frac{\text{Sum of all the values}}{\text{Number of values}}$$

The formula is often written as:

$$\mu = \frac{\Sigma x}{n}$$

where:

(i) μ, pronounced as mu, is the symbol for the mean.

Note: Strictly speaking, μ should be called the **arithmetic mean**.

(ii) Σ, the Greek capital letter, pronounced sigma, means 'the sum of' (i.e. Σx means 'add up all the x-values').

(iii) n is the number of values of x.

(iv) You can use your calculator to add up a list of numbers, i.e. Σx is very easy to do on a calculator.

Mode

The mode of a set of items is the **item that occurs most often**. If there are no repeated items, then the mode does not exist. It's that simple!

Median

> When the values are arranged in ascending or descending order of size, then the **median** is the middle value. If the number of values is even, then the median is the average of the two middle values.

Note: Half the values lie below the median and half the values lie above the median.

EXAMPLE 1

The ages of the seven dwarfs are as follows.

Name	Happy	Doc	Sleepy	Sneezy	Dopey	Grumpy	Bashful
Age	685	702	498	539	402	685	619

(i) Find the mean age.

(ii) Find the (mode) modal age.

(iii) Find the median age.

Solution:

(i) Mean age $= \dfrac{\text{Sum of all their ages}}{\text{Number of dwarfs}} = \dfrac{\Sigma x}{n}$

$\text{Mean} = \dfrac{685 + 702 + 498 + 539 + 402 + 685 + 619}{7}$

$\mu = \text{Mean} = \dfrac{4{,}130}{7} = 590$

(ii) Mode = 685   The number that occurs most often

(Happy and Grumpy are twins!)

(iii) Median = Middle value in ascending or descending order

$= 702, 685, 685, \mathbf{619}, 539, 498, 402$

Median = 619

EXAMPLE 2

Find the mean, mode and median of 4, 0, 2, 6, 8, 2, 6, 6.

Solution:

$\text{Mean} = \dfrac{\text{Sum of all the values}}{\text{Number of values}} = \dfrac{\Sigma x}{n}$

$\text{Mean} = \dfrac{4 + 0 + 2 + 6 + 8 + 2 + 6 + 6}{8}$

$\mu = \text{Mean} = \dfrac{34}{8} = 4{\cdot}25$

Mode = 6, the number that occurs most often in the list

Median = middle value in the list 0, 2, 2, 4, 6, 6, 6, 8 in ascending order. Since there is an even number of numbers, we take the average of the two middle ones, 4 and 6.

$$\therefore \text{Median} = \frac{4+6}{2} = \frac{10}{2} = 5$$

Note: The mean and the median need not necessarily be members of the original set of values, while the mode, if it exists, is always a member of the original set of values.

A note on averages

Average	Advantages	Disadvantages
Mean	• Useful for further analysis. • Uses all the data. • Easy to calculate.	• Distorted by extreme results. • Mean is not always a given data value.
Mode	• Easy to find. • Not influenced by extreme values.	• Not very useful for further analysis. • May not exist.
Median	• Useful for further analysis. • Unaffected by extremes. • Easy to calculate if data are ordered.	• Not always a given data value. • Can be difficult to calculate.

Exercise 4.1

Find the mean, mode and median for questions 1–4.

1. 3, 7, 2, 5, 3

2. 10, 4, 5, 4, 12, 2, 8, 5, 4

3. 6·2, 9, 6·4, 7·4, 2·5

4. 2·8, 3·1, 6·7, 1·4, 5·6, 8·6

5. A waitress kept a record of her tips given to her each day for seven days.
   The record read: €3·68, €10·11, €2·93, €5·42, €1·94, €6·19, €5·15.
   (i) Calculate (a) the mean and (b) the median amount of tips given to her per day.
   (ii) Give a reason why there is no mode in the record.

6. The mean of five numbers is 9. Find the sum of the numbers.

7. The mean of the six numbers 10, 7, 3, 4, 9, x is 7. Find x and, hence, the median.

8. The mean of eight numbers is 9. When one of the numbers is taken away, the mean is increased by 1. Find the number that is taken away.

9. A footballer had an average of three points in his last seven games. How many points must he score in his next match if he is to increase his average to four?

10. Find the mean of $4a + 6$, $a - 3$, $7a + 12$, $3 - a$ and $4a + 7$.

11. (i) The mode of the nine numbers 2, 3, 7, 4, 9, 2, x, 3, 5 is x. How many different values of x are possible?

(ii) Given that x is also the median of the nine values, what is the exact value of x?

12. Dani sat a class maths test every week for five weeks. Her marks (out of 10) were recorded.

Week	One	Two	Three	Four	Five
Test result	2	7	9	2	8

Which of the three measures of average (mean, mode, median) would Dani use to describe her result to her parents, given that she wants to show her result in the best possible light? Give a reason for your answer.

13. Nine students on a school tour spent the following amounts:

€120   €65   €52   €47   €40   €28   €30   €34   €34

(i) Find the mean, mode and median.

(ii) In your view, which measure (mean, mode, median) describes the data most accurately? Justify your answer.

14. The temperature in degrees Celsius was measured at noon each day for 10 days:

22, 19, 27, 16, 21, 22, 18, 31, 23, 20.

(i) Find:
   (a) The mean
   (b) The median
   (c) The mode temperature

(ii) Which average best describes the temperature and why?

Frequency distribution table for discrete (countable) data

If the values in a distribution are arranged in ascending or descending order, showing their corresponding frequencies, the distribution is called a **frequency distribution**.

Note: If the values and frequencies are given in a table, it is called a **frequency distribution table**.

EXAMPLE

A casino owner tested a new six-sided die by throwing it 36 times and recording the results.

$$4 \quad 3 \quad 2 \quad 6 \quad 3 \quad 1 \quad 2 \quad 5 \quad 6 \quad 1 \quad 1 \quad 3$$
$$2 \quad 2 \quad 5 \quad 6 \quad 4 \quad 5 \quad 1 \quad 5 \quad 5 \quad 3 \quad 6 \quad 2$$
$$1 \quad 1 \quad 6 \quad 4 \quad 5 \quad 3 \quad 2 \quad 2 \quad 3 \quad 5 \quad 6 \quad 1$$

Show these results on a frequency distribution table.

What conclusions, if any, might the casino owner draw from the results?

What further action, if any, might the casino owner take?

Justify your statements.

Solution:

Frequency distribution table

Score on die	1	2	3	4	5	6
Tally	||||| ||	||||| ||	|||||		|||	||||| ||	|||||	
Frequency	7	7	6	3	7	6

In making 36 throws of the die, the casino owner might expect each score to appear six times (36 throws ÷ 6 numbers = 6 times each). Since the score of 4 appears only three times, it might be concluded the die is not fair (**biased**). Hence, the new six-sided die would be rejected.

However, the casino owner might decide that 36 throws is not enough. The experiment might be repeated with another 36 (or more) throws. This course of action would give a more accurate description of the situation.

Mean, mode and median for discrete frequency distributions

Mean

To find the mean of a frequency distribution, do the following.

1. Multiply each value by its corresponding frequency.
2. Sum all these products.
3. Divide this sum by the total number of frequencies.

That is:

$$\mu = \frac{\Sigma fx}{\Sigma f}$$

(i) x is the value of each measurement

(ii) f is the frequency of each measurement

(iii) Σfx is the sum of all the fx values

(iv) Σf is the sum of all the frequencies

Note: You can use your calculator to calculate the mean, μ.

$\mu = \bar{x}$ on many calculators. You may need to consult your calculator manual.

Mode

To find the mode of a frequency distribution, check the frequency distribution table. The mode is the number (score) with the largest frequency, i.e. the most common number (score) in the distribution.

Median

As the values are arranged in order of size, the median can be read directly from a frequency distribution table by looking for the middle value, or the average of the two middle values if there is an even number of values.

 EXAMPLE

A test consisted of five questions. One mark was awarded per question for a correct solution and no marks for an incorrect solution. The following frequency distribution table shows how a class of students scored in the test.

Mark	0	1	2	3	4	5
Number of students	1	3	6	9	7	4

Calculate: **(i)** the mean **(ii)** the modal (mode) mark **(iii)** the median mark.

Solution:

(i) Mean

$$\mu = \text{Mean} = \frac{\Sigma fx}{\Sigma f} = \frac{1(0) + 3(1) + 6(2) + 9(3) + 7(4) + 4(5)}{1 + 3 + 6 + 9 + 7 + 4}$$

$$= \frac{0 + 3 + 12 + 27 + 28 + 20}{30}$$

$$= \frac{90}{30} = 3$$

$\therefore$ The mean = 3 marks

(ii) **Mode** (or modal mark)

Check the table given in the question.

The largest frequency (number of students) = 9.

Note: 9 is not the answer.

The mode is 3 marks, since nine students scored 3 marks.

(iii) **Median**

There are 30 values altogether. Therefore, the median is the average of the 15th and 16th mark. The first mark is 0, the next three are each 1 mark and the next six are 2 marks each. The next nine are 3 marks each and these include the 15th and 16th mark.

$$\therefore \text{ The median } = \frac{3+3}{2} = 3 \text{ marks.}$$

Exercise 4.2

Find (i) the mean (ii) the mode and (iii) the median of each of the following discrete frequency distributions in questions 1–6.

1.

Value	1	2	3	4
Frequency	8	6	4	2

2.

Value	0	1	2	3	4	5	6
Frequency	1	7	6	5	2	6	3

3.

Value	1	3	5	7	9	11	13	15
Frequency	1	2	5	7	6	3	2	2

4.

Value	8	10	12	14	16	18	20
Frequency	4	6	9	10	9	6	4

5.

Value	0	1	2	3	4	5	6	7	8	9
Frequency	6	8	10	7	3	5	4	2	1	1

6.

Value	10	11	12	13	14	15	16
Frequency	4	7	9	5	6	8	1

7. A die was thrown 40 times and the frequency of each score was as follows.

Value	1	2	3	4	5	6
Frequency	7	7	8	9	5	4

   (i) Find the median score.

  (ii) Find the modal (mode) score.

 (iii) Calculate the mean of these scores.

  (iv) The die was then thrown another 10 times. The mean of these 10 throws was 3·5. Calculate the overall mean for all 50 throws.

8. A test consisting of eight questions was given to 40 pupils. One mark was awarded per question for a correct solution and no marks for an incorrect solution. The results were as follows.

$$
\begin{array}{cccccccccc}
3 & 2 & 5 & 6 & 1 & 3 & 5 & 7 & 1 & 4 \\
2 & 4 & 3 & 7 & 4 & 8 & 6 & 3 & 2 & 3 \\
6 & 5 & 6 & 1 & 5 & 5 & 2 & 4 & 5 & 4 \\
5 & 4 & 2 & 3 & 4 & 3 & 4 & 5 & 3 & 5
\end{array}
$$

   (i) Represent the information in a frequency distribution table.

  (ii) Calculate the mean mark per pupil.

 (iii) Calculate the median mark.

  (iv) What is the mode?

   (v) If the pass mark was 4, what percentage of the pupils failed the test?

  (vi) Ten other pupils did the same test. The mean mark then for the 50 pupils was unchanged. Calculate the sum of the marks for the 50 pupils.

 (vii) A second set of 50 pupils did the same test and the mean for the 100 pupils was increased by one mark. Calculate the mean mark for the second set of 50 pupils.

9. In a survey of 82 households, the bar chart represents the number of people in each of those households.

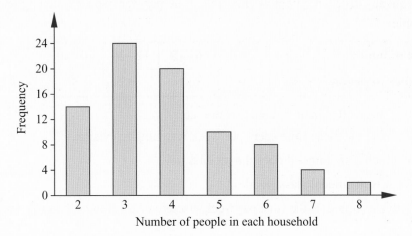

(i)   Draw a frequency distribution table.

(ii) Hence or otherwise, find the median and the mode.

(iii) Find the total number of people in the 82 households.

(iv) Find the mean number of people in each household.

(v)   Comment on the fact that the survey did not record:

  (a) Any one-person household

  (b) Any nine-person household

Discrete or continuous grouped frequency distributions

Sometimes the range of values is very wide and it is not suitable to show all the values individually. When this happens, we arrange the values into suitable groups called **class intervals**, such as 0–10, 10–20, etc. When the information is arranged in class intervals, it is not possible to calculate the exact value of the mean. However, it is possible to estimate it by using the **mid-interval value** of each class interval. The easiest way to find the mid-interval value is to add the two extreme values and divide by 2.

For example, in the class interval 30–50, add 30 and 50 and divide by 2,

i.e. $\dfrac{30 + 50}{2} = \dfrac{80}{2} = 40.$ $\therefore$ 40 is the mid-interval value.

Otherwise, the procedure for estimating the mean is the same as in the previous section.

Use the formula $\mu = \dfrac{\Sigma fx}{\Sigma f}$, taking x as the mid-interval value.

EXAMPLE

The frequency distribution below shows the time per week spent watching television by 37 people.

Time in hours	0–2	2–6	6–12	12–20	20–30
Number of people	5	9	12	6	5

Note: 0–2 means 0 is included but 2 is not, etc.

 (i) Estimate the mean time spent per week watching television.

 (ii) In which class interval does the median lie?

 (iii) What is the modal class (mode)?

 (iv) In this example, is the time per week discrete or continuous? Justify your answer.

Solution:

We assume the data to be at mid-interval values.

It is good practice to rewrite the table using these mid-interval values.

New table:

Time in hours (mid-interval values)	1	4	9	16	25
Number of people	5	9	12	6	5

(i) Mean $= \mu = \dfrac{\Sigma fx}{\Sigma f} = \dfrac{5(1) + 9(4) + 12(9) + 6(16) + 5(25)}{5 + 9 + 12 + 6 + 5} = \dfrac{370}{37} = 10$

∴ The mean number of hours spent watching television per week is 10 hours.

(ii) There are 37 people altogether. The middle one is the 19th person. Therefore, we require the class interval in which the 19th person lies.

By looking at the table, we find that the time spent watching television by the 19th person lies in the 6–12 hour class interval.

∴ The median lies in the 6–12 hour class interval.

(iii) The mode is 6–12 hours, with 12 people spending such times watching television: 12 is the largest number of people watching TV in the five class intervals.

(iv) As time is measurable, we could conclude a person could spend 1·25 hours or 1·26 hours watching TV.

∴ You could conclude that the time (hours) in this example is continuous.

Exercise 4.3

Assuming that the data can be taken at mid-interval values, calculate the mean of each of the following grouped frequency distributions in questions 1–8. In each case, state in which class interval the median lies. Also write down the modal class.

1.
Value	0−2	2−4	4−6	6−8
Frequency	12	9	6	3

2.
Value	1−5	5−9	9−13	13−17	17−21
Frequency	5	8	7	5	3

3.
Value	0−20	20−40	40−60	60−80	80−100
Frequency	2	5	8	6	4

4.
Value	0−2	2−6	6−12	12−20
Frequency	4	4	6	11

5.
Value	5−15	15−35	35−45	45−75
Frequency	15	37	14	9

6.
Value	0−5	5−10	10−20	20−35	35−40	40−50
Frequency	3	5	6	9	5	2

7.
Value	0−60	60−120	120−180	180−240
Frequency	18	35	31	16

8.
Value	0−5	5−15	15−25	25−50
Frequency	10	21	47	22

9. A survey of 80 students gave the amount of money spent per month in the school canteen.

Amount in €	0−8	8−16	16−24	24−32	32−40
Number of students	8	12	20	24	16

Note: 0–8 means 0 is included but 8 is not, etc.

(i) Taking the amounts at the mid-interval values, show that the mean amount of money spent per student was €22·80.

(ii) 'The money amount in euro is a continuous variable.' Do you agree or disagree with this statement? Justify your answer.

10. A department store carried out a survey on the length of time a number of people spent shopping in their store. The table shows the length of time spent shopping in 10-minute intervals.

Time interval in minutes	0–10	10–20	20–30	30–40	40–50	50–60	60–70
Number of shoppers	30	x	24	30	40	20	10

Note: 0–10 means 0 is included but 10 is not, etc.

(i) If the average number of shoppers for the first, second and third intervals was 30, calculate the value of x.

(ii) Using mid-interval values, calculate the average shopping time in the store.

(iii) What is the least number of shoppers who completed their shopping within 35 minutes?

(iv) In which class interval does the median lie?

(v) Name the modal class.

(vi) Comment on the mean, mode and median values you found. Do you think that any one of the three averages is better or worse than the others to help describe the situation? Explain your reasoning.

(vii) Describe two difficulties the store may have encountered when carrying out this survey.

Variability of data

Each of these sets of numbers has a mean of 4, but the spread of each set is different.

(a) 4, 4, 4, 4, 4

(b) 1, 3, $3\frac{1}{2}$, 4·2, 8·3

(c) −196, −49, 25, 66, 174

There is no variability in set (a), while the numbers in set (c) are much more spread out than in set (b).

There are different ways of measuring the variability or spread of a distribution.
One is the **range**. Another is the **standard deviation**.

The range

The **range** is based on the extreme values of the distribution.

Range = highest value − lowest value.

- In (a) the range = 4 − 4 = 0.
- In (b) the range = 8·3 − 1 = 7·3.
- In (c) the range = 174 − (−196) = 370.

The range is often used to measure variation because it is quick and easy to calculate.

A list of data with a small range tells us the data are more consistent than similar data with a bigger range.

The standard deviation (σ)
The **standard deviation** (σ, pronounced sigma) is an important and useful measure of spread. It gives a measure of the deviations from the mean, μ. It is calculated using all the values in the distribution.

To calculate σ:

- For each reading x, calculate $x - \mu$, its deviation from the mean.
- Square this deviation to give $(x - \mu)^2$. Note that irrespective of whether the deviation was positive or negative, this is now positive.
- Find $\Sigma (x - \mu)^2$, the sum of all these values.
- Find the average by dividing the sum by n, the number of readings. This gives $\dfrac{\Sigma(x - \mu)^2}{n}$.
- Finally, take the positive square root of $\dfrac{\Sigma(x - \mu)^2}{n}$ to obtain the standard deviation, σ.

The standard deviation, σ, of a set of n numbers with mean μ is given by:

$$\sigma = \sqrt{\frac{\Sigma(x - \mu)^2}{n}} \qquad \text{(see the mathematical tables)}$$

Let's return to **(a)** from before.

For the set 4, 4, 4, 4, 4, find the standard deviation, σ.

Since $x - \mu = 4 - 4 = 0$ for every reading, $\sigma = \sqrt{\dfrac{0 + 0 + 0 + 0 + 0}{5}}$.

Hence, there is no deviation from the mean.

Let's return to **(b)** from before.

For the set 1, 3, 3·5, 4·2, 8·3, find the standard deviation, σ.

$$\Sigma(x - \mu)^2 = (1 - 4)^2 + (3 - 4)^2 + (3\cdot5 - 4)^2 + (4\cdot2 - 4)^2 + (8\cdot3 - 4)^2$$
$$= 9 + 1 + 0\cdot25 + 0\cdot04 + 18\cdot49$$
$$= 28\cdot78$$

$$\sigma = \sqrt{\frac{\Sigma(x - \mu)^2}{n}} = \sqrt{\frac{28\cdot78}{5}} = 2\cdot39916 \approx 2\cdot4$$

Finally, let's return to **(c)** from before.

For the set −196, −49, 25, 66, 174, find the standard deviation, σ.

$$\Sigma(x - \mu)^2 = (-196 - 4)^2 + (-49 - 4)^2 + (25 - 4)^2 + (66 - 4)^2 + (174 - 4)^2$$
$$= 75{,}994$$

$$\sigma = \sqrt{\frac{\Sigma(x - \mu)^2}{n}} = \sqrt{\frac{75{,}994}{5}} = 123\cdot3 \text{ to one decimal place}$$

Notes:

- Set **(c)** has a much higher standard deviation than set **(b)**, confirming that it is much more spread about the mean.
- Standard deviation units are the same as the units of the data.
- Standard deviations are useful when comparing sets of data. The higher the standard deviation, the greater the variability in the data.

You can use your calculator to calculate the standard deviation, σ. The statistical mode on your calculator makes calculating standard deviation easy and routine. However, you may need to consult your calculator manual to learn this.

Empirical rule (68%, 95% or almost all)

For many large populations, the **empirical rule** provides an estimate of the approximate percentage of observations that are contained within one, two or three standard deviations of the mean.

- Approximately 68% of the observations are in the interval $\mu \pm 1\sigma$.
- Approximately 95% of the observations are in the interval $\mu \pm 2\sigma$.
- Almost all of the observations are in the interval $\mu \pm 3\sigma$.

EXAMPLE

Consider a very large number of candidates applying for third level college places through the CAO points system. Suppose the mean number of CAO points μ, is 350 points and has a standard deviation, σ, of 80 points. Then using the empirical rule

- $\mu \pm 1\sigma = 350 \pm 80$ points   covers 68% of candidates
- $\mu \pm 2\sigma = 350 \pm 160$ points   covers 95% of candidates
- $\mu \pm 3\sigma = 350 \pm 240$ points   covers almost all candidates

Hence the values for the corresponding CAO points using the empirical rule are shown on the following normal distribution curve.

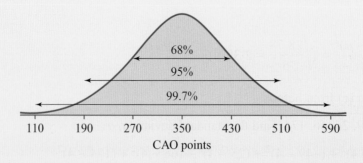

Exercise 4.4

Calculate the standard deviation (i) with a calculator (ii) without a calculator of each of the following arrays of numbers for questions 1–9 (answers correct to two decimal places).

1. 1, 2, 3, 4, 5
2. 2, 5, 6, 8, 10, 11
3. 4, 5, 6, 9
4. 1, 2, 2, 3, 4, 6
5. 4, 8, 10, 10, 11, 11
6. 5, 8, 11, 14, 17
7. 2, 4, 5, 7, 11, 13
8. 9, 12, 4, 6, 10, 7
9. 12, 4, 9, 8, 7, 11, 5

10. The standard deviation of the array of numbers 2, 8, 3, 7, 6, 4, 5 is k. Calculate the value of k.

11. Show that the following arrays of numbers have the same standard deviation.
     (i) 3, 4, 6, 8, 9   (ii) 7, 8, 10, 12, 13

12. The array of numbers 1, 2, 4, 5, 8, 16 has mean μ and standard deviation σ. Verify that $\mu - \sigma = 1$.

13. The array of numbers 1·8, 2·6, 4·8, 7·2 has mean μ and standard deviation σ. Verify that $\mu - \sigma = 2$.

14. Show that the mean of the array of numbers 3, 6, 7, 5·5, 3·5 is 5. Hence, calculate the standard deviation, correct to one decimal place.

15. Two machines, X and B, are used to pack biscuits. A random sample of 10 packets was taken from each machine and the mass of each packet was measured to the nearest gram.
     (i) Find the standard deviation of the masses of the packets taken in the sample from each machine.

Machine X (mass in g)	195	197	197	198	199	199	200	200	201	204
Machine B (mass in g)	191	193	194	197	199	200	202	203	205	206

     (ii) By comparing the results for the standard deviations, comment on which machine is more reliable.

16. The size, mean and standard deviation of three different data sets are given in the table below.

	P	Q	R
Size (N)	62	203	11
Mean (μ)	10	5	4
Standard deviation (σ)	9	3	0

     Complete the sentences below by inserting the relevent letter or numbers in each space.
     (i)   The biggest data set is _____ and the smallest is _____.
     (ii) In general, the data in set _____ are the biggest.
     (iii) The data in set _____ are more spread out than the data in other sets.
     (iv) List the elements in set R. { _____ }
     (v)   If the sets P and R are combined, the mode is most likely to be _____.

17. Hailey, Ned and Bren spent the day fishing. They caught four different types of fish and recorded the type and mass (correct to the nearest 0·1 kg) of each fish caught. At 18:00 hours they summarised the results as follows.

	Number of fish by type				All fish caught	
	Perch	Salmon	Trout	Pike	Mean mass (kg)	Standard deviation (kg)
Hailey	2	1	7	2	2·1	0·8
Ned	5	1	8	2	1·5	0·5
Bren	1	0	1	0	2·0	0

(i) 'The mass of each fish caught by Bren was 2 kg.' Justify this statement from the data.

(ii) 'Hailey probably caught the biggest fish.' Do you agree or disagree with this statement? Explain your answer using the data.

(iii) Before leaving the waterside, Bren catches one more fish and weighs it. He then announces that if this extra fish is included with the other two fish he caught, the standard deviation is 1·0 kg. Find the mass of this extra fish, correct to the nearest 0·1 kg.

18. The masses of a group of students were found to be approximately normal with a mean of 62 kilograms and a standard deviation of 6 kilograms.

On the normal curve, the arrows indicate intervals of one standard deviation.

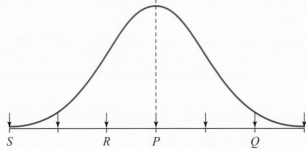

What is the approximate value of the mass at the following?
(i) *P*   (ii) *Q*   (iii) *R*   (iv) *S*

19. Steel nails are produced so that their length is normally distributed with a mean of 4·25 cm. If 95% of their lengths are between 4·2075 cm and 4·2925 cm, then what is the approximate standard deviation from the mean.

Standard deviation of a frequency distribution

To calculate the standard deviation, σ, of a frequency distribution, we use the following formula.

$$\sigma = \sqrt{\frac{\Sigma f(x - \mu)^2}{\Sigma f}}$$ in the book of Formulae and Tables

- x represents the values, or mid-interval values.
- f represents the frequency of the values.
- μ represents the mean value.
- Σ means 'add up'.

As before, you can use your calculator to calculate the standard deviation, σ.

 EXAMPLE

Fifty boxes of matches were taken and a record made of the number of matches per box. The results were as follows.

Number of matches per box	47	48	49	50	51
Frequency	6	9	18	13	4

(i) Find the mean number of matches per box and the standard deviation, correct to two decimal places. Do this question (a) without using a calculator (b) using a calculator.

(ii) Hence, estimate the number of matchboxes that are within the range $(\mu - \sigma, \mu + \sigma)$. Comment on your reasoning.

Solution:

(i) (a)

No. of matches per box (x)	Frequency (f)	fx
47	6	282
48	9	432
49	18	882
50	13	650
51	4	204
	$\Sigma f = 50$	$\Sigma fx = 2450$

$$\text{Mean} = \mu = \frac{\Sigma fx}{\Sigma f} = \frac{2450}{50} = 49$$

For standard deviation, σ:

f	x	$x - \mu$	$(x - \mu)^2$	$f(x - \mu)^2$
6	47	$47 - 49$	$(-2)^2 = 4$	24
9	48	$48 - 49$	$(-1)^2 = 1$	9
18	49	$49 - 49$	$(0)^2 = 0$	0
13	50	$50 - 49$	$(1)^2 = 1$	13
4	51	$51 - 49$	$(2)^2 = 4$	16
$\Sigma f = 50$				$\Sigma f(x - \mu)^2 = 62$

$$\sigma = \sqrt{\frac{\Sigma f(x - \mu)^2}{\Sigma f}} = \sqrt{\frac{62}{50}} = 1\cdot 11 \text{ correct to two decimal places}$$

(b) Using a calculator quickly gives the same answers. Check your operating manual if you are not sure how to proceed. If you do not have the manual, ask for help from a friend or a teacher.

We now calculate:

$\mu - \sigma = 49 - 1\cdot 11 = 47\cdot 89$

$\mu + \sigma = 49 + 1\cdot 11 = 50\cdot 11$

(ii) Hence, estimate the number of matchboxes that are within the range (47·89, 50·11).

Number of matches per box	47	48	49	50	51
Frequency	6	9	18	13	4

Our answer counts the number of matchboxes that have 48 or 49 or 50 matches within the range (47·89, 50·11).

The number of matchboxes within the range

$= 9 + 18 + 13 = 40$

The reasoning is based on the fact that boxes with 47 matches are lower than the required range, while boxes with 51 matches are above the required range.

Note: For grouped frequency distributions, the standard deviation is calculated in exactly the same way, except that x stands for the mid-interval value.

Exercise 4.5

Find the mean and standard deviation, correct to two decimal places, of each of the following frequency distributions in questions 1–4 (i) without using a calculator (ii) using a calculator. In each case, state if the information (values) in the question is discrete or continuous.

1.

Value	1	2	3	4	5
Frequency	2	3	5	3	2

2.

Value	2	6	8	9	10	13
Frequency	3	4	2	6	5	2

In questions 3 and 4, assume the data can be taken at the mid-interval values.

3.

Value	0–4	4–8	8–12	12–16	16–20
Frequency	2	3	9	7	3

4.

Value	0–20	20–40	40–60	60–80
Frequency	11	14	9	6

5. Twenty pupils were given a problem to solve. The following grouped frequency distribution table gives the number of pupils who solved the problem in the given time interval.

Time (minutes)	0–4	4–12	12–24	24–40
Frequency	3	8	7	2

Note: 0–4 means 0 is included but 4 is not, etc.

   (i) In which interval does the median lie?

  (ii) Explain what is meant by **median** solving time.

Assuming the data can be taken at the mid-interval values, calculate:

(iii) The mean

(iv) The standard deviation, correct to two decimal places

6. (i) The times taken to get to school on seven consecutive mornings were (in minutes) 22, 40, 28, 62, 48, 24 and 56. Calculate the mean and standard deviation of these journey times.

  (ii) How many of these journeys were shorter than the mean time by more than one standard deviation?

7. The following table shows the length of time for which 120 people have been unemployed.

Time in months	0–2	2–4	4–6	6–8	8–10	10–12
Number of people	14	17	24	36	18	11

Note that the interval 4–6, for example, represents $4 \le$ time < 6.

   (i) Write down the modal class.

  (ii) Is the data discrete or continuous?

(iii) Calculate the mean time and the standard deviation, correct to one decimal place, using the mid-interval values.

(iv) Hence, estimate the number of people who have been unemployed for a time that is within one standard deviation of the mean time.

Histogram

A **histogram** is often used to display information contained in a frequency distribution. It is similar to a bar chart with no gaps between the bars, and the two are often confused. It is worth remembering that bar charts can only represent discrete data, while histograms can represent discrete or continuous data. The essential characteristic of a histogram is that the **area of each rectangle represents the frequency**, and the sum of the areas of the rectangles is equal to the sum of the frequencies.

Drawing a histogram is straightforward.

1. Decide on the length of the base for each rectangle in the diagram. Make sure all rectangles have the same width.
2. Draw each rectangle the correct height (or length) to represent the information it displays.
3. Each rectangle must touch its neighbour.
4. Label each axis.
5. Label each rectangle clearly.
6. Give the histogram a title to describe the information.

Note: For the sake of drawing a histogram or using a histogram to work out frequencies, we say the area of the rectangle represents the frequency. However, mathematically we say that the **area of each rectangle is proportional to the frequency** of the corresponding class, i.e. if one class has a frequency twice that of another, then the area of the rectangle representing this class will have twice the area of the rectangle representing the other class, etc.

EXAMPLE

The following frequency distribution gives the number of marks obtained by students in an examination.

Mark	0–20	20–40	40–60	60–80	80–100
Number of students	8	21	8	10	24

Note: 0–20 means 0 is included but 20 is not, etc.

(i) Represent the data with a histogram. Name the modal class. In which class interval does the median lie?

(ii) On your histogram, indicate clearly where the median lies. Write down your value for the median.

Solution:

(i) There are five divisions: 0–20, 20–40, 40–60, 60–80, 80–100.

∴ We require five rectangles, all with the same width.

The heights of each rectangle are 8, 21, 8, 10, 24.

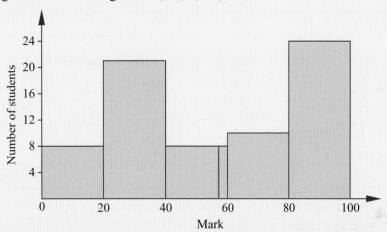

The modal class is the class with the greatest number of students in it.

∴ Modal class = (80–100), where 80 ≤ mark < 100.

The median is associated with the 'middle' student.

Notice that $8 + 21 + 8 + 10 + 24 = 71$, the total number of students.

The median is thus associated with the 36th student.

Hence $8 + 21 + 8 = 37$ students.

This tells us the median is in the class 40–60 mark.

To get an exact value for the median:

Note $\quad 8 + 21 + 8 = 37$

and $\quad 8 + 21 + 7 = 36$

(ii) From this we can conclude that $\frac{7}{8}$ of the third rectangle is required for the median mark. Hence the red line on the histogram gives us a median value of approximately 58.

Exercise 4.6

Construct a histogram to represent each of the following grouped frequency distributions.

1.

Interval	0–20	20–40	40–60	60–80	80–100
Frequency	20	8	22	21	20

2.

Interval	0–10	10–20	20–30	30–40
Frequency	7	8	15	24

3.

Interval	0–100	100–200	200–300	300–400	400–500
Frequency	12	8	30	9	15

4.

Interval	0–40	40–80	80–120	120–160
Frequency	32	24	100	36

Given the histogram

Sometimes we are given the histogram already drawn and we need to calculate the frequencies represented by the rectangles. We are usually given the area of one of the rectangles (which represents the frequency) and its height (read directly from the diagram). We can then work out the remaining frequencies from the information given.

In histograms, it is useful to know that

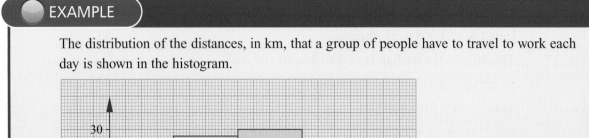

Frequency = area of rectangle = base × height

EXAMPLE

The distribution of the distances, in km, that a group of people have to travel to work each day is shown in the histogram.

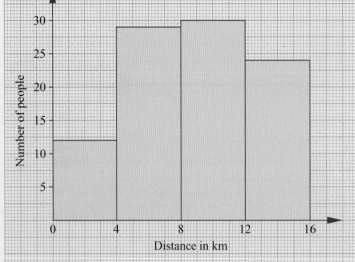

Given that the distribution has mean $\mu = 8\cdot4$ km and standard deviation $\sigma = 4$ km, mark on the histogram $\mu - \sigma$ and $\mu + \sigma$.

Hence, estimate the number of people in the interval $(\mu - \sigma, \mu + \sigma)$.

Solution:

We have $\quad \mu - \sigma = 8\cdot4 - 4 = 4\cdot4$

and $\quad\quad\quad \mu + \sigma = 8\cdot4 + 4 = 12\cdot4$

Now return to the original graph.

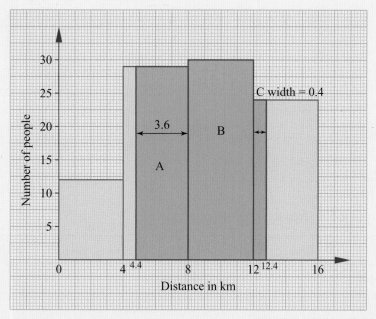

The heights (frequencies) on the histogram are 12, 28, 30 and 24 respectively.

To find the number of people who travelled between 4·4 km and 12·4 km, we find

area A + area B + area C

$$= \left(\frac{3\cdot6}{4}\right)[28] + 30 + \left(\frac{0\cdot4}{4}\right)[24]$$

$$= 25\cdot2 + 30 + 2\cdot4$$

$$= 57\cdot6$$

We can thus answer 57 people.

Whatever answer we give will be an approximation.

55, 56, 57, 58 or 59 people would also be acceptable here.

Exercise 4.7

1. The distribution of the ages of people at a meeting is shown in the histogram.

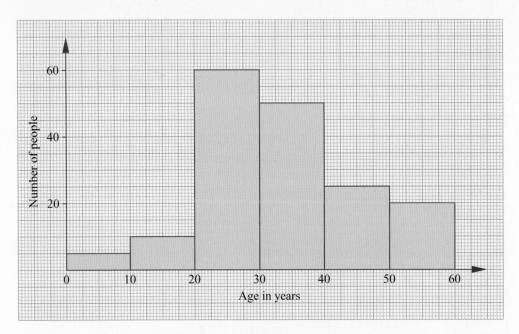

(i) Complete the corresponding frequency distribution table.

Age (years)	0–10	10–20	20–30	30–40	40–50	50–60
Number of people			60			

(ii) How many people were at the meeting?

(iii) Given that the distribution has mean $\mu = 43$ years and standard deviation $\sigma = 15$ years, mark on the histogram $\mu - \sigma$ and $\mu + \sigma$. Hence, estimate the number of people in the interval $(\mu - \sigma, \mu + \sigma)$.

2. The claims made against an insurance company for a certain year are shown in the histogram.

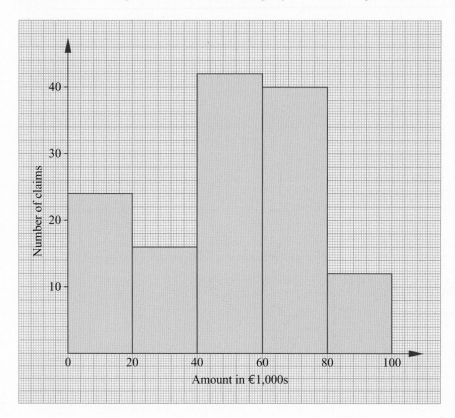

(i) Complete the corresponding frequency distribution table.

Amount (€1,000s)	0–20	20–40	40–60	60–80	80–100
Number of claims			42		

(ii) In which interval does the median lie?

(iii) By taking the mid-interval value of the median score in euro, find an estimate for the total amount paid out by the company in the year.

3. The histogram shows the distribution of the distance, in km, that students have to travel to school.

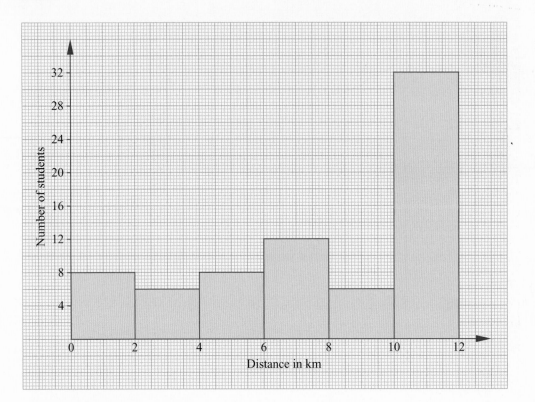

(i) Complete the corresponding frequency distribution table.

Distance (km)	0–2	2–4	4–6	6–8	8–10	10–12
Number of students		6				

(ii) Assuming the data can be taken at the mid-interval values, calculate:

   (a) The mean to the nearest integer

   (b) The standard deviation, correct to two decimal places

(iii) Estimate the percentage (to the nearest integer) of students who have travelled a distance that is within one standard deviation of the mean distance.

4. The distribution of contributions, in euro, given to a charity by a number of people is shown in the histogram below.

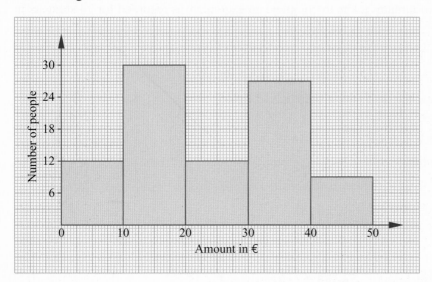

   (i) Complete the corresponding frequency distribution table.

Amount in €	0–10	10–20	20–30	30–40	40–50
Number of people		30			

  (ii) By taking the data at the mid-interval values, calculate:

   (a) μ, the mean contribution

   (b) σ, the standard deviation, correct to the nearest euro

 (iii) You interview two people from the group of people who made a contribution to the charity. The two people interviewed claim to have donated a total of €150. Would you be surprised by this claim? Justify your answer.

 (iv) You interview three other people from the group. Using $\mu + \sigma$ from above, what is the maximum amount you could expect these three people to claim to have contributed in total?

Stem and leaf diagrams

Stemplots are sometimes referred to as **stem and leaf diagrams**. They can be useful ways of presenting data. However, they are generally only useful for small amounts (e.g. a maximum of 30) of data. Stemplots can be used to compare two samples by showing the results together on a back-to-back stemplot.

EXAMPLE 1

The number of minutes taken to complete an exercise was recorded for 24 students in a class. The results were as follows.

> 20   9   36   24   17   32   25   21   14   8   26   38
> 18   15   21   8   11   23   6   37   25   32   17   36

(i) Represent the data with a stem and leaf plot.

Calculate:

(ii) The range

(iii) The median

(iv) The lower quartile

(v) The upper quartile

(vi) The interquartile range

Solution:

(i) The smallest value is 6 and the largest value is 38.

Let the intervals be 0–9, 10–19, 20–29, 30–39.

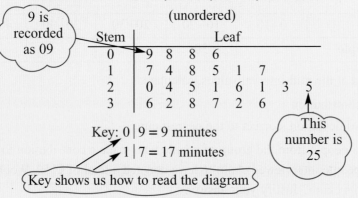

9 is recorded as 09

(unordered)

Stem	Leaf
0	9 8 8 6
1	7 4 8 5 1 7
2	0 4 5 1 6 1 3 5
3	6 2 8 7 2 6

Key: 0|9 = 9 minutes

1|7 = 17 minutes

Key shows us how to read the diagram

This number is 25

Number of minutes taken to complete an exercise.

(ordered)

Stem	Leaf
0	6 8 8 9
1	1 4 5 7 7 8
2	0 1 1 3 4 5 5 6
3	2 2 6 6 7 8

Key: 0|9 = 9 minutes

1|7 = 17 minutes

Enter the leaves, crossing out the values as you record them. This is called an **unordered** stem and leaf plot. Then create a new stem and leaf plot so that the leaves are in increasing order. This is called an **ordered** stem and leaf plot.

(ii) Range = largest value − smallest value = 38 − 6 = 32 minutes.

(iii) The median mark (Q_2) is the time value halfway through the distribution.

The halfway value is between the 12th and 13th values

$= \frac{1}{2}[21 + 21] = 21$

∴ The median = 21 minutes.

(iv) The lower quartile (Q_1) is the value one-quarter of the way through the distribution.

This one-quarter value is between the 6th and 7th values

$= \frac{1}{2}[14 + 15] = 14\frac{1}{2}$

∴ The lower quartile (Q_1) = $14\frac{1}{2}$ minutes.

(v) The upper quartile (Q_3) is the value three-quarters of the way through the distribution.

This three-quarters value is between the 18th and 19th values

$= \frac{1}{2}[26 + 32] = 29$

∴ The upper quartile (Q_3) = 29 minutes.

(vi) The interquartile range

$= Q_3 − Q_1$

$= 29 − 14\frac{1}{2}$

$= 14\frac{1}{2}$ minutes

Note: The interquartile range is more useful than the range.

Here is a diagram to help clarify the situation.

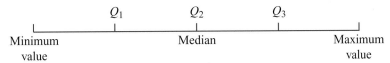

The median (Q_2) is the value that subdivides the ordered data into two halves.

The quartiles (Q_1 and Q_3) subdivide the data into quarters.

EXAMPLE 2

Use a stem and leaf diagram (stemplot) to compare the examination marks in History and Geography for a class of 20 primary school students.

History	75	69	58	58	46	44	32	50	57	77
	81	61	61	45	31	44	53	66	48	53
Geography	52	58	68	77	38	85	43	44	55	66
	65	79	44	71	84	72	63	69	79	72

Use the stemplots to find the median mark of History and the median mark of Geography.

Solution:

The first four entries for History (75, 69, 58, 58) and for Geography (52, 58, 68, 77) are entered onto a back-to-back stemplot, as follows.

Key: History 9 | 6 means 69		History		Geography		*Key:* Geography 5 | 2 means 52

```
Key: History        3           Key: Geography
9 | 6 means 69       4           5 | 2 means 52

              8 8  | 5 | 2 8
                9  | 6 | 8
                5  | 7 | 7
                   | 8 |
```

The completed diagram before rearranging:

```
            1 2 | 3 | 8
      8 4 5 4 6 | 4 | 3 4 4
    7 3 3 0 8 8 | 5 | 2 8 5
        6 1 1 9 | 6 | 8 6 5 3 9
            7 5 | 7 | 7 9 1 2 2 9
              1 | 8 | 5 4
```

The final diagram, arranged in order:

Key: History 8 | 5 means 58				*Key:* Geography 6 | 3 means 63

```
Key: History          History | | Geography       Key: Geography
8 | 5 means 58            2 1 | 3 | 8              6 | 3 means 63
                  8 6 5 4 4 | 4 | 3 4 4
                8 8 7 3 3 0 | 5 | 2 5 8
                    9 6 1 1 | 6 | 3 5 6 8 9
                        7 5 | 7 | 1 2 2 7 9 9
                          1 | 8 | 4 5
```

From the diagram, it is clear that the class had higher marks in Geography than in History and it appears that they performed better in Geography. This would, however, depend on the standard of marking used in the two examinations. It would also depend on the standards of questions used in the two examinations.

The median for both subjects is associated with the middle result when the results are written in order.

The median for both subjects is the average of the 10th and 11th results in the final diagram.

History	Geography
53 and 57 are the relevant results	66 and 68 are the relevant results
∴ Median for History $= \dfrac{53 + 57}{2}$ $= 55$ marks	∴ Median for Geography $= \dfrac{66 + 68}{2}$ $= 67$ marks

A comparison of the medians reinforces our belief that the marks for Geography are greater than the marks for History.

Line plots

A line plot uses symbols – usually $\times$s or dots – to represent the frequency of a piece of data.

EXAMPLE

A teacher carried out a survey into the way her class travelled to school.

Mode of transport	Walk	Cycle	Bus	Car	Train
Number of students	8	4	10	7	1

(i) How many students are in the class?

(ii) Represent the data on a line plot.

Solution:

(i) $8 + 4 + 10 + 7 + 1 = 30$

(ii)

```
                    ×
                    ×
                    ×
        ×           ×       ×
        ×           ×       ×
        ×           ×       ×
        ×           ×       ×
        ×    ×      ×       ×
        ×    ×      ×       ×
        ×    ×      ×       ×
        ×    ×      ×       ×       ×
      ─────────────────────────────────
      Walk  Cycle  Bus    Car     Train
              Mode of transport
```

Exercise 4.8

1. A stemplot is given below, but it does not have a key.

Stem	Leaf
4	9
5	1 4
5	7 ⑧ 9
6	2 3 3 4
6	5 6 6 6 7 7
7	0 3 4
7	6

State the value ringed and the width of the interval that it is in when the diagram illustrates the following.

(i) The times taken for a race, where $7\,|\,3$ represents 7·3 minutes.

(ii) The lengths, in metres (m) to two decimal places, of components where $7\,|\,3$ represents 0·73 m.

(iii) The masses, in grams (g) to three decimal places, of components where $7\,|\,3$ represents 0·073 g.

2. Using a suitable key in each case, construct a stem and leaf diagram to represent the following data.

(i) The marks gained by a class of students in an English test:

$$82 \quad 59 \quad 66 \quad 41 \quad 60 \quad 69 \quad 64 \quad 77 \quad 64 \quad 58$$
$$55 \quad 69 \quad 82 \quad 62 \quad 58 \quad 50 \quad 71 \quad 76 \quad 70 \quad 66$$

(ii) The weights, in kg, for dogs in a show:

$$6{\cdot}4 \quad 5{\cdot}4 \quad 6{\cdot}7 \quad 5 \quad 5{\cdot}8 \quad 7{\cdot}7 \quad 8{\cdot}6 \quad 6{\cdot}1 \quad 6{\cdot}6 \quad 7{\cdot}5 \quad 5{\cdot}2 \quad 5{\cdot}9$$

(iii) The heights (in cm) of students in a class:

161	151	155	171	140
159	154	157	156	166
141	146	150	161	171
158	182	181	169	176
166	161	184	154	167

3. Forty students sat a general knowledge test. Each student was given a grade as in the table below.

A	C	F	D	B	B	D	E
B	B	A	D	C	C	A	B
C	E	F	A	B	B	B	E
C	D	F	D	A	C	A	D
D	B	B	C	C	B	B	A

   (i) Display the data on a line plot.

   (ii) Write down the modal grade (mode).

4. A group of students use the random button on a calculator to select a number between 0 and 50. Here are the results:

22	12	1	2	10	27	22
25	22	17	9	13	13	27
29	47	39	11	32	10	43
10	22	19	4	33	33	49
17	40	5	2	26	23	1

   (i) How many students are in the group?
   (ii) Represent the data on a stem and leaf diagram. Include a suitable key.
   (iii) Use the diagram to calculate:
       (a) The range
       (b) The median
       (c) The lower quartile
       (d) The upper quartile
       (e) The interquartile range
   (iv) State the mode, if it exists.

5. The following table shows the results of a group of boys and a group of girls in an Irish language test.

Boys   22, 18, 27, 38, 28, 17, 32, 30, 22, 24
Girls   28, 24, 31, 33, 20, 40, 41, 23, 31, 29

(i) Represent the data on a suitable back-to-back ordered stem and leaf diagram.

(ii) What conclusion can you make by examining this diagram? Explain your answer.

6. The ordered stem and leaf diagram is used to compare the examination marks in Mathematics and Physics for 14 Leaving Certificate students.

Key: 5|2 means 52

9 4	4	7
7 5 1	5	2 5
4 2 0	6	1 1 3 6 4
5	7	2 7 9
6 2 2 1	8	4

Describe five errors in the diagram above.

7. The pulse rates of 30 workers in a factory were measured before and after taking exercise.

Before: 110, 93, 81, 75, 73, 73, 48, 53, 69, 69, 66, 111, 100, 93, 90, 50, 57, 64, 90, 111, 91, 70, 70, 51, 79, 93, 105, 51, 66, 98.

After: 117, 84, 77, 108, 130, 69, 77, 84, 84, 86, 95, 125, 96, 104, 104, 137, 143, 70, 80, 131, 145, 106, 130, 109, 137, 75, 104, 72, 97, 80.

(i) Display the data in a back-to-back stemplot. (Use class intervals 40–49, 50–59, 60–69, etc.)

(ii) Calculate the median value (a) before and (b) after taking exercise.

(iii) Calculate the range of values of pulse rates (a) before and (b) after taking exercise.

(iv) By analysing your answers to (i), (ii) and (iii), what conclusions can you draw?

(v) This investigation of the factory workers' pulse rates arose from comments that these workers were unusually athletic. State **one** additional piece of information that you would need in order to decide whether that is true.

8. A teacher recorded the times taken by 20 boys to swim one length of the pool. The times are given to the nearest second.

(i) Using the intervals 24–25, 26–27, etc., draw a stem and leaf diagram to illustrate the results.

32	31	26	27	27	32	29	26	25	25
29	31	32	26	30	24	32	27	26	31

(ii) The teacher later recorded the times taken by 20 girls to swim one length of the pool. The times are given to the nearest second. Display the data for boys and girls in a back-to-back stemplot. (Use the intervals 24–25, 26–27, etc.)

25	34	29	26	27	27	33	28	26	24
30	31	33	25	29	25	33	26	26	32

(iii) By considering two statistical terms, e.g. range, median, mean, mode, what conclusions can you draw when comparing the times for the two groups?

Scatter diagrams

A **scatter diagram** shows the relationship between two variables. It is sometimes called a scatter plot.

Note: Variables are quantities that vary.

To draw a scatter diagram, we plot points on a graph. Remember x-axis/y-axis graphs?

EXAMPLE

A class of students took examinations in English and French. The marks they obtained are as follows.

Student	1	2	3	4	5	6	7	8	9	10
English	65	45	40	55	60	80	50	30	70	65
French	60	60	55	70	80	85	40	50	70	80

(i) Plot the data on a scatter diagram.

(ii) Make a comment on the diagram in the context of the question.

Solution:

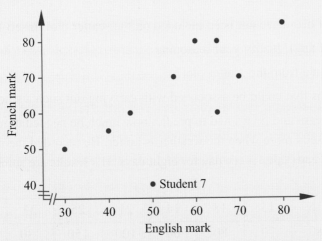

(iii) With the exception of student 7, there is a strong correspondence between the two sets of marks. The students who do well at English are those who also do well at French.

Note: In statistics, we say student 7 is an outlier. Outliers are values that are unusual with the rest of the data.

Exercise 4.9

1. An economics student wants to find out whether the length of time people spend in education affects the income they earn. The student carries out a small study. Fifteen adults are asked to state their annual income and the number of years they spent in full-time education. The data are given in the table below, as well as a partially completed scatter diagram.

Years of education	Income (€1,000s)
11	65
11	28
12	30
13	35
13	43
14	55
15	38
16	45
16	38
17	55
17	60
17	30
17	58
17	65
19	70

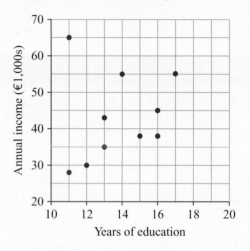

   (i)   The last five rows of data have not been included on the scatter plot. Insert them now.

   (ii) Highlight outliers (if any). Justify your reasoning.

   (iii) What can you conclude from the scatter plot?

   (iv) Suggest two problems that could be associated with carrying out such a study.

2. Ray made and sold ice cream and he wanted to predict how much he needed to make each day. He believes he sells more when the weather is hotter. He recorded the maximum temperature and the ice cream sales every day for eight days. His results are summarised in the table.

Temperature (°C)	16	15	18	14	21	25	23	24
Sales in €	80	70	80	60	100	150	130	130

   (i)   Draw a scatter diagram of this data.

   (ii) Do you agree with Ray's claim?

   (iii) Ray can use the graph to predict sales depending on the temperature. Can you estimate what his expected sales would be on a day with a maximum temperature of 22°C?

3. One measure of personal fitness is the time taken for an individual's pulse rate to return to normal after strenuous exercise; the greater the fitness, the shorter the time. Pat and Nora have the same normal pulse rates. Following a short programme of strenuous exercise, both recorded their pulse rates p at time t minutes after they had stopped exercising. Nora's results are given in the table below.

Time (minutes)	t	0·5	1·0	1·5	2·0	3·0	4·0	5·0
Pulse rate for Nora	p	125	113	102	94	81	83	71

(i) Draw a scatter diagram to show Nora's data.

(ii) Pat's results are given in the table below. Using a different colour pen, plot the scatter points for Pat on the same diagram as Nora's data.

Time (minutes)	t	0·5	1·0	1·5	2·0	3·0	4·0	5·0
Pulse rate for Pat	p	122	118	111	108	96	88	77

(iii) Giving a reason, state who you consider to be fitter.

(iv) Are there any outliers in either set of data? Explain.

4.

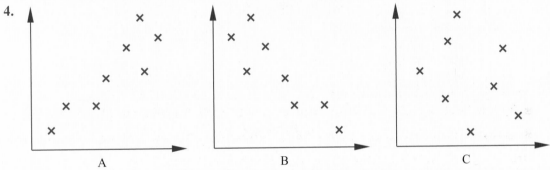

A   B   C

Match the scatter diagrams A, B, C with the statements P, Q, R.

P—As you get older, your eyesight disimproves.

Q—Students who are good at maths are usually good at physics.

R—There is no connection between height and intelligence.

5. Students in Germany investigated the link between altitude (height above sea level) in metres and mean July midday temperature. Their findings were as follows.

Altitude (m)	300	600	900	1,200	1,500	1,800	2,100
Mean July midday temp (°C)	22	19	16	18	15	9	8

(i) Illustrate the data on a scatter diagram.

(ii) Do you think the data indicates a link between altitude and mean July midday temperature?

(iii) Estimate the mean July midday temperature:
    (a) At an altitude of 1,000 m
    (b) At an altitude of 2,400 m

Frequency curves

This data shows the ages of people attending a school concert (numbers are rounded to the nearest 10).

Age	0–10	10–20	20–30	30–40	40–50	50–60	60–70
Frequency	20	190	180	140	90	70	10

Note: 0–10 means 0 years but not 10 years, etc.

Draw a frequency histogram and a frequency polygon to illustrate this data.

Solution:

To draw a frequency histogram, first work out the best scale to use.

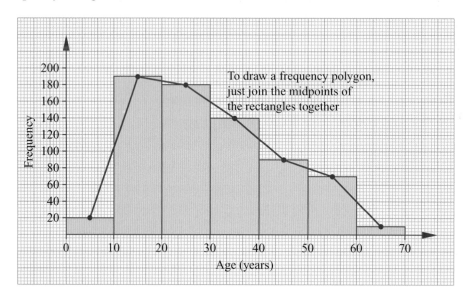

When the number of intervals is large, the frequency polygon consists of a large number of line segments. The frequency polygon approaches a smooth curve, known as a frequency curve.

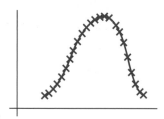

The shape of a distribution

If distributions represented by a vertical line graph or a histogram are illustrated using a frequency curve, it is easier to see the general 'shape' of the distribution. For example:

(i) Uniform or rectangular

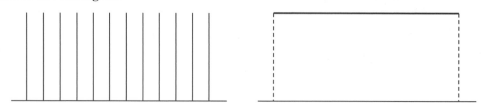

In a **uniform or rectangular distribution**, the data are evenly spread throughout the range.

(ii) **The normal distribution**

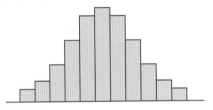 

This symmetrical, bell-shaped distribution is known as a **normal distribution**.

An approximately normal distribution occurs when measuring quantities such as heights, masses or examination marks.

In this type of curve, mean = median = mode.

(iii) *Positive skew*

A **positively skewed distribution** could occur when considering, for example:

- The number of children in a family.
- The age at which women marry.
- The distribution of wages in a firm.

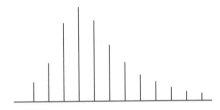 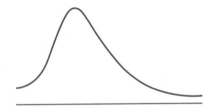

In a positively skewed distribution, there is a long tail at the *positive* end of the distribution.

In this type of curve, mean > median.

(iv) **Negative skew**

A **negatively skewed distribution** could occur when considering, for example:

- Reaction times for an experiment.
- Daily maximum temperatures for a month in the summer.

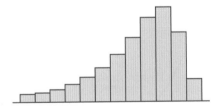 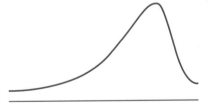

In a negatively skewed distribution, there is a long tail at the *negative* end of the distribution.

In this type of curve, mean < median.

(v) Reverse J-shape

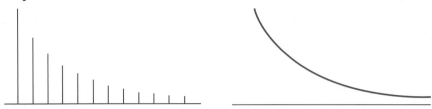

In a **J-shaped (reverse) distribution**, an initial bulge is followed by a long tail.

A special note on 'tail' in statistics and probability:

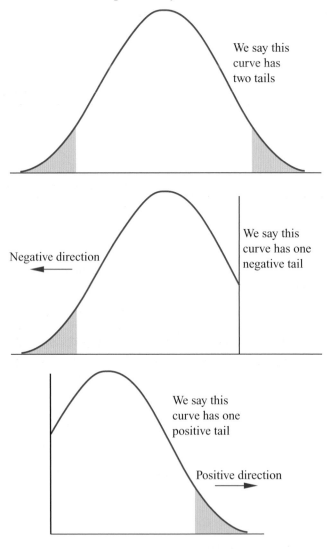

We say this curve has two tails

Negative direction

We say this curve has one negative tail

We say this curve has one positive tail

Positive direction

When we consider curves similar to **(iii)** and **(iv)**, we always focus on the tail.

In **(iii)** the tail is at the positive end, hence we say the curve is positively skewed.

In **(iv)** the tail is at the negative end, hence we say the curve is negatively skewed.

Exercise 4.10

1. From the list of the following five curve descriptions, match each one with the correct common shape.

   (i) Normal curve/bell shape

   (ii) Uniform/rectangular

   (iii) Reverse J-shape

   (iv) Positively skewed

   (v) Negatively skewed

   (a)

   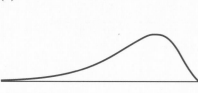

   (b)

   (c)

   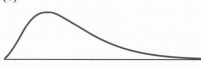

   (d)

   (e)

2. The yearly income of workers in the Netherlands is given in the following table.

Yearly income	0– 40,000	40,000– 80,000	80,000– 120,000	120,000– 160,000	160,000– 200,000	200,000– 240,000	240,000– 280,000
Percentage of workers	30%	40%	15%	8%	4%	2%	1%

   (i) Draw a histogram and hence a frequency polygon to illustrate this data.

   (ii) How would you describe the shape of this distribution?

3. A research physician obtained the following histogram with a sample of 400 diabetics.

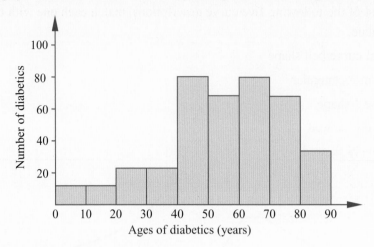

   (i) Is the distribution symmetric?

  (ii) Identify the overall shape of the distribution.

 (iii) In considering the shape of a distribution, it is helpful to observe the number of peaks (highest points). A distribution is said to be **unimodal** if it has one peak, **bimodal** if it has two peaks and **multimodal** if it has three or more peaks.

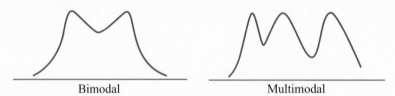

   Is the distribution above unimodal, bimodal or multimodal?

4. The following is a frequency histogram for the number of questions answered incorrectly on an eight-question fraction quiz by each of the 50 students in a sixth class from primary school.

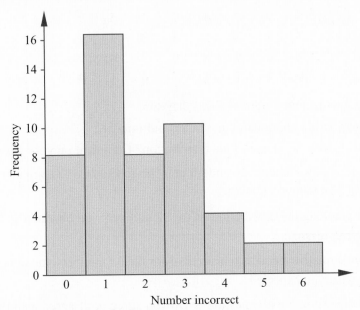

(i) Identify the overall shape of the distribution.

(ii) State whether the distribution is unimodal, bimodal or multimodal.

5. The following is a stem and leaf diagram for the lengths of stay in Ireland obtained from a sample of 36 Australian residents who travelled here one year.

```
0 | 5 3 3 1 6 2 1 1 8 5 3 3
1 | 6 3 1 5 4 0 2 7 8 0 2 2
2 | 1 0 1 7 1
3 | 1 2
4 | 1 4 8
5 | 6
6 | 4
```

Key: 3|1 = 31 days

(i) Identify the overall shape of the distribution.

(ii) Is the distribution unimodal, bimodal or multimodal?

(iii) Find the median.

(iv) Find the interquartile range.

6. Thirty-two students were asked to pick a digit between 0 and 9 inclusive. The results were as follows.

$$
\begin{array}{cccccccc}
8 & 9 & 9 & 4 & 2 & 1 & 5 & 9 \\
7 & 7 & 7 & 5 & 3 & 3 & 1 & 4 \\
4 & 6 & 9 & 8 & 9 & 3 & 4 & 7 \\
8 & 9 & 7 & 1 & 7 & 4 & 1 & 4
\end{array}
$$

   (i) Illustrate the data on a stem and leaf diagram.

  (ii) Is the distribution unimodal, bimodal or multimodal?

 (iii) Can you classify the shape of the distribution? Comment on your answer.

7. Use a table of random numbers, a random number generator or a computer to obtain 32 random integers between 0 and 9.

   (i) Without graphing the distribution of the 32 numbers you obtained, guess its shape and explain your reasoning.

  (ii) Construct a relative frequency histogram for the 32 numbers you obtained. Is its shape roughly what you expected?

 (iii) Compare question 6 with question 7. Do you agree or disagree with the following statement:

    'The results in both questions are similar.' Justify your answer.

Correlation and causality

Correlation implies a connection between two variables.

For example, people who are good at maths are usually good at physics. This is a general trend to which there will often be exceptions.

Causality implies a direct link between two variables. One variable causes the change in the other variable.

For example, consider the outside temperature and the amount of oil used for central heating. The lower the temperature, the greater the amount of oil used: one variable directly causes the other to change.

Sometimes there is no direct link between two variables, but they are connected by a third variable.

For example, in the past generation the number of microwave ovens and the number of mobile phones have both increased. One is not directly related to the other, but they are both related to changes in technology.

Another example:

The number of people attending music festivals in Europe is constantly increasing, while the number of people worldwide suffering from malnutrition is constantly increasing.

Can we assume going to music festivals is causing malnutrition? The link to both increases is probably the growth of world population.

It is possible to find correlations between variables that are unlikely to be connected. This is spurious correlation.

Here are five scatter diagrams that are typical of what we meet.

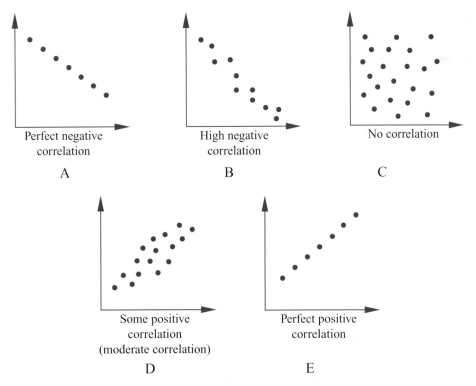

We get negative correlation where increasing values of one variable are associated with generally decreasing values of the other variable.

We get positive correlation where increasing values of one variable are associated with generally increasing values of the other variable.

EXAMPLE

The examination placings of seven students were as follows.

	Statistics placing	Mathematics placing
A	2	1
B	1	3
C	4	7
D	6	5
E	5	6
F	3	2
G	7	4

(i) Illustrate the placings on a scatter diagram.

(ii) Classify the correlation from the diagram using two words from the following list:

Positive   Negative   None

Weak   Strong   Moderate

(iii) Would you consider any points on the diagram to be outliers? Explain.

(iv) 'A small number of data points can make it difficult to claim strong correlation.' Discuss.

Solution:

Points are (2, 1), (1, 3), (4, 7), etc.

(i)

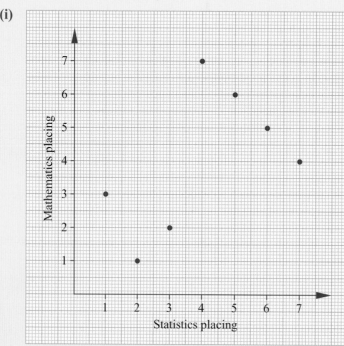

(ii) Weak positive.

Using two words to describe the correlation seems to hint that the word 'none' in the list is not required here.

We often find ambiguous/unclear results and we simply do our best to answer the question.

(iii) Some observors might suggest that (7, 4) and (4, 7) are outliers. However, the answer is that there are no obvious outliers: all pairs seem OK.

(iv) I agree with the statement. My intuition tells me there is probably a positive correlation between Statistics placings and Mathematics placings.

A bigger number of students, such as 12 or even 20, would clarify the situation. Seven students is too few for a clear correlation (if it exists) to become apparent.

Note: The examiner may not agree with this discussion. However, the argument makes sense, and that is what will be required in the examination.

Exercise 4.11

1. To test the effect of a new drug, 12 patients were examined before the drug was administered and given an initial score (I) depending on the severity of various symptoms. After taking the drug they were examined again and given a final score (F). A decrease in score represented an improvement. The scores for the 12 patients are given in the table below.

Patient	Score	
	Initial (I)	Final (F)
1	60	49
2	23	12
3	18	13
4	14	4
5	42	28
6	34	27
7	32	20
8	30	20
9	41	34
10	25	15
11	20	16
12	50	40

(i) Plot the data on a scatter diagram.

(ii) How would you describe the correlation of the data?
    (a) Negative correlation
    (b) No correlation
    (c) Positive correlation

(iii) Which of the following three words would you use with your answer from (ii)?
    (a) Moderate
    (b) None
    (c) Strong

(iv) On average, what improvement would you expect for a patient whose initial score was 35? Explain your answer.

2. The following table shows the marks (x) obtained in a Christmas examination and the marks (y) obtained in the following summer examination by a group of 10 students.

Student	Christmas (x)	Summer (y)
A	55	66
B	35	51
C	56	63
D	57	34
E	66	49
F	79	70
G	80	84
H	84	84
I	52	53
J	60	67

(i) Construct a scatter plot.

(ii) What can you conclude from the scatter plot?

(iii) (a) Which student showed the most improvement from Christmas to summer?
    (b) Which student showed the most disimprovement from Christmas to summer?
    (c) Could (a) and (b) be considered outliers? Comment on your answer.

(iv) An eleventh student obtained a mark of 70 in the Christmas examination but was absent from the summer examination. Estimate the mark that you think this student would have obtained in the summer examination. Justify your answer.

3. A school owns a minibus that is used for transporting students to sports fixtures and on school visits. For each trip, the mileage and the petrol consumption are recorded. The tank is topped up with petrol at the end of each trip.

A statistics teacher decides to record the number of students transported, x, and the petrol consumption, y, in km per litre for each trip. The following table shows the data recorded for a number of trips.

Trip	A	B	C	D	E	F	G	H	I	J
x	14	2	16	9	12	5	7	7	15	11
y	8·07	8·98	8·02	8·42	8·39	8·21	8·69	8·85	8·13	8·19

(i) Draw a scatter diagram of the data.

(ii) 'The scatter diagram shows a strong positive correlation for the data.' Discuss.

(iii) On one of the trips, a large amount of heavy equipment was carried in addition to the students. Identify the most likely trip, giving a reason.

(iv) Suggest one error the statistics teacher might make gathering and recording the data.

4. State the type of correlation for each of the following data sets.

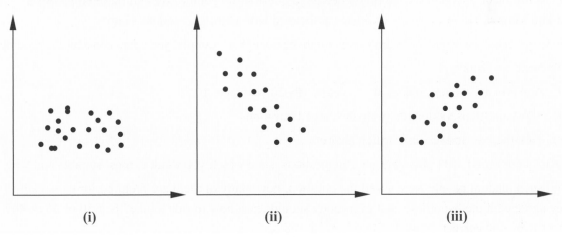

(i)   (ii)   (iii)

5. The following table shows the number of solicitors, x, and the number of cars stolen last week, y, for a sample of towns in Ireland.

x	12	5	11	19	5	21	3	4	17
y	14	3	21	28	8	43	1	12	30

    (i) Construct a scatter diagram for the data.

   (ii) (3, 1) represents three solicitors, one car stolen. This is clearly an outlier. Discuss.

  (iii) Comment on the degree of correlation suggested by the data.

  (iv) Comment on the suggestion that most car thieves are solicitors.

Hypothesis and testing a hypothesis

Statistics help to make decisions

We may decide to test a theory, such as everybody should learn how to ride a bike.

This is called a **hypothesis**.

In testing a hypothesis, data may be collected or given.

To collect data, a questionnaire could be used to carry out a survey.

We may be given data from a source, e.g. from the Central Statistics Office.

To test our theory/hypothesis, we might decide to question 60 people. We call these 60 people a random sample. There are many problems associated with getting a random sample.

Discuss in class how a questionnaire/survey might be done. For example, you could consider the headings:

  (i) Male vs. female

 (ii) Age (young, mature, old vs. 0−10 years, 10−20 years, etc.)

(iii) Short questions vs. longer, more developed questions

(iv) Tick-the-box answers vs. written answers

In each case for (i)−(iv) plus your own suggestions, state which you think is most suitable and why.

If 60 such random people were asked the question, how many of them are required for us to claim they agree with the hypothesis that everybody should learn how to ride a bike? Is it 30 or 35 or 40? There is no one correct answer!

Exercise 4.12

1. Design a questionnaire to test a hypothesis on a school issue, e.g. we should have a student council or a non-uniform day is a great way of fundraising.

    (i) Carry out a survey.

    (ii) Analyse the results to see whether the hypothesis is valid.

    (iii) Use statistical diagrams to support your conclusions.

2. Design a questionnaire to test the hypothesis that your local community should provide a youth club.

    (i) Carry out a survey.

    (ii) Analyse the results to see if the hypothesis is valid.

    (iii) Support your conclusions with statistical data and diagrams.

    (iv) Carry out another survey with a questionnaire to find out what activities are important for young people.

3. In a maths test, 50 students in transition year obtained the following results given on the stem and leaf diagram.

0	8 7 5
1	6 8 4 5 1 1 7 8 9 7 9
2	7 1 8 9 2 7 3 3 1 8 7 2 6 7 3 8 9 8 1 5 9
3	1 5 7 8 1 1 3 5 7
4	2 3 5 1 8 4

Key: $1\,|\,6$ = Score 16

By analysing the above information, test the hypothesis that most students scored more than 28.

4. (i) Measure the heights of 30 boys and 30 girls and record their measurements on a back-to-back stemplot.

    (ii) Compare the two stemplots using another statistical method.

    (iii) Test the hypothesis that boys are taller than girls.

    (iv) Do you accept or reject the hypothesis? Explain your choice with reasons based on the results you generated.

5. In a furniture factory, 20 pieces of material are cut into the following lengths.

169	169	172	170
172	170	169	171
169	174	169	169
171	170	171	171
170	165	165	174

(i) Complete the following frequency table.

Length	Tally	Frequency
165		
169		
170		
171		
172		
174		

(ii) Find the mean and the standard deviation correct to the nearest integer. Hence, test the hypothesis that 90% of the lengths are within ± one standard deviation of the mean.

Line of best fit

When working with scatter diagrams, we attempt to make sense of the pattern. That is, we attempt to link the scatter with a trend line. We call this line the **line of best fit**. In most scatter diagrams, there are many lines of best fit.

EXAMPLE

A marketing manager investigates the effect of advertising expenditure on company sales. The manager has a hypothesis that an increase in advertising expenditure results in an increase of company sales. The company accounts department provides the following information.

Advertising expenditure in € (x)	800	1,000	1,200	1,200	1,500	1,600	1,800	1,900	2,000	2,200	2,600
Company sales in € (y)	20,000	20,000	25,000	22,000	26,000	26,000	32,000	31,000	30,000	34,000	32,000

(i) Draw a scatter diagram to illustrate the data.

(ii) Does the scatter diagram verify the hypothesis? Explain your answer.

(iii) The manager thinks that it would be useful to have a straight line graph to read off. Where would such a straight line be drawn?

(iv) Using this line of best fit, the manager estimates the expected company sales (in €). If €2,100 is spent on advertising, what is the manager's estimate using this line?

Solution:

(i) Points are (800, 20,000), (1,000, 20,000), (1,200, 25,000), etc.

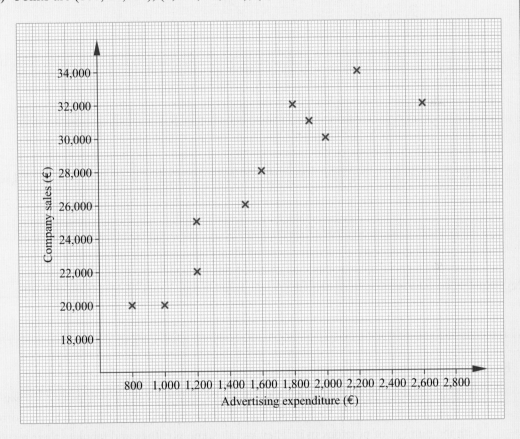

(ii) The scatter diagram shows a clear positive correlation between advertising expenditure and company sales, so the hypothesis is verified.

(iii) The manager draws the line of best fit so that it follows the trend of the plotted points. In this example, there is not one unique line of best fit.
This line should have a similar number of points on each side.

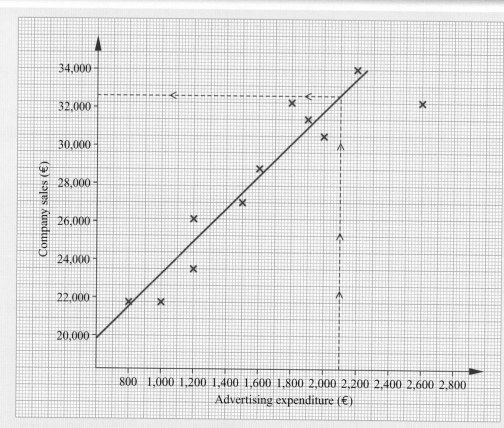

(iv) Finally, using the line of best fit on the scatter diagram (follow the dotted line), we see that advertising expenditure of €2,100 indicates expected company sales of approximately €32,500.

Exercise 4.13

1. Some agricultural science students are investigating the size of potatoes in 5 kg bags. They are investigating the hypothesis that the median mass of potatoes in a bag correlates with the number of potatoes in it. They weigh some potatoes and tabulate their results.

Median mass of potatoes (to nearest gram)	72	87	96	105	110	125	136	142	147	159	174	192
Number of potatoes per bag	50	51	36	40	45	35	35	36	40	28	32	25

(i) Draw a scatter diagram to illustrate the data.

(ii) Which of the following does the scatter diagram show?

(a) No correlation (b) Positive correlation (c) Negative correlation

Explain your answer.

(iii) The students agree to draw a line of best fit. Draw your idea of where they put the line of best fit on the scatter diagram.

(iv) From your line of best fit, estimate the number of potatoes in a bag with a median mass of potatoes of 120 g.

2. A manager of a large store selling women's clothing does a survey of 10 customers and finds the following.

Woman's age (years)	18	21	36	45	23	53	25	37	30	32
Annual expenditure on clothes (€)	330	300	180	120	310	200	200	150	250	190

(i) Show the data on a scatter diagram.

(ii) The manager expected to find a strong negative correlation. Was he correct? Explain your answer.

(iii) Draw a line of best fit and use it to estimate:

(a) The age of a woman with annual expenditure on clothes of €225

(b) The expected amount of annual expenditure in euro of a 40-year-old woman

(iv) Are your answers to (a) and (b) above reliable? Give a reason for each.

3. Vincent had a collection of old pennies. The following table shows how old each coin was and how much it weighed.

Age (years) x	51	47	53	33	39	46	42	48	28	36
Weight (grams) y	7·3	9·5	6	11·1	10·4	8·5	9·7	7·4	11·5	11·6

(i) Find the (average) mean age of the coins.

(ii) Find the (average) mean weight of the coins.

(iii) Draw a scatter graph to represent the data.

(iv) Comment on the type of correlation (if any).

(v) Plot the mean age and mean weight point (x, y) and label it K.

(vi) Draw a line of best fit through the mean age and mean weight point, K.

4. The scatter graph, complete with a line of best fit, shows the ages and the number of road traffic accidents for men.

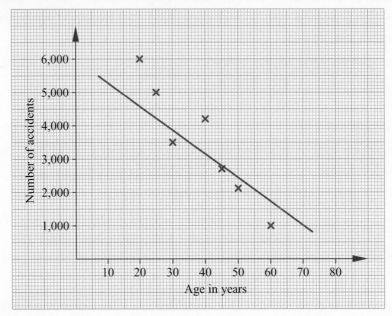

   (i) Is the correlation shown positive or negative? Justify your choice.

  (ii) Estimate the number of accidents for 35-year-olds.

 (iii) Estimate the number of accidents for 80-year-olds.

 (iv) Estimate the number of accidents for 15-year-olds.

  (v) Which of (ii), (iii) or (iv), if any, would be most reliable? Justify your answer.

5. The scatter graph, complete with a line of best fit, shows the amount in euro gambled on a fruit machine and the amount in euro paid out to 12 different gamblers.

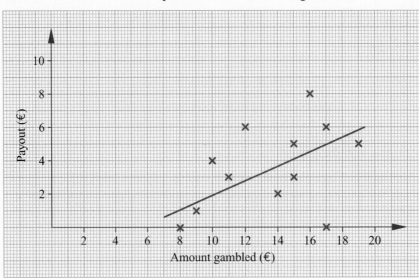

Using the line of best fit, answer the following.

    (i) What was the greatest amount lost by any one gambler?

   (ii) A new player decides to gamble €13. How much could that player expect the machine to pay out?

  (iii) Eamonn has €5 to gamble. What could he reasonably expect his payout to be? Explain your answer.

  (iv) Shaun claims to have received a payout of €10. Do you believe him? Justify your answer.

Given the mean of a frequency distribution

We are often given the mean of a frequency distribution and need to find one of the values or frequencies. Essentially, we are given an equation in disguise and by solving this equation we can calculate the missing value or frequency.

EXAMPLE

The table below shows the ages of children in a creche.

Age	1	2	3	4	5
Number of children	4	7	9	x	5

If the mean age is 3, find the value of x.

Solution:

Equation given in disguise: Mean = 3

$$\therefore \frac{4(1) + 7(2) + 9(3) + x(4) + 5(5)}{4 + 7 + 9 + x + 5} = 3$$

$$\frac{4 + 14 + 27 + 4x + 25}{x + 25} = 3$$

$$\frac{4x + 70}{x + 25} = 3$$

$$4x + 70 = 3(x + 25) \text{ [multiply both sides by } (x + 25)]$$

$$4x + 70 = 3x + 75$$

$$4x - 3x = 75 - 70$$

$$x = 5$$

Exercise 4.14

1. In the following frequency distribution, the mean is 2. Find the value of x.

Number	1	2	3	4
Frequency	x	11	3	1

2. In the following frequency distribution, the mean is 5. Find the value of x.

Number	3	4	5	6
Frequency	2	x	5	6

3. The result of a survey of the number of passengers carried by taxi in a town was recorded as follows.

Number of passengers	1	2	3	4	5
Number of taxis	3	t	9	6	4

    (i) If the mean number of passengers carried per taxi was 3, find the value of t.

    (ii) How many taxis were in the survey?

4. The following grouped frequency distribution table shows the number of hours secondary school students spent watching TV in one particular week.

Time in hours	4–6	6–8	8–10	10–12	12–14
Number of students	2	8	5	x	3

    Note: 4–6 means 4 is included but 6 is not, etc.

    (i) Using the mid-interval values, the mean time spent watching TV was calculated to be 9 hours. Find the value of x.

    (ii) A comment was made that this frequency distribution table result did not accurately represent the time spent by secondary school students watching TV. Make one statement in response to the comment.

5. People attending a course were asked to choose one of the whole numbers from 1 to 12. The results were recorded as follows.

Number	1–3	4–6	7–9	10–12
Number of people	4	7	x	8

    Using mid-interval values, 7 was calculated as the mean of the numbers chosen. Find the value of x.

Misuses of statistics

Misleading graphs and diagrams

Many advertisements frequently use graphs and diagrams to present information. In most cases the graphs and diagrams are well presented and give an honest and fair representation of the facts. However, some are deliberately drawn to mislead. The most common methods to present correct information in misleading graphs and diagrams are to use a false origin, insert no scale or a non-uniform scale on the vertical axis or drawing graphs with unequal widths and dimensions. Other misleading methods to watch out for are using a biased sample or a sample that is too small; deliberate omissions, errors and exaggerations; misleading comparisons; and using unreliable sources.

Consumers should try to spot misleading graphs and diagrams, errors, omissions and exaggerations when presented with information (statistics).

EXAMPLE

Briefly comment on these bar charts, which represent the number of cars sold over two years on a garage forecourt.

Solution:

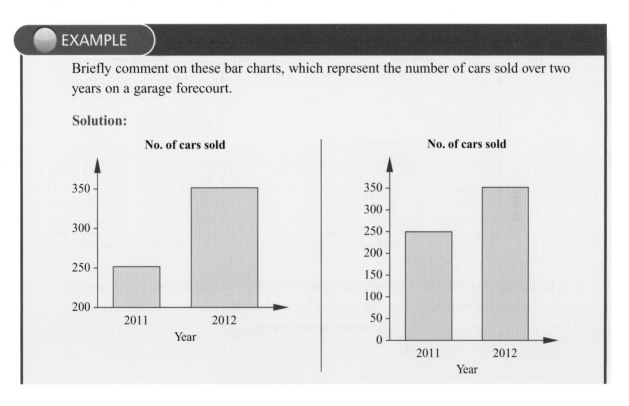

This bar chart is misleading in two ways.

1. The vertical axis gives the misleading impression that car sales in 2012 were three times greater compared to 2011 (indicating a 200% increase). However, the vertical (sales) axis does not start at zero.

2. The second bar is drawn much wider than the first bar, also giving the misleading impression that car sales were much greater in 2012 than in 2011.

When the whole bar chart is drawn correctly, with the vertical (sales) axis starting at zero and the second bar having the same width, it clearly shows that car sales have increased. However, they have not even doubled (actual increase was 40%).

Note:

$350 - 250 = 100$ (actual increase)

$$\% \text{ increase} = \frac{100}{250} \times 100 = 40\%$$

Exercise 4.15

1. In each case, give two reasons why the graphs are misleading.

   (i) **Sales soar**

   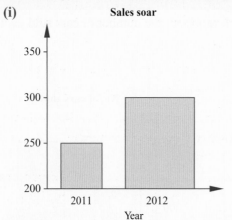

   (ii) **Profits dive**

   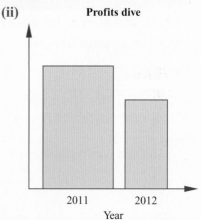

2. This bar chart is drawn to compare the amount of money, in euro, raised for charity by two classes. Give three reasons why the bar chart is misleading.

   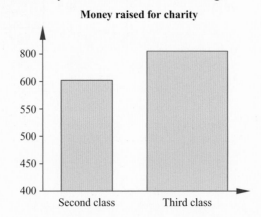

3. A car manufacturer produces two makes of car, A and B. They sell twice as much of B as A. The following diagram has been drawn to represent this information. Explain why the diagram is misleading.

A   B

4. The diagram has been drawn to represent the number of trucks sold over a 10-year period. Give two reasons why this diagram is misleading.

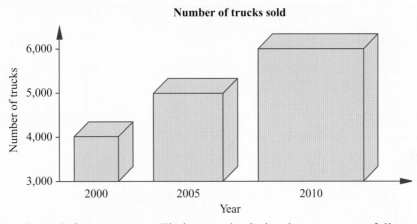

Number of trucks sold

5. Seven people work for a company. Their annual salaries, in euro, are as follows:

    180,000   40,000   40,000   40,000   40,000   40,000   40,000

    The company decides to advertise for another employee. The company claims in the advertisement that the average salary is €60,000 per year. Is the company trying to mislead with this advertisement? Give reasons for your answer.

6. The bar chart below summarises the results of 420 throws of a die. A person says that this graph indicates that the die is biased in favour of six. Do you think that the die is biased? Justify your answer.

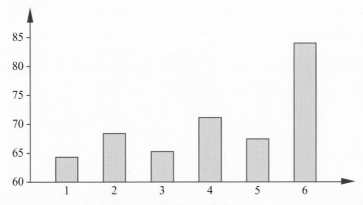

7. A cat food manufacturer makes a cat food called KATT food. The manufacturer claims that eight out of 10 owners said that their cats preferred KATT food. Comment on how this claim could be misleading.

Perimeter and area

Formulae required (see the booklet of formulae and tables)

1. Rectangle 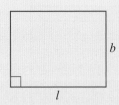	**2. Square**
Area $= lb$ Perimeter $= 2l + 2b = 2(l + b)$	Area $= l^2$ Perimeter $= 4l$
3. Triangle 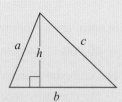	**4. Triangle** 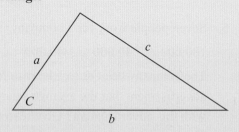
Area $= \frac{1}{2} bh$ Perimeter $= a + b + c$	Area $= \frac{1}{2} ab \operatorname{Sin} C$ Area $= \sqrt{s(s-a)(s-b)(s-c)}$ Taking $s = \dfrac{a + b + c}{2}$
5. Parallelogram 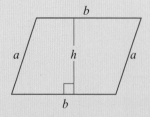	**6. Trapezium, a quadrilateral with two parallel sides of unequal length** 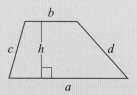
Area $= bh$ Perimeter $= 2a + 2b$ $\qquad\quad = 2(a + b)$	Area $= \left(\dfrac{a + b}{2}\right) h$ Perimeter $= a + c + b + d$

7. Circle (disc)

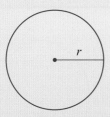

Area = πr^2

Circumference = $2\pi r$ = perimeter

8. Sector of a circle

Area = $\dfrac{\theta}{360} \times \pi r^2$

Length of arc = $\dfrac{\theta}{360} \times 2\pi r$

$\left(\text{Similar to circle with } \dfrac{\theta}{360} \text{ in front of formulae}\right)$

Perimeter = $r + \dfrac{\theta}{360}(2\pi r) + r$

$= 2r + \dfrac{\theta}{360}(2\pi r)$

EXAMPLE 1

The right-angled triangle shown in the diagram has sides of length 10 cm and 24 cm.

(i) Find the length of the third side.

(ii) Find the length of the perimeter of the triangle.

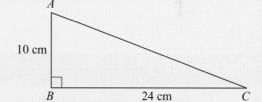

Solution:

(i) Using Pythagoras' theorem:

$|AC|^2 = |AB|^2 + |BC|^2$

$|AC|^2 = 10^2 + 24^2$

$|AC|^2 = 100 + 576 = 676$

$|AC| = \sqrt{676} = 26$ cm

(ii) Perimeter = $|AB| + |BC| + |CA| = 10 + 24 + 26 = 60$ cm

EXAMPLE 2

The figure is made up of a semicircle and a triangle (all dimensions are in cm).

Find the area of the figure in cm². (Assume $\pi = \frac{22}{7}$.)

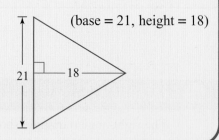

Solution:

Split the figure up into regular shapes, for which we have formulae to calculate the area.

Find the area of each shape separately and add these results together.

1. Area of semicircle

    $= \frac{1}{2}\pi r^2$ (radius $= \frac{21}{2}$)

    $= \frac{1}{2} \times \frac{22}{7} \times \frac{21}{2} \times \frac{21}{2}$

    $= 173{\cdot}25$ cm²

2. Area of triangle   (base = 21, height = 18)

    $= \frac{1}{2}bh$

    $= \frac{1}{2} \times 21 \times 18$

    $= 189$ cm²

Area of figure = area of semicircle + area of triangle

               $= 173{\cdot}25 + 189 = 362{\cdot}25$ cm²

EXAMPLE 3

The diagram represents a sector of a circle of radius 15 cm.
$|\angle POQ| = 72°$.

(i) Find the area of the sector OPQ, in terms of π.
(ii) Find the perimeter of the sector (assume $\pi = 3{\cdot}14$).

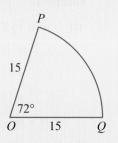

Solution:

(i) Area of sector

$$= \frac{\theta}{360} \times \pi r^2$$

$$= \frac{72}{360} \times \pi \times 15 \times 15$$

$$= \frac{1}{5} \times \pi \times 15 \times 15$$

$$= 45\pi \text{ cm}^2$$

(ii) Length of arc PQ

$$= \frac{\theta}{360} \times 2\pi r$$

$$= \frac{72}{360} \times 2 \times 3{\cdot}14 \times 15$$

$$= \frac{1}{5} \times 2 \times 3{\cdot}14 \times 15$$

$$= 18{\cdot}84 \text{ cm}$$

Perimeter $= 15 + 15 + 18{\cdot}84 = 48{\cdot}84$ cm

Notes: **1.** When using $\pi = \frac{22}{7}$, it is good practice to write the radius as a fraction. For example, $21 = \frac{21}{1}$ or $4{\cdot}5 = \frac{9}{2}$.

2. If a question says 'give your answer in terms of π', then leave π in the answer: do not use $3{\cdot}14$ or $\frac{22}{7}$ or your calculator for π.

EXAMPLE 4

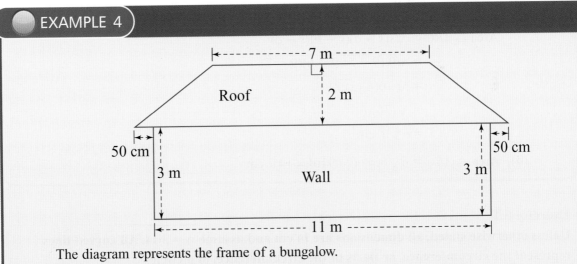

The diagram represents the frame of a bungalow.
Find the total area of the diagram in square metres.

Solution:
Note: 50 cm = 0·5 m. It is vital that all calculations be done in the same units (in this case, metres).

151

Area of wall = lb
$= (11)(3)$
$= 33 \text{ m}^2$

Area of roof $= \left(\dfrac{a+b}{2}\right)h$

$a = 0{\cdot}5 + 11 + 0{\cdot}5 = 12$

$b = 7$

$h = 2$

Area of roof $= \left(\dfrac{12+7}{2}\right)2 = 19\,\text{m}^2$

Total area $= 33 + 19 = 52 \text{ m}^2$

EXAMPLE 5

Find the area of the triangle *ABC*:

(i) In the form $p\sqrt{p}$, where $p \in \mathbb{N}$

(ii) Correct to one decimal place

Solution:

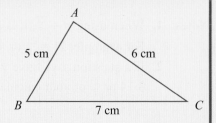

(i) $s = \dfrac{5 + 6 + 7}{2} = 9$

Area $\triangle ABC = \sqrt{s(s-a)(s-b)(s-c)}$

$\qquad = \sqrt{9\,(9-5)(9-6)(9-7)}$

$\qquad = \sqrt{(9)(4)(3)(2)}$

$\qquad = \sqrt{(36)(6)}$

$\qquad = 6\sqrt{6} \text{ cm}^2$

(ii) Area $\triangle ABC = 6\sqrt{6} = 6(2{\cdot}0916) = 14{\cdot}7 \text{ cm}^2$

Exercise 5.1

Unless otherwise stated, all dimensions are in cm and assume $\pi = 3{\cdot}14$. **All curved lines represent the circumference, or parts of the circumference, of a circle.**

Find: (i) the perimeter (ii) the area of each of the following shapes in questions 1–9.

1.
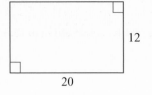

2.
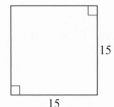

3.
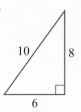

4.

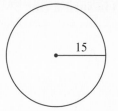

5.

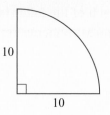

6.

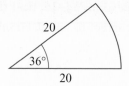

7.

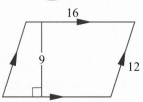

8.

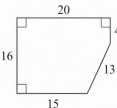

9.

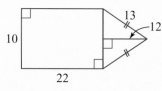

10. Calculate the area of the figure in the diagram.

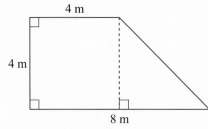

11. Calculate the area of the shaded region in the diagram.

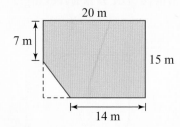

12. A right-angled triangle has sides of length 8 cm, 15 cm and 17 cm. Find its area.

13. The Department of the Environment designs a flag consisting of a blue triangle, *OPQ*, on a white background, *OCBA*, to display on beaches that have a very high standard of water purity.

The flag *OABC* is a rectangle with

$|OA| = 1$ m and $|OC| = 80$ cm.

P is the midpoint of [*CB*] and *Q* is the midpoint of [*AB*]. Calculate the area of the blue section of the flag.

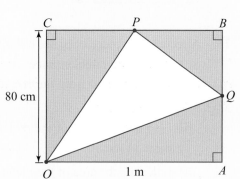

In questions 14–16, find the area of each of the following triangles (i) in surd form (ii) correct to one decimal place. All measurements are in cm.

14.

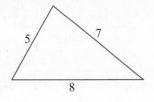

15.

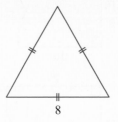

16.

Find the area of each of the following trapeziums in questions 17–19. All measurements are in cm.

17.

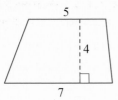

18.

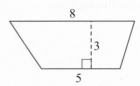

19.

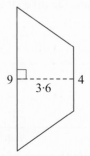

Calculate the area of the shaded region in questions 20–22, where *ABCD* is a rectangle and *PQRS* is a square.

20.

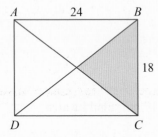

21.

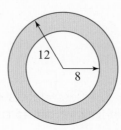

22.

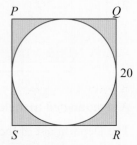

23. A rectangular piece of metal has a width of 16π cm. Two circular pieces, each of radius 8 cm, are cut from the rectangular piece, as shown.

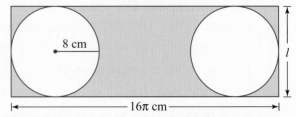

   (i) Find the length, *l*, of the rectangular piece of metal.

   (ii) Calculate the area of the metal not used (i.e. the shaded section), giving your answer in terms of π.

   (iii) Express the area of the metal not used as a percentage of the total area.

24. A rectangle has length 21 cm and width 20 cm.

    (i) Find the area of the rectangle.

    (ii) Find the length of the diagonal.

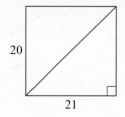

25. A circle is inscribed in a square, as shown. The radius of the circle is 9 cm.

    (i) Find the perimeter of the square.

    (ii) Calculate the area of the square.

26. The rear windscreen wiper of a car rotates on an arm 42 cm long. The wiper blade is 27 cm long. The wiper rotates through an angle of 120°, as shown in the diagram.

    Calculate the area of the windscreen cleaned by the wiper in terms of π.

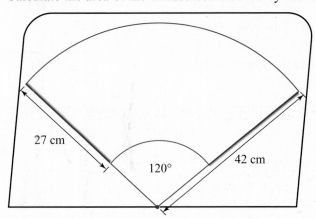

27. A circle with a radius of 7 cm has the trapezium *PQRS* inscribed as shown in the diagram. Calculate the shaded area.

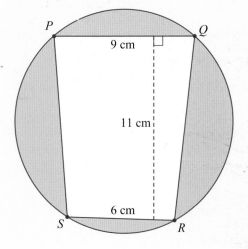

28. A circle with a radius of 3·5 cm is inscribed in the triangle XYZ, as shown in the diagram. Calculate the shaded area correct to the nearest integer, where $\pi = \frac{22}{7}$.

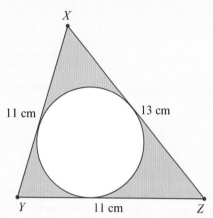

29. A running track is made up of two straight parts and two semicircular parts, as shown in the diagram. The length of each of the straight parts is 90 m. The diameter of each of the semicircular parts is 70 m. Calculate the length of the track correct to the nearest metre, taking $\pi = 3·14$.

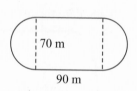

30. The diagram shows the perimeter of a running track consisting of two straight sections of length l and two semicircular sections at each end of radius $\dfrac{100}{\pi}$ m, as shown.

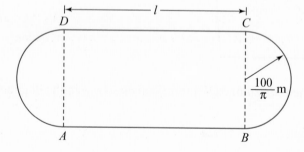

(i) Given that the perimeter of the track measures 400 m, find l.

(ii) A 1,500 m race starts at the point A and goes in the direction ABCD. At what point does the race finish?

(iii) An athlete completes this distance in 3 minutes 26 seconds. Find her average speed in m/s, correct to one decimal place.

31. The circle p has a radius of 4 cm. The circle k has a radius double the radius of the circle p. k and p touch at the point W. The circles are enclosed in the trapezium $ABCD$, as shown.

$|AB| = 27$ cm and $|DC| = 18$ cm.

Find the shaded area in the form $x - y\pi$, where $x, y \in N$.

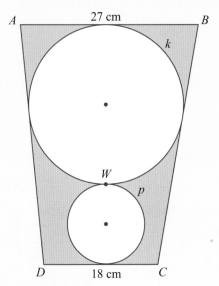

Given the perimeter or area

In some equations we are given the perimeter, the circumference or the area and asked to find missing lengths. Basically we are given **an equation in disguise** and we solve this equation to find the missing length.

EXAMPLE 1

The perimeter of a rectangle is 180 m. If length : breadth = 2 : 1, find the area of the rectangle.

Solution:

Let the length $= 2x$ and the breadth $= x$.

Equation given in disguise:

$$\text{Perimeter} = 180$$
$$\therefore \quad 2x + x + 2x + x = 180$$
$$6x = 180$$
$$x = 30$$

$\therefore$ Breadth $= 30$ m

and length $= 2x = 2(30) = 60$ m

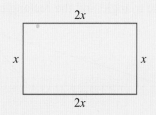

$$\text{Area} = l \times b$$
$$= 60 \times 30$$
$$= 1,800$$
$$\therefore \quad \text{Area} = 1,800 \text{ m}^2$$

EXAMPLE 2

The circumference of a circle is 37·68 cm. Calculate its area (assume $\pi = 3 \cdot 14$).

Solution:

Equation given in disguise:

Circumference = 37·68 cm

$\therefore \qquad 2\pi r = 37 \cdot 68$

$2(3 \cdot 14)r = 37 \cdot 68$

$6 \cdot 28r = 37 \cdot 68$

$r = \dfrac{37 \cdot 68}{6 \cdot 28} = 6$ cm

$\text{Area} = \pi r^2$

$= 3 \cdot 14 \times 6 \times 6$

$= 113 \cdot 04$

$\therefore$ Area of circle $= 113 \cdot 04$ cm^2

Exercise 5.2

If not given, drawing a rough diagram may help in solving the following problems.

1. The diagram shows a rectangle of length 42 cm.
   The area of the rectangle is 966 cm^2.

   (i) Find the height of the rectangle.

   (ii) Find the area of the shaded triangle.

   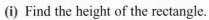

   42 cm

2. The area of a rectangle is 320 cm^2. If its length is 40 cm, calculate:

   (i) Its breadth   **(ii)** Its perimeter

3. **(i)** The perimeter of a square is 36 cm. Calculate its area.
   (ii) The area of a square is 25 cm^2. Calculate its perimeter.

4. The area of the triangle is 80 cm^2.
   The length of the base is 20 cm.
   Calculate its perpendicular height, h cm.

   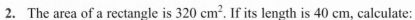

   h

   20 cm

5. The triangle and the rectangle have equal area. Find h.

   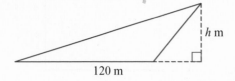

   h m

   120 m

   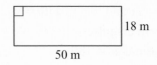

   18 m

   50 m

6. The length and breadth of a rectangle are in the ratio 3 : 2, respectively. The length of the rectangle is 12 cm. Find its breadth and its area.

7. The perimeter of a rectangle is 120 m. If length : breadth = 3 : 1, find the area of the rectangle.

8. The area of a rectangle is 128 m². If length : breadth = 2 : 1, find the length and the breadth of the rectangle.

The table below shows certain information on circles, including the value of π to be used. In each case, write down the equation given in disguise and use this to find the radius and complete the table.

	π	Circumference	Area	Radius
9.	π	$10\,\pi$		
10.	π		$9\,\pi$ m²	
11.	π		$6{\cdot}25\,\pi$ cm²	
12.	$\frac{22}{7}$	264 cm		
13.	$\frac{22}{7}$		616 m²	
14.	$3{\cdot}14$	157 mm		
15.	$3{\cdot}14$		1,256 m²	
16.	π		$30{\cdot}25\,\pi$ cm²	
17.	$\frac{22}{7}$		346·5 m²	
18.	$3{\cdot}14$		452·16 cm²	

19. A piece of wire is 308 cm in length.

308 cm

The wire is bent into the shape of a circle.
Calculate the radius of the circle.
(Assume $\pi = \frac{22}{7}$.)

20. A piece of wire of length 66 cm is in the shape of a semicircle, as shown.
Find the radius length of the semicircle.
(Assume $\pi = \frac{22}{7}$.)

66 cm

21. The semicircular shape shown in the diagram has a diameter of 16 cm. Taking $\pi = 3{\cdot}14$:

(i) Find the length of the perimeter of the shape, correct to the nearest centimetre.

(ii) Find the area of the shape, correct to the nearest square centimetre.

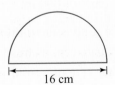

16 cm

22. The diagram shows a small circle drawn inside a larger circle. The small circle has an area of 25π cm^2. The larger circle has a circumference of 16π cm. Calculate the area of the shaded region in terms of π.

23. The area of the sector shown is 31·4 cm^2. Calculate the value of r. (Assume $\pi = 3\cdot14$.)

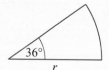

24. The area of the sector shown is 12·56 cm^2. Calculate the value of r. (Assume $\pi = 3\cdot14$.)

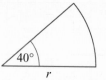

25. The area of the trapezium shown is 68·25 cm^2. Calculate the value of h.

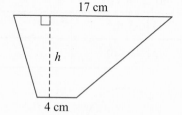

26. The area of the trapezium shown is 198 cm^2. Calculate the value of x.

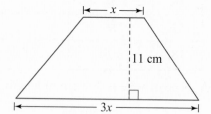

Volume and surface area

The **volume** of a solid is the amount of space it occupies.

Volume is measured in cubic units, such as cubic metres (m^3) or cubic centimetres (cm^3).

Capacity is the volume of a liquid or gas and is usually measured in litres.

Note: 1 litre = 1,000 cm^3 = 1,000 ml

The **surface area** of a solid is the **total area of its outer surface**. It is measured in square units such as square metres or square centimetres.

To calculate the surface area of a solid you have to find the area of each face and add them together (often called the total surface area). With some objects, such as a sphere, the surface area is called the curved surface area.

Note: It is usual to denote volume by V and surface area by SA.

Rectangular solids

Formulae required

1. Rectangular solid (cuboid)	**2. Cube**
$V = lbh$	$V = l^3$
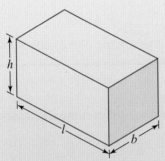	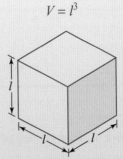
$SA = 2lb + 2lh + 2bh$	$SA = 6l^2$

EXAMPLE 1

The volume of a rectangular block is 560 cm^3.
Its length is 14 cm and its breadth is 8 cm.

(i) Find its height. **(ii)** Find its surface area.

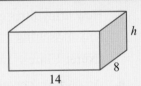

Solution:

(i) Equation given in disguise:

Volume = 560 cm^3

$(14)(8)h = 560$

$112h = 560$

$h = \frac{560}{112} = 5$ cm

(ii) Surface area

$= 2lb + 2lh + 2bh$

$= 2(14)(8) + 2(14)(5) + 2(8)(5)$

$= 224 + 140 + 80$

$= 444$ cm^2

EXAMPLE 2

The surface area of a cube is 96 cm^2.
Calculate its volume.

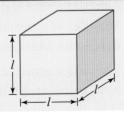

Solution:

Let the length of one side of the cube be l cm. Equation given in disguise:

Surface area = 96 cm^2

$$6l^2 = 96$$
$$l^2 = 16$$
$$l = 4 \text{ cm}$$

Volume = l^3
$$= 4^3$$
$$= 64 \text{ cm}^3$$

Thus, the volume of the cube is 64 cm^3.

Exercise 5.3

In questions 1–3, find **(i)** the volume **(ii)** the surface area of a solid rectangular block with the following dimensions.

1. 6 cm, 5 cm, 4 cm   **2.** 12 m, 8 m, 6 m   **3.** 20 mm, 9 mm, 7 mm

4. The volume of a rectangular block is 480 cm^3.
Its length is 12 cm and its breadth is 8 cm.
Calculate:

(i) Its height   **(ii)** Its surface area

5. How many litres of water can be stored in a rectangular tank measuring 1·5 m by 70 cm by 50 cm?

(Note: 1 litre = 1,000 cm^3)

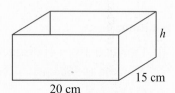

6. An open rectangular tank (no top) is full of water.
The volume of water in the tank is 2·4 litres.
If its length is 20 cm and its breadth is 15 cm, find:

(i) Its height   **(ii)** Its surface area
(Note: 1 litre = 1,000 cm^3)

7. How many rectangular packets of tea measuring 12 cm by 4 cm by 4 cm can be packed into a cardboard box measuring 96 cm by 36 cm by 32 cm?

8. The volume of a cube is 27 cm^3. Calculate its surface area.

9. The volume of a cube is 64 cm^3. Calculate its surface area.

10. The surface area of a cube is 24 cm^2. Calculate its volume.

11. The surface area of a cube is 150 cm^2. Calculate its volume.

12. The sides of a rectangular block are in the ratio 2 : 3 : 7. If its volume is 2,688 cm^3, find its dimensions and hence its surface area.

13. The surface area of a solid rectangular block is 258 cm^2. If its breadth is 6 cm and height is 5 cm, calculate: **(i)** Its length   **(ii)** Its volume

14. A jeweller buys a rectangular block of gold of length 4 cm, width 3 cm and height 2 cm. 1 cm³ of gold costs €500.

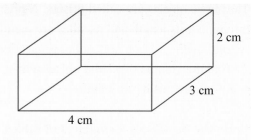

   (i) Calculate the cost of the block of gold.

   (ii) The jeweller needs 250 mm³ of gold to make a gold ring. How many rings can be made from the block?

   (iii) Each ring is sold for €150. Calculate the amount of profit the jeweller makes on each ring.

15. A solid rectangular metal block has length 12 cm and width 5 cm. The volume of the block is 90 cm³.

   (i) Find the height of the block in cm.

   (ii) Find the total surface area of the block in cm².

   (iii) Each cm³ of the metal has a mass of 8·4 g. The total mass of a number of these metal blocks is 113·4 kg. How many blocks are there?

Uniform cross-section

Many solid objects have the same cross-section throughout their length.

Here are some examples.

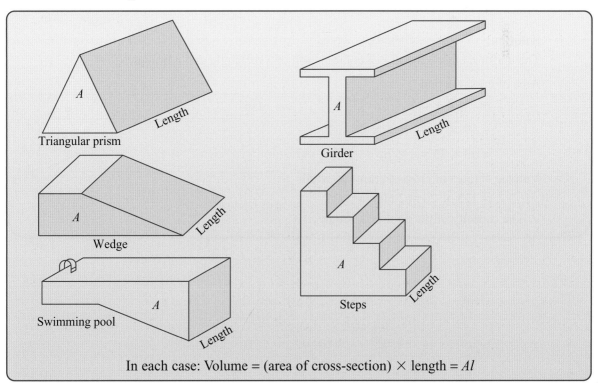

Triangular prism

Girder

Wedge

Steps

Swimming pool

In each case: Volume = (area of cross-section) × length = Al

The above objects are called prisms. A prism is a solid object which has the same cross-section throughout its length and its sides are parallelograms.

A solid cylinder has a uniform cross-section, but it is not a prism.

To find the volume of a solid object with a uniform cross-section, find the area of the cross-section and multiply this by its length.

From the booklet of formulae and tables

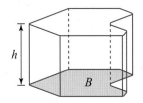

$$V = Bh$$

Solid of uniform cross-section (prism)
taking B as the area of the base

EXAMPLE

The diagram shows the design of a swimming pool. Calculate the capacity of the pool in m^3.

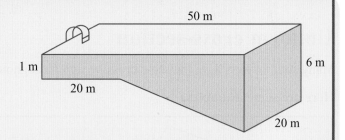

Solution:

The uniform cross-section is a combination of a rectangle and a triangle.

Area of cross-section

$$= l \times b + \tfrac{1}{2}bh$$

$$= 50 \times 1 + \tfrac{1}{2} \times 5 \times 30$$

$$= 50 + 75 = 125 \text{ m}^2$$

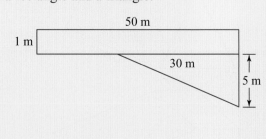

Volume = (area of cross-section) × width

$$= 125 \times 20 = 2{,}500 \text{ m}^3$$

∴ The capacity of the pool is 2,500 m^3.

Exercise 5.4

Calculate the volume of each of the following solids in questions 1–6 (all dimensions are in cm).

1.

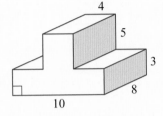

2.

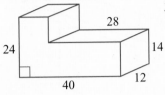

3.

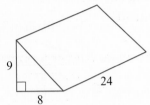

4.

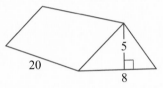

5.

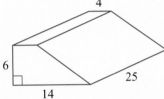

6.

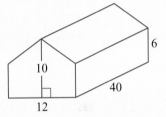

Questions 7, 8 and 9 each show a prism with one of the bases shaded. Calculate the volume of each prism. (All dimensions are in cm.)

7.

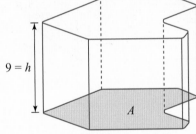

Area of base, $A = 14·8$

8.

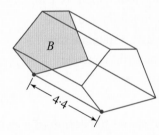

Area of base, $B = 27·5$

9.

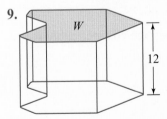

Area of base, $W = 93·25$

10. The diagram shows a steel girder.
    (i) Calculate the area of its cross-section (shaded region).
    (ii) Calculate the volume, in cm³, of steel used to manufacture it.

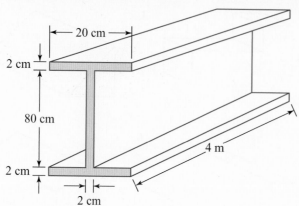

11. Five rectangular-shaped concrete steps are constructed as shown. Each step measures 1·2 m by 0·4 m and the total height is 1 m, with each step having the same height of 0·2 m. Calculate the volume of the solid concrete construction.

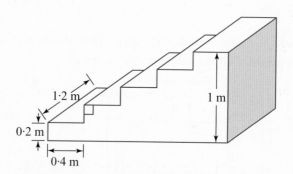

12. The diagram shows the design of a swimming pool.
    (i) Calculate the capacity of the pool in m³.
    (ii) Calculate the time, in hours and minutes, taken to fill the pool with water if the water is delivered by a pipe at the rate of 10 m³/min.
    (iii) Calculate the cost of heating the water for 15 hours if the average cost per cubic metre per hour is 0·08 c.

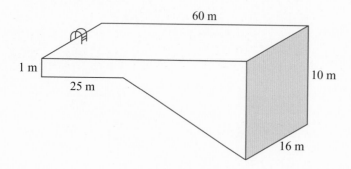

13. The diagram shows a triangular prism which has sloping sides that are perpendicular to each other.

    (i) Calculate the area of its cross-section (the shaded region).

    (ii) If its volume is 120 cm^3, find x.

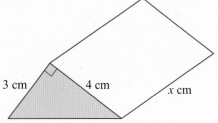

3 cm   4 cm x cm

Cylinder, sphere and hemisphere

Formulae required (see the booklet of formulae and tables)

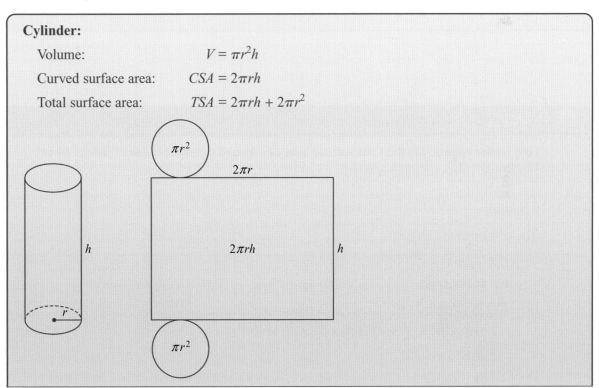

Cylinder:

Volume:	$V = \pi r^2 h$
Curved surface area:	$CSA = 2\pi rh$
Total surface area:	$TSA = 2\pi rh + 2\pi r^2$

πr^2

$2\pi r$

h

$2\pi rh$

h

r

πr^2

Sphere:

Volume: $V = \frac{4}{3}\pi r^3$

Curved surface area: $CSA = 4\pi r^2$

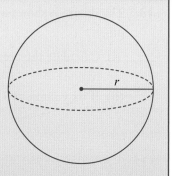

Hemisphere:

Volume: $V = \frac{2}{3}\pi r^3$

Curved surface area: $CSA = 2\pi r^2$

Total surface area: $TSA = 2\pi r^2 + \pi r^2 = 3\pi r^2$

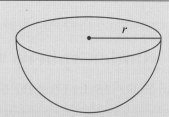

EXAMPLE 1

Find **(i)** the volume **(ii)** the total surface area of a closed cylindrical can of radius 14 cm and height 10 cm (assume $\pi = \frac{22}{7}$).

Solution:

(i) $V = \pi r^2 h$

$V = \frac{22}{7} \times \frac{14}{1} \times \frac{14}{1} \times \frac{10}{1}$

$V = 6,160 \text{ cm}^3$

(ii) $TSA = 2\pi rh + 2\pi r^2$

$= \frac{2}{1} \times \frac{22}{7} \times \frac{14}{1} \times \frac{10}{1} + \frac{2}{1} \times \frac{22}{7} \times \frac{14}{1} \times \frac{14}{1}$

$= 880 + 1,232$

$= 2,112 \text{ cm}^2$

h	$2\pi rh$
	$2\pi r$

$+$ πr^2 $+$ πr^2

EXAMPLE 2

A solid sphere has a radius of 6 cm. Calculate **(i)** its volume **(ii)** its curved surface area. (Assume $\pi = 3\cdot14$.)

Solution:

(i) $V = \frac{4}{3}\pi r^3$

$\quad\quad = \frac{4}{3} \times 3\cdot14 \times 6 \times 6 \times 6$

$\quad\quad = 904\cdot32 \text{ cm}^3$

(ii) $CSA = 4\pi r^2$

$\quad\quad\quad = 4 \times 3\cdot14 \times 6 \times 6$

$\quad\quad\quad = 452\cdot16 \text{ cm}^2$

Exercise 5.5

Complete the following table, which gives certain information about various closed cylinders.

	π	Radius	Height	Volume	Curved surface area	Total surface area
1.	$\frac{22}{7}$	7 cm	12 cm			
2.	3·14	15 cm	40 cm			
3.	π	8 mm	11 mm			
4.	$\frac{22}{7}$	3·5 m	10 m			
5.	3·14	12 cm	40 cm			
6.	π	13 mm	30 mm			

Complete the following table, which gives certain information about various spheres.

	π	Radius	Volume	Curved surface area
7.	$\frac{22}{7}$	21 cm		
8.	3·14	9 m		
9.	π	6 mm		
10.	$\frac{22}{7}$	10·5 cm		
11.	3·14	7·5 cm		
12.	π	1·5 m		

Complete the following table, which gives certain information about various hemispheres.

	π	Radius	Volume	Curved surface area	Total surface area
13.	π	15 mm			
14.	π	$1\frac{1}{2}$ cm			
15.	$\frac{22}{7}$	42 cm			
16.	3·14	12 m			

17. A hollow plastic pipe has an external diameter of 16 cm and an internal diameter of 10 cm. Calculate the volume of plastic in 2 m of pipe. (Assume $\pi = 3\cdot14$.)

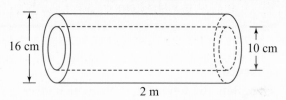

18. **(i)** The perimeter of a square lawn is 96 m. Find the area of the lawn in m².

    (ii) A garden roller in the shape of a cylinder has a diameter of 75 cm and is 1 m wide, as shown in the diagram. Calculate the curved surface area of the roller in m², correct to one decimal place.

    (iii) What percentage of the lawn will be rolled when the roller has completed nine revolutions?

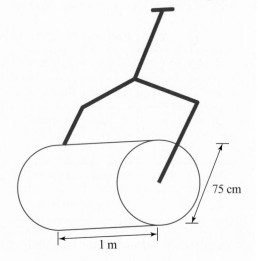

19. A cylindrical jug has a radius of 6 cm and a height of 40 cm. If the jug is full of lemonade, how many cylindrical tumblers, each with a radius of 4 cm and a height of 10 cm, can be filled from the jug?

20. A machine part consists of a hollow sphere floating in a closed cylinder full of oil. The height of the cylinder is 28 cm, the radius of the cylinder is 15 cm and the radius of the sphere is $\frac{21}{2}$ cm. Taking π to be $\frac{22}{7}$, find the volume of:

    (i) The cylinder
    (ii) The sphere
    (iii) The oil

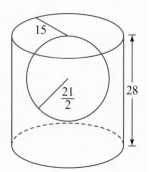

Cone

Formulae required (see the booklet of formulae and tables)

Volume: $V = \frac{1}{3}\pi r^2 h$

Curved surface area: $CSA = \pi r l$

Total surface area: $TSA = \pi r l + \pi r^2$

Pythagoras' theorem: $l^2 = r^2 + h^2$

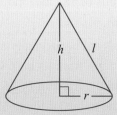

Notes: l is called the slant height.

A cone is often called a **right circular cone**, as its vertex is directly above the centre of the base and its height is at right angles to the base.

EXAMPLE 1

A right circular cone has a height of 12 cm and a base radius of 5 cm. Find:

(i) Its volume   **(ii)** Its curved surface area (assume $\pi = 3.14$)

Solution:

(i) Volume of cone

$= \frac{1}{3}\pi r^2 h$

$= \frac{1}{3} \times 3.14 \times 5 \times 5 \times 12$

$= 314 \text{ cm}^3$

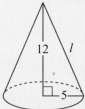

(ii) Slant height is missing

$l^2 = r^2 + h^2$

$l^2 = 5^2 + 12^2$

$l^2 = 25 + 144$

$l^2 = 169$

$l = 13 \text{ cm}$

Curved surface area

$= \pi r l$

$= 3.14 \times 5 \times 13$

$= 204.1 \text{ cm}^2$

EXAMPLE 2

(i) A right circular cone has a height of 10 cm and a base radius of 18 cm. Find its volume in terms of π.

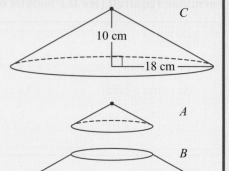

(ii) The cone is cut horizontally to its base at a height of 5 cm from its base into two sections, a cone A and a frustum B, as shown.

(a) Find the radius of the cone A.

(b) Find the volume of the cone A in terms of π.

(c) Hence or otherwise, calculate the volume of the frustum B in terms of π.

Solution:

(i) Volume of cone $C = \frac{1}{3}\pi r^2 h$

$$= \frac{1}{3}\pi(18)^2(10)$$

$$= 1{,}080\pi \text{ cm}^3$$

(ii) (a) We must use similar triangles to find the radius of cone A.

$$\frac{r}{R} = \frac{h}{H}$$

$$\frac{r}{18} = \frac{5}{10}$$

$$10\,r = 90$$

$$r = 9 \text{ cm}$$

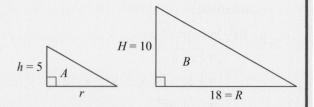

(b) Volume of cone $A = \frac{1}{3}\pi r^2 h$

$$= \frac{1}{3}\pi(9)^2(5)$$

$$= 135\,\pi \text{ cm}^3$$

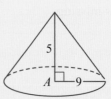

Method 1: Use subtraction

(c) Volume of frustum B = volume of cone C − volume of cone A

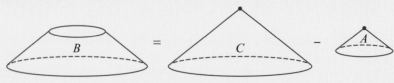

$$1{,}080\pi \qquad - \qquad 135\pi \quad = \quad 945\pi \text{ cm}^3$$

Method 2: Use the formula for the volume of a frustum (see the booklet of formulae and tables)

$$V = \tfrac{1}{3}\pi h(R^2 + Rr + r^2)$$
$$= \tfrac{1}{3}\pi(5)[18^2 + 18(9) + (9)^2]$$
$$= \tfrac{1}{3}\pi(5)(324 + 162 + 81)$$
$$= \tfrac{1}{3}\pi(5)(567) = 945\pi \text{ cm}^3$$

Exercise 5.6

Complete the following table, which gives certain information about various cones.

	π	Radius	Height	Slant height	Volume	Curved surface area
1.	π	8 cm	6 cm			
2.	$\frac{22}{7}$		20 mm	29 mm		
3.	3·14	3 cm		5 cm		
4.	π	1·5 m		2·5 m		
5.	3·14		9 cm	41 cm		
6.	π	8 m		17 m		
7.	$\frac{22}{7}$	2·8 cm	4·5 cm			
8.	π	4·8 mm		5 mm		
9.	π	12 m	35 m			
10.	3·14	11 cm		61 cm		

11. A cone has a radius length of 7 cm and a height of 2·4 cm.

    Calculate: **(i)** Its volume   **(ii)** Its total surface area (assume $\pi = \frac{22}{7}$)

12. A cone has a radius length of 18 cm and a height of 16·25 cm.

    Calculate: **(i)** Its volume   **(ii)** Its total surface area (assume $\pi = 3·14$)

13. **(i)** A right circular cone, C, has a height of 15 cm and a base
with a radius of 12 cm. Find its volume in terms of π.

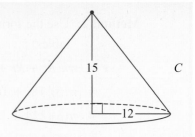

(ii) The cone C is cut horizontally and divided into two
sections, as in the diagram. Section A is a cone and
section B is a frustum.

    (a) Write down the height of cone A. Justify your
answer for h.

    (b) Find, in terms of π, the volume of cone A.

    (c) Hence or otherwise, calculate the volume of the
(frustum) section B in terms of π.

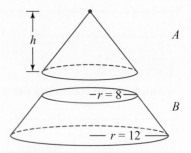

14. A right circular cone S has dimensions given
in cm, as in the diagram. S is cut horizontally
to its base and divided into two sections,
P and Q.

    (i) Write down the radius, r, of the cone S.
Justify your answer for r.

    (ii) Find the volume of S, correct to one
decimal place, with $\pi = 3.14$.

    (iii) Hence or otherwise, find the volume of
the (frustum) section Q, correct to one
decimal place, with $\pi = 3.14$.

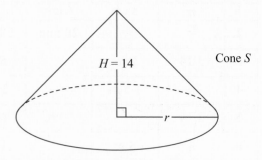

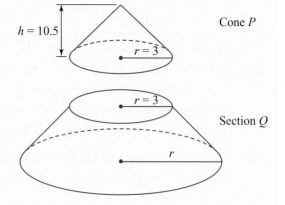

15. A right circular cone M has dimensions given in cm, as in the diagram. M is divided horizontally to its base into two sections, J and K.

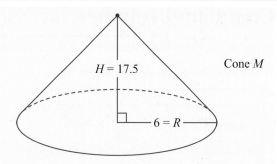

Cone M

$H = 17.5$

$6 = R$

    (i) Write down the radius, r, of the cone J. Justify your answer for r.

    (ii) Find the volume of J, taking $\pi = \frac{22}{7}$.

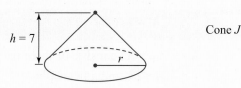

Cone J

$h = 7$

r

    (iii) Find the volume of the (frustum) section K, with $\pi = \frac{22}{7}$.

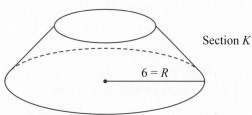

Section K

$6 = R$

16.   **(i)** A cone has radius x and height $3x$. Find its volume in term of π and x.

    (ii) A second cone has twice the radius and half the height of the first cone. Find the ratio of the volume of the second cone to the volume of the first.

17. An egg timer consists of two identical cones of height 6 cm and base radius 4 cm. Sand occupies half the volume of one cone and flows from one to the other at a rate of $\frac{4\pi}{45}$ cm^3 per second.

    (i) Calculate the volume of each cone in terms of π.

    (ii) Calculate the length of time it takes for the sand to flow from one cone into the other.

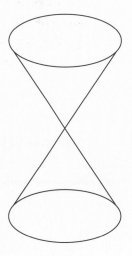

Compound volumes

Many of the objects we need to find the volume of will be made up of different shapes.

When this happens, do the following.

1. Split the solid up into regular shapes for which we have formulae to calculate the volume or surface area.

2. Add these results together (sometimes we subtract these results).

EXAMPLE 1

A solid object consists of three parts: a cone of height 8 cm, A, a cylinder, B, and a hemisphere, C, each having a radius of 6 cm, as shown. If the height of the object is 26 cm, calculate its volume in terms of π.

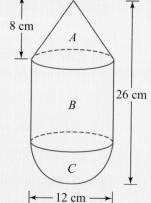

Solution:

A: Volume of cone $= \frac{1}{3}\pi r^2 h$

$\quad\quad = \frac{1}{3}\pi \times 6 \times 6 \times 8$

$\quad\quad = 96\pi \ \text{cm}^3$

B: Volume of cylinder $= \pi r^2 h$

$\quad\quad = \pi \times 6 \times 6 \times 12$

$\quad\quad = 432\pi \ \text{cm}^3$

C: Volume of hemisphere $= \frac{2}{3}\pi r^3$

$\quad\quad = \frac{2}{3}\pi \times 6 \times 6 \times 6$

$\quad\quad = 144\pi \ \text{cm}^3$

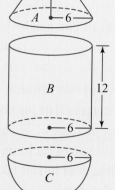

Total volume = volume of cone + volume of cylinder + volume of hemisphere

$\quad\quad = (96\pi + 432\pi + 144\pi) \ \text{cm}^3 = 672\pi \ \text{cm}^3$

EXAMPLE 2

An ashtray consists of a solid block with a cone excavated to contain the ash. The radius of the cone is 10 cm with a depth of 6 cm. The sides of the block touch the base circle of the cone, as in the diagram.

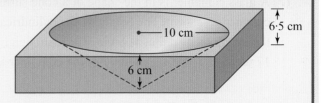

    10 cm   6·5 cm   6 cm

  (i) Find the volume of the cone (take $\pi = 3\cdot14$).

 (ii) Find the volume of the block.

(iii) Hence, find the volume of material that makes up the ashtray.

(iv) Comment on the effectiveness or otherwise of this ashtray design. Suggest an alternative design from the shapes covered in this chapter.

Solution:

  (i)   Volume of cone $= \frac{1}{3}\pi r^2 h$

$$= \tfrac{1}{3}(3\cdot14)(10)^2(6) = 628\,\text{cm}^3$$

 (ii)   Volume of block $= lbh$

$$= (20)(20)(6\cdot5) = 2{,}600\,\text{cm}^3$$

(iii)   Volume of ashtray material $= 2{,}600 - 628 = 1{,}972\ \text{cm}^3$

(iv)   The useful space in this ashtray is 628 cm^3.

$$\Rightarrow \tfrac{628}{2{,}600} \times 100 \approx 24\% \text{ of the total volume}$$

It follows that 76% (100% − 24%) of this ashtray consists of material. In my opinion, this is too much material from both a practical and cost viewpoint. A good ashtray design should have more space than material.

In addition, the extremely pointed vertex at the base is not very effective and might be a safety issue (ash not properly crushed to extinguish the spark). My suggestion for a more efficient design would be a cylindrical space inside a solid cylinder, as in thediagram. You can make your own design.

Exercise 5.7

1. A glass container is in the shape of a cone surmounted by a cylinder, as shown. The height of the cylindrical part is 20 cm and the length of its radius is 8 cm. The slant height of the cone is 17 cm. Show that the volume of the container is $1,600\pi$ cm^3.

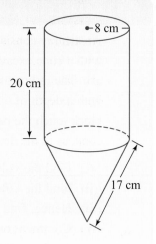

2. A test tube consists of a hemisphere of diameter 3 cm surmounted by a cylinder, as shown. The total height of the test tube is $16\frac{1}{2}$ cm. Calculate, in terms of π, the volume of the test tube.

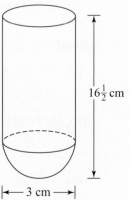

3. A boiler is in the shape of a cylinder with hemispherical ends, as shown in the diagram. The total length of the boiler is 30 m and its diameter is 12 m. Find in terms of π:
   (i) Its volume
   (ii) Its surface area

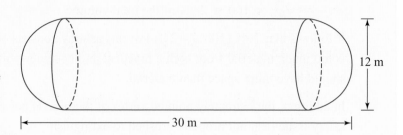

4. A solid object consists of three parts: a hemisphere, a cylinder and a cone, as shown, each having a diameter of 18 cm. If the height of the cone is 12 cm and the total height is 35 cm, calculate its volume and surface area in terms of π.

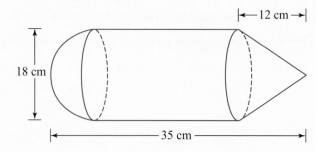

5. A buoy consists of an inverted cone on top of a
   hemisphere, as shown. If the radius of the hemisphere is 6 cm
   and the height of the cone is 9·1 cm, calculate, assuming
   $\pi = 3\cdot14$:
   (i) The volume of the buoy
   (ii) The surface area of the buoy

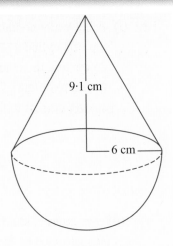

6. A tent has dimensions as shown in the diagram.

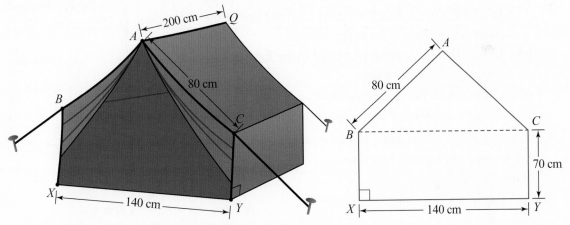

   (i) Find the area of the rectangular section $BXYC$.
   (ii) Show that the area of the triangular section $ABC = 700\sqrt{15}$ cm.
   (iii) Given that the tent has uniform length $= |AQ| = 200$ cm,
        calculate its volume to the nearest cm^3.

7. A wax crayon is in the shape of a cylinder of diameter 10 mm, surmounted
   by a cone of slant height 13 mm.
   (i) Show that the vertical height of the cone is 12 mm.
   (ii) Show that the volume of the cone is 100π mm^3.
   (iii) Given that the volume of the cylinder is 15 times the volume of the cone,
        find the volume of the crayon, in cm^3, correct to two decimal places.
   (iv) How many complete crayons like this one can be made from 1 kg of wax,
        given that each cm^3 of wax weighs 0·75 grams?

8. **(i)** A hot water container is in the shape of a hemisphere on top of a cylinder, as shown. The hemisphere has a radius of 25 cm and the container has a height of 100 cm. Find the internal volume of the container in litres, giving your answer correct to the nearest litre.

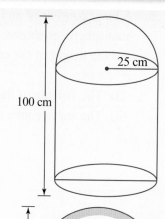

(ii) An external solid plastic lagging jacket 5 cm thick is constructed to fit exactly around the hot water container and in the same shape. The jacket does not cover the bottom of the container. Find the total volume of the container, including the lagging jacket.

(iii) Hence, find the volume of plastic in the lagging jacket correct to the nearest litre.

(iv) Comment on the suggestion that the lagging jacket should cover the bottom of the container.

9. The dimensions of the gable end of a garage (the rectangle and triangle put together) are shown in the diagram.

   (i) Find the exterior area of the gable end.

   (ii) The length of the garage is 8·25 m. Find its volume.

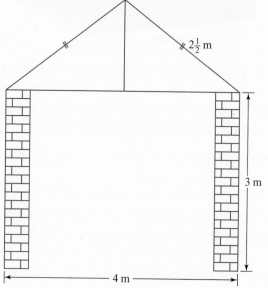

10. A solid sphere with a radius of 21 cm has a vertical cylindrical shaft with a radius of 1 cm drilled through its centre, *c*.

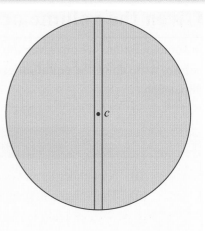

    (i) Calculate the volume remaining when the shaft is drilled. Take $\pi = \frac{22}{7}$.

    (ii) Show that Volume cylinder : Volume sphere = 1 : 294.

Note: The shaft is not an absolute cylinder – it has a slight bulge at each end. However, at the scale involved here it is not significant.

11.

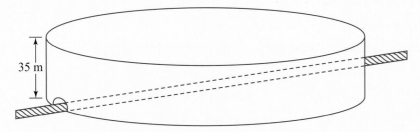

35 m

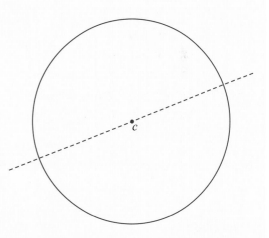

A stadium is designed in the shape of a cylinder. The stadium has a height of 35 m and a radius of 100 m. A light rail line is constructed in a tunnel which passes directly through the centre, *c*, of the stadium on a ground-level track. The face of the tunnel is a semi-circle. The tunnel is half cylindrical in shape with a radius of 5 m.

    (i) Find the volume of the stadium including the rail line in terms of π.

    (ii) Find the volume of the rail tunnel in terms of π.

    (iii) Hence, express the volume of the rail tunnel as a percentage of the volume of the stadium in the form $\frac{a}{b}\%$ where $a, b \in \mathbb{N}$.

Given the volume or surface area

In some questions we are given the volume or surface area and asked to find a missing dimension. As before, write down the **equation given in disguise** and solve this equation to find the missing dimension.

EXAMPLE

(i) A cylinder has a volume of 192π cm^3. If its radius is 4 cm, calculate its height.

(ii) The volume of a sphere is $\frac{32}{3}\pi$cm^3. Calculate its radius.

Solution:

(i) Equation given in disguise:

$$\text{Volume of cylinder} = 192\pi \text{ cm}^3$$

$$\pi r^2 h = 192\pi$$

$$r^2 h = 192 \qquad \text{(divide both sides by } \pi)$$

$$16h = 192 \qquad \text{(put in } r = 4)$$

$$h = 12 \text{ cm} \qquad \text{(divide both sides by 16)}$$

(ii) Equation given in disguise:

$$\text{Volume of sphere} = \frac{32}{3}\pi \text{cm}^3$$

$$\frac{4}{3}\pi r^3 = \frac{32}{3}\pi$$

$$4\pi r^3 = 32\pi \qquad \text{(multiply both sides by 3)}$$

$$4r^3 = 32 \qquad \text{(divide both sides by } \pi)$$

$$r^3 = 8 \qquad \text{(divide both sides by 4)}$$

$$r = 2 \text{ cm} \qquad \text{(take the cube root of both sides)}$$

Exercise 5.8

1. A cylinder has a volume of 720π cm^3. If its radius is 6 cm, calculate:
    (i) Its height   (ii) Its curved surface area in terms of π

2. The curved surface area of a sphere is 144π cm^2. Calculate:
    (i) Its radius   (ii) Its volume in terms of π

3. The volume of a cone is 320π cm^3. If the radius of the base is 8 cm, calculate its height.

4. The volume of a solid sphere is 36π cm^3. Calculate:
   (i) Its radius
   (ii) Its surface area in terms of π

5. A solid cylinder has a volume of 96π cm^3. If its height is 6 cm, calculate:
   (i) Its radius
   (ii) Its total surface area in terms of π

6. The curved surface area of a cylinder is 628 cm^2 and its radius is 5 cm. Calculate:
   (i) Its height
   (ii) Its volume (assume $\pi = 3\cdot14$)

7. A solid cylinder has a volume of 462 m^3. If the height is 12 m, assuming $\pi = \frac{22}{7}$, calculate:
   (i) Its radius
   (ii) Its total surface area

8. The curved surface area of a cone is 60π cm^2. If the radius of its base is 6 cm, calculate:
   (i) Its slant height
   (ii) Its volume in terms of π

9. A cone has a volume of $\frac{160}{3}\pi$ cm^3. If the radius of the base is 4 cm, find its height.

10. The radius of a cylinder is 2·8 cm and its volume is 49·28 cm^3. Calculate, assuming $\pi = \frac{22}{7}$:
    (i) Its height
    (ii) Its curved surface area

11. The volume of a solid cylinder is 401·92 m^3. If its height is 8 m, calculate, assuming $\pi = 3\cdot14$:
    (i) Its radius
    (ii) Its total surface area

12. The volume of a cone is $1,215\pi$ cm^3. If the height is five times the radius of the base, calculate the height of the cone.

13. A buoy at sea is in the shape of a hemisphere with a cone on top, as in the diagram. The radius of the base of the cone is 0·9 m and its vertical height is 1·2 m.
    (i) Find the vertical height of the buoy.
    (ii) Find the volume of the buoy in terms of π.
    (iii) When the buoy floats, 0·8 m of its height is above water. Find, in terms of π, the volume of that part of the buoy that is above the water.

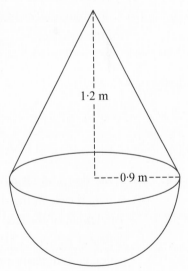

14. A fishing float consists of a cone on a hemisphere, each of radius 5 cm. The cone's volume is $1\frac{1}{5}$ times that of the hemisphere.

    (i) Find the volume of the hemisphere in terms of π.

    (ii) Find the volume of the cone in terms of π and h.

    (iii) Hence or otherwise, find the value of h.

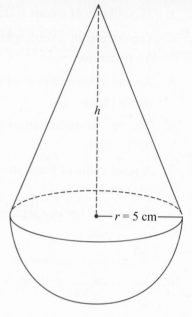

15. A team trophy for the winners of a football match is in the shape of a sphere supported on a cylindrical base, as shown. The diameter of the sphere and of the cylinder is 21 cm.

    (i) Find the volume of the sphere in terms of π.

    (ii) The volume of the trophy is $6{,}174\pi$ cm³. Find the height of the cylinder.

21 cm

16.   (i) Write down, in terms of π, the volume of a hemisphere with a radius of length $4\frac{1}{2}$ cm.

    (ii) A pencil case in the shape of a cylinder with a hemisphere at each end is shown. The length of the case is 23 cm and the diameter is 9 cm. Calculate the volume of the pencil case in terms of π.

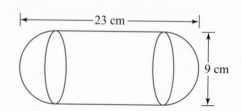

23 cm

9 cm

Equal volumes

Many questions involve equal volumes with a missing dimension. As before, write down the **equation given in disguise** and solve this equation to find the missing dimension.

Notes:

1. Moving liquid

In many questions we have to deal with moving liquid from one container to another container of different dimensions or shape. To help us solve the problem, we use the following fact:

> The volume of the moved liquid does not change.

2. Recasting

Many of the questions we meet require us to solve a recasting problem. What happens is that a certain solid object is melted down and its shape is changed. We use the following fact:

> The volume remains the same after it is melted down.

3. Displaced liquid

In many questions we have to deal with situations where liquid is displaced by immersing or removing a solid object. In all cases the following principle helps us to solve these problems:

> Volume of displaced liquid = volume of immersed or removed solid object

In problems on moving liquid or recasting or displaced liquid, it is good practice not to put in a value for π (i.e. do **not** put in $\pi = \frac{22}{7}$ or $\pi = 3\cdot14$), as the πs normally cancel when you write down the equation given in disguise.

EXAMPLE 1

A sphere of radius 15 cm is made of lead. The sphere is melted down. Some of the lead is used to form a solid cone of radius 10 cm and height 27 cm. The rest of the lead is used to form a cylinder of height 25 cm. Calculate the length of the radius of the cylinder.

Solution:

Equation given in disguise:

Volume of cylinder + volume of cone = volume of sphere

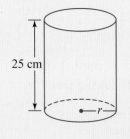 + 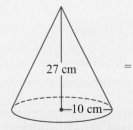 = 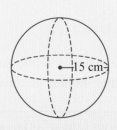 (diagram of the situation)

$$\pi r^2 h + \tfrac{1}{3}\pi r^2 h = \tfrac{4}{3}\pi r^3$$

$$r^2 h + \tfrac{1}{3}r^2 h = \tfrac{4}{3}r^3 \quad \text{(divide each part by } \pi)$$

$$25r^2 + \tfrac{1}{3}(10)(10)(27) = \tfrac{4}{3}(15)(15)(15) \quad \text{(put in given values)}$$

$$25r^2 + 900 = 4{,}500 \quad \text{(simplify)}$$

$$25r^2 = 3{,}600 \quad \text{(subtract 900 from both sides)}$$

$$r^2 = 144 \quad \text{(divide both sides by 25)}$$

$$r = 12 \text{ cm} \quad \text{(take the square root of both sides)}$$

Therefore, the radius of the cylinder is 12 cm.

EXAMPLE 2

(i) Find, in terms of π, the volume of a solid metal sphere of radius 6 cm.

(ii) Five such identical spheres are completely submerged in a cylinder containing water. If the radius of the cylinder is 8 cm, by how much will the level of the water drop if the spheres are removed from the cylinder?

Solution:

(i) Volume of sphere $= \tfrac{4}{3}\pi r^3 = \tfrac{4}{3}\pi(6)(6)(6) = 288\pi \text{ cm}^3$

(ii) Diagram:

Old situation  New situation  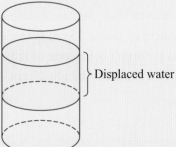 Displaced water

Equation given in disguise:

Volume of displaced water = volume of five spheres

Diagram:

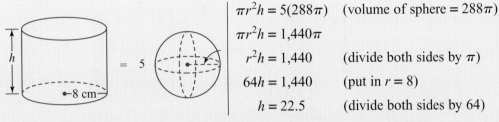

$\pi r^2 h = 5(288\pi)$ (volume of sphere = 288π)

$\pi r^2 h = 1{,}440\pi$

$r^2 h = 1{,}440$ (divide both sides by π)

$64h = 1{,}440$ (put in $r = 8$)

$h = 22.5$ (divide both sides by 64)

Thus, the level of water in the cylinder would fall by 22·5 cm.

EXAMPLE 3

(i) The volume of a hemisphere is 486π cm^3. Find the radius of the hemisphere.

(ii) Find the volume of the smallest rectangular box that the hemisphere will fit into.

Solution:

(i) Volume $\frac{1}{2}$ sphere $= \frac{1}{2}\left[\frac{4}{3}\pi r^3\right]$

$486\pi = \frac{2}{3}\pi r^3$

$486 = \frac{2}{3}r^3$

$1{,}458 = 2r^3$

$729 = r^3$

$9 \text{ cm} = r$

(ii)

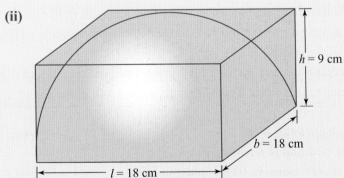

$h = 9$ cm

$b = 18$ cm

$l = 18$ cm

Volume rectangular box $= l \times b \times h$

$= 18 \times 18 \times 9$

$= 2{,}916 \text{ cm}^3$

Exercise 5.9

Find the missing dimensions in questions 1–6. In each case, the volumes are equal (all dimensions in centimetres).

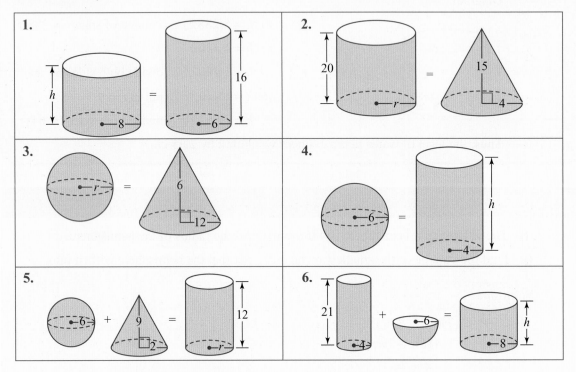

7. A solid lead cylinder of base radius 2 cm and height 15 cm is melted down and recast as a solid cone of base radius 3 cm. Calculate the height of the cone.

8. (i) A solid cylinder made of lead has a radius of length 15 cm and a height of 135 cm. Find its volume in terms of π.

   (ii) The solid cylinder is melted down and recast to make four identical right circular solid cones. The height of each cone is equal to twice the length of its base radius. Calculate the base radius length of the cones.

9. A cylinder of internal diameter 8 cm and height 18 cm is full of liquid. The liquid is poured into a second cylinder of internal diameter 12 cm. Calculate the depth of the liquid in this second cylinder.

10. A spherical golf ball has a diameter of 4 cm.

   (i) Find the volume of the golf ball in terms of π.

   (ii) A cylindrical hole on a golf course is 10 cm in diameter and 12 cm deep. The hole is half full of water. Calculate the volume of water in the hole in terms of π.

   (iii) The golf ball is dropped into the hole. Find the rise in the level of the water, correct to two decimal places.

11. A solid metal rectangular block 30 cm by 24 cm by 15 cm is melted down and recast into cubes of side 3 cm. How many such cubes are made?

12. A solid is in the shape of a hemisphere on top of a cone, as in the diagram.

    (i) The volume of the hemisphere is 18π cm^3.
Find the radius of the hemisphere.

    (ii) The slant height of the cone is $3\sqrt{5}$ cm.
Show that the vertical height of the cone is 6 cm.

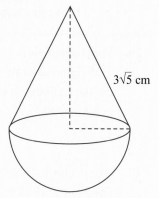

    (iii) Show that the volume of the cone equals the volume of the hemisphere.

    (iv) This solid is melted down and recast in the shape of a solid cylinder. The height of the cylinder is 9 cm. Calculate its radius.

13.   **(i)** The diameter of a solid metal sphere is 9 cm. Find the volume of the sphere in terms of π.

    (ii) The sphere is melted down. All of the metal is used to make a solid shape which consists of a cone on top of a cylinder, as shown in the diagram. The cone and the cylinder both have a height of 8 cm. The cylinder and the base of the cone both have a radius of r cm. Calculate r, correct to one decimal place.

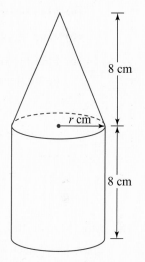

14.   **(i)** A steelworks buys steel in the form of solid cylindrical rods of radius 10 cm and length 30 m. The steel rods are melted to produce solid spherical ball bearings. No steel is wasted in the process. Find the volume of steel in one cylindrical rod in terms of π.

    (ii) The radius of a ball bearing is 2 cm. How many such ball bearings are made from one steel rod?

    (iii) Ball bearings of a different size are also produced. One steel rod makes 225,000 of these new ball bearings. Find the radius of the new ball bearings.

15. **(i)** A rectangular tank has a height of 4 m and a width of 3 m. Find its length if its volume is 96 m³.

   (ii) The tank is filled with water and a hole is drilled through its base. The water escapes at the rate of 50 litres per second. How long will it take to empty the tank in minutes?

16. Water flows through a cylindrical pipe at the rate of 12 cm per second. The diameter of the pipe is 8 cm. The water flows into an empty cylindrical tank of radius 24 cm. What is the depth of the water after one minute?

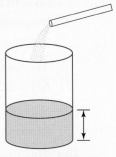

17. **(i)** A golf ball has a diameter of 3 cm. Find its volume in terms of π.

   (ii) Four golf balls fit exactly into a cylindrical tube, as shown.

   (a) Find the radius and height of the tube.

   (b) Find the volume of the tube in terms of π.

   (c) Find the fraction of the volume of the cylinder that is taken up by the four golf balls.

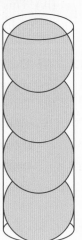

18. Sweets made from a chocolate mixture are in the shape of solid spherical balls. The diameter of each sweet is 3 cm. 36 sweets fit exactly in a rectangular box which has an internal height of 3 cm.

   (i) The base of the box is a square. How many sweets are there in each row?

   (ii) What is the internal volume of the box?

   (iii) The 36 sweets weigh 675 g. What is the weight of 1 cm³ of the chocolate mixture? Give your answer correct to one decimal place.

19. A vitamin capsule is in the shape of a cylinder with hemispherical ends. The length of the capsule is 20 mm and the diameter is 6 mm.

   (i) Calculate the volume of the capsule, giving your answer correct to the nearest mm³, taking $\pi = 3\cdot14$.

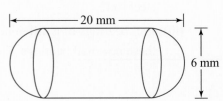

(ii) A course of these vitamins consists of 24 capsules. The capsules are stacked in three rows of eight in a box, as shown in the diagram. Write down:

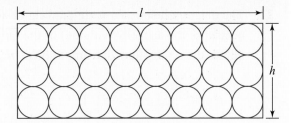

(a) The length, l

(b) The height, h

(c) The width of the box

(iii) Hence, calculate the volume of the box in mm^3.

(iv) How much of the internal volume of the box is not occupied by the capsules?

20. A wax candle is in the shape of a right circular cone. The height of the candle is 7 cm and the diameter of the base is 6 cm.

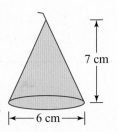

(i) Find the volume of the wax candle, correct to the nearest cm^3.

(ii) A rectangular block of wax measuring 25 cm by 12 cm by 12 cm is melted down and used to make a number of these candles. Find the maximum number of candles that can be made from the block of wax if 4% of the wax is lost in the process.

21. (i) Soup is contained in a cylindrical saucepan which has an internal radius of 14 cm. The depth of the soup is 20 cm. Calculate, in terms of π, the volume of soup in the saucepan.

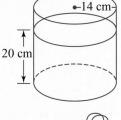

(ii) A ladle in the shape of a hemisphere with an internal radius of length 6 cm is used to serve the soup. Calculate, in terms of π, the volume of soup contained in one full ladle.

(iii) The soup is served into cylindrical cups, each with an internal radius of length 4 cm. One ladleful is placed in each cup. Calculate the depth of the soup in each cup.

(iv) How many cups can be filled from the contents of the saucepan if each cup must contain exactly one full ladle?

22. The diagram below is a scale drawing of a hopper tank used to store grain. An estimate is needed of the capacity (volume) of the tank. The figure of the man standing beside the tank allows the scale of the drawing to be estimated.

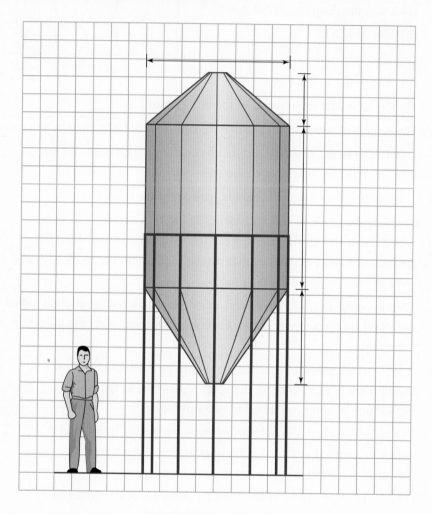

  (i) Give an estimate, in metres, of the height of an average adult man.

 (ii) Using your answer to part (i), estimate the dimensions of the hopper tank. Write your answers in the spaces provided on the diagram in metres.

(iii) Taking the tank to be a cylinder with a cone above and below, find an estimate for the capacity of the tank in cubic metres.

Trapezoidal rule

The trapezoidal rule gives a concise formula to enable us to make a good approximation of the area of an irregular shape.

Consider the diagram below.

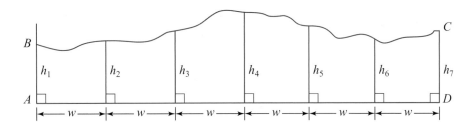

To find the area of the figure *ABCD*, do the following.

1. Divide the figure into a number of strips of equal width. (Note: The number of strips can be even or odd.)

2. Number and measure each height, h.

3. Use the following formula:

$$\text{Area} = \frac{W}{2}[h_1 + h_7 + 2(h_2 + h_3 + h_4 + h_5 + h_6)]$$

$$\text{Area} = \frac{\text{Width}}{2}[\text{first height} + \text{last height} + 2(\text{sum of all remaining heights})]$$

Note: The greater the number of strips taken, the greater the accuracy.

EXAMPLE 1

Use the trapezoidal rule to estimate the area of the figure below.

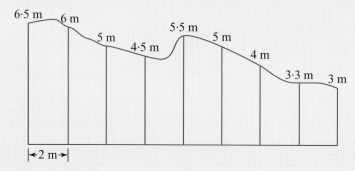

Solution:

$$\text{Area} = \frac{W}{2}[\text{first height} + \text{last height} + 2(\text{sum of all remaining heights})]$$

$$\text{Area} = \frac{W}{2}[h_1 + h_9 + 2(h_2 + h_3 + h_4 + h_5 + h_6 + h_7 + h_8)]$$

Now $h_1 = 6.5$, $h_2 = 6$, $h_3 = 5$, $h_4 = 4.5$, $h_5 = 5.5$, $h_6 = 5$, $h_7 = 4$, $h_8 = 3.3$, $h_9 = 3$

$$\text{Area} = \frac{2}{2}[6.5 + 3 + 2(6 + 5 + 4.5 + 5.5 + 5 + 4 + 3.3)]$$

$$\text{Area} = 1[9.5 + 2(33.3)]$$

$$\text{Area} = 76.1 \text{ m}^2$$

If an irregular shape has no straight edge it can be broken up into two regions, each with its own straight edge, as in the diagram. We then apply the trapezoidal rule in the normal way, except we treat both heights on each side of the line as one height in using the formula (see the next example).

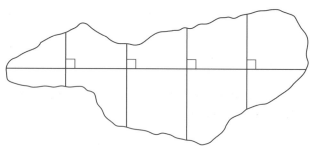

Sometimes we also have to deal with an equation in disguise.

EXAMPLE 2

A surveyor makes the following sketch in estimating the area of a building site, where k is the length shown. Using the trapezoidal rule, she estimates that the area of the site is 175 m². Find k.

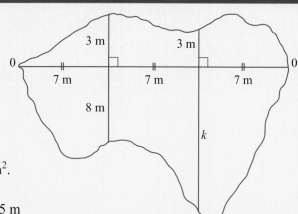

Solution:

Estimated area of building site = 175 m².

$$\therefore \frac{W}{2}[h_1 + h_4 + 2(h_2 + h_3)] = 175 \text{ m}$$

$$\boxed{\begin{array}{l} h_1 = 0 \\ h_2 = 3 + 8 = 11 \\ h_3 = 3 + k \\ h_4 = 0 \end{array}}$$

$$\frac{7}{2}[0 + 0 + 2(11 + 3 + k)] = 175$$

$$\frac{7}{2}[22 + 6 + 2k] = 175$$

$$77 + 21 + 7k = 175$$

$$7k = 175 - 77 - 21$$

$$7k = 77$$

$$k = 11 \text{ m}$$

Exercise 5.10

Use the trapezoidal rule to estimate the area of the following figures in questions 1–6 (all dimensions are in m).

1.

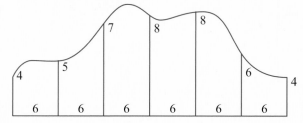

2.

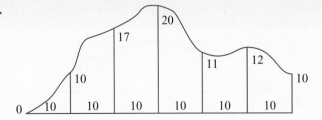

3.

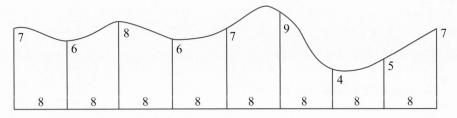

4.

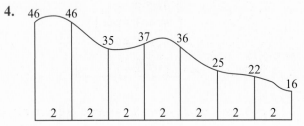

5.

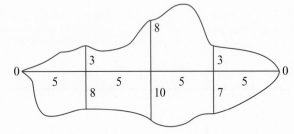

6.

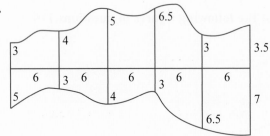

7. A sketch of a piece of land is shown. Using the trapezoidal rule, the area of the piece of land is estimated to be 270 m². Calculate the value of k.

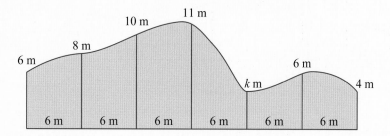

8. Using the trapezoidal rule, the area of the figure below was estimated to be 205 cm². Calculate the value of h.

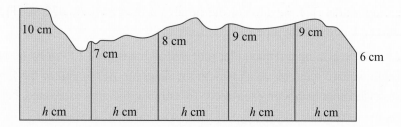

9. The sketch shows a field $ABCD$ which has one uneven edge. At equal intervals of 6 m along $[BC]$, perpendicular measurements of 7 m, 8 m, 10 m, 11 m, 13 m, 15 m and x m are made to the top of the field.

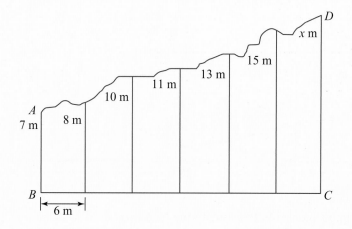

Using the trapezoidal rule, the area of the field is calculated to be 410 m². Calculate the value of x.

10. The sketch shows a flood caused by a leaking underground pipe that runs from A to B.

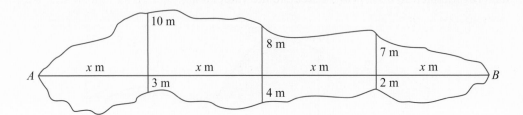

At equal intervals of x m along $[AB]$, perpendicular measurements are made to the edges of the flood. The measurements to the top edge are 10 m, 8 m and 7 m. The measurements to the bottom edge are 3 m, 4 m and 2 m. At A and B, the measurements are 0 m.

Using the trapezoidal rule, the area of the flood is estimated to be 672 m². Find x and hence write down the length of the pipe.

11. Archaeologists excavating a rectangular plot $ABCD$ measuring 120 m by 60 m divided the plot into eight square sections, as shown on the diagram. At the end of the first phase of the work, the shaded area had been excavated. To estimate the area excavated, perpendicular measurements were made to the edge of the excavated area, as shown.

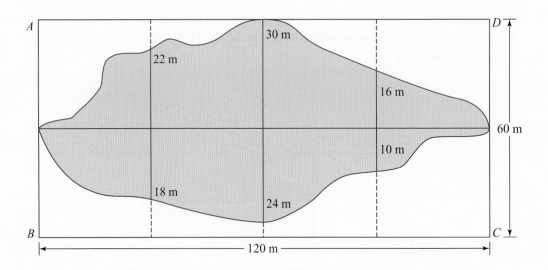

(i) Use the trapezoidal rule to estimate the area excavated.

(ii) Express the excavated area as a percentage of the total area.

12. In order to estimate the area of the irregular shape below, a horizontal line is drawn across the widest part of the shape and three offsets (perpendicular line) are drawn at equal intervals along this line.

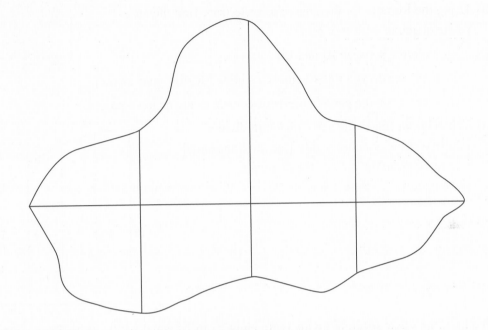

(i) Measure the horizontal line and the offsets in centimetres.

(ii) Make a rough sketch of the shape in your answerbook and record the measurements on it. Use the trapezoidal rule with these measurements to estimate the area of the shape.

13. The sketch shows a piece of land which borders the side of a straight road [AB]. The length of [AB] is 63 m. At equal intervals along [AB], perpendicular measurements are made to the boundary, as shown on the sketch.

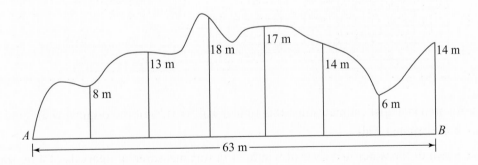

(i) Use the trapezoidal rule to estimate the area of the piece of land.

(ii) The land is valued at €380,000 per hectare. Find the value of the piece of land.

(Note: 1 hectare = 10,000 m²)

14. The diagram shows a quadrant of a circle of radius 10.

    (i) Using the trapezoidal rule, estimate the area of the quadrant (all dimensions are in cm).

    (ii) Using the formula for the area of a circle, πr^2, find the area of the quadrant with $\pi = 3 \cdot 14$.

    (iii) Find the error between **(i)** and **(ii)**.

    (iv) Which answer do you think is most accurate? Justify your answer.

    (v) Hence, calculate the percentage error correct to the nearest integer.

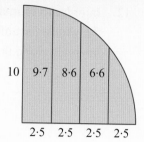

    (vi) The diagram shows the same quadrant divided into five strips of equal width. Use the trapezoidal rule to estimate the area of the quadrant.

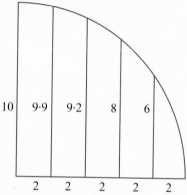

    (vii) Given the same quadrant divided into eight strips of equal width, write down your estimate for the area without doing any calculations. Justify your answer.

15. (i) The front face of a stone wall of a ruined castle is shown in the diagram. All distances are measured in metres. The heights are measured at intervals of 2·4 m along the base line. Use the trapezoidal rule to calculate the area of the front face of the stone wall.

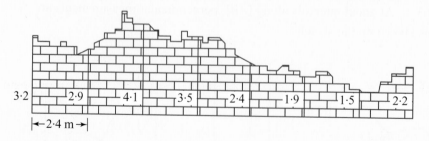

    (ii) An archaeologist estimates that this ruined wall is 16% of the original wall. Find the area of the original wall.

16. The depth of the water in a river of width 20 m was measured at intervals of 4 m, starting from one bank and ending at the other. The results are recorded in the following table.

Distance from the bank (m)	0	4	8	12	16	20
Depth (m)	0·6	0·8	1·4	2·1	1·9	0·7

(i) Use the trapezoidal rule to estimate the area of a cross-section of the water at this point.

(ii) At this point of the river, it was calculated that the water was flowing at a speed of $\frac{1}{2}$ m per second. Find the volume of water passing this point each minute **(a)** in cubic metres **(b)** in litres.

17. The diagram shows the curve $y = x^2 + 2$ in the domain $0 \leq x \leq 5$, where $x \in \mathbb{R}$.

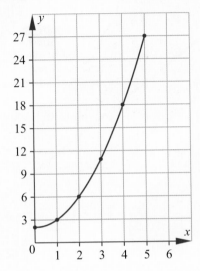

(i) Copy the following table, then complete it using the equation of the curve.

x	0	1	2	3	4	5
y						

(ii) Hence, use the trapezoidal rule to estimate the area between the curve and the x-axis.

(iii) The actual area between the curve and the x-axis is $51\frac{2}{3}$ square units. Find the percentage error in the estimate, correct to one decimal place.

(iv) Comment on how effective you think the trapezoidal rule is in this case.

18. A Geography class is required to estimate the area of Carlingford Lough from a map with a scale of 1 : 70,000.

An axis line *ABCDEF* is drawn and divided into five equal segments (of 3 cm each), as shown.

(i) Complete the following table by writing down the values of x and y by measuring from the map. Give your answers correct to the nearest half centimetre.

Through the point	A	B	C	D	E	F
Perpendicular distance from shore to shore in cm	0	$3\frac{1}{2}$	$3\frac{1}{2}$	x	y	$2\frac{1}{2}$

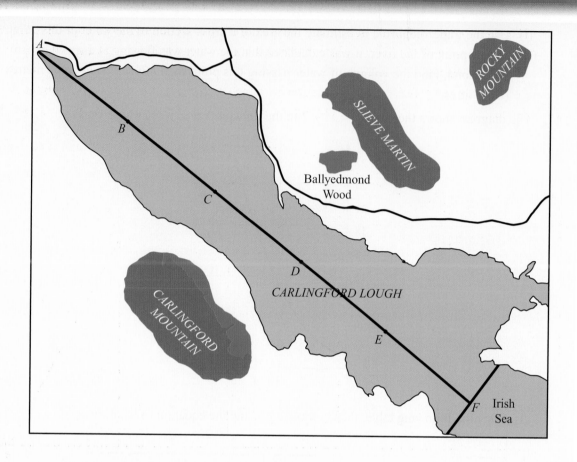

(ii) Use the trapezoidal rule to estimate the following.

 (a) The area in cm² of Carlingford Lough as outlined on the map, correct to the nearest cm².

 (b) The area in km² of Carlingford Lough as outlined, correct to the nearest km².

 (c) Comment on the accuracy or otherwise of the trapezoidal rule in this situation. Justify your comment.

19. The diagram below shows a shape with two straight edges and one irregular edge. By dividing the edge [AB] into five equal intervals, use the trapezoidal rule to estimate the area of the shape.

Record your constructions and measurements on the diagram. Give your lengths correct to the nearest half cm and your area correct to the nearest cm².

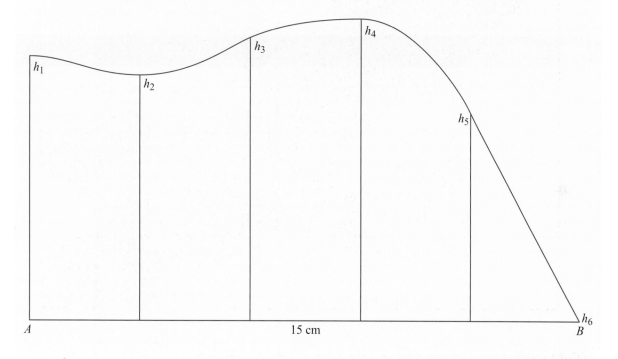

15 cm

Nets of 3D shapes

A line has only one **dimension** – length (1D).

A flat shape has two dimensions – length and width (2D).

A **solid** shape has three dimensions – length, width and height (3D).

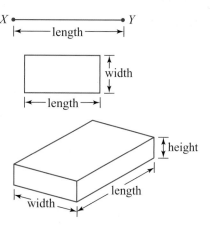

When a 3D shape is opened out, the flat shape is called the **net**.

 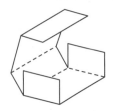 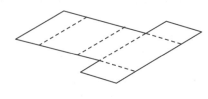

EXAMPLE

(i) This is a **net** of a solid cube.

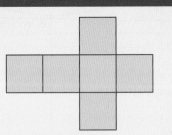

This is how it folds up to make the cube.

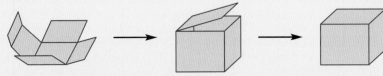

There can be many different nets for one rectangular solid, e.g. this is also a net of a solid cube.

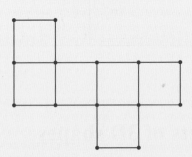

(ii) This is a net for a cuboid that is 4 cm by 2 cm by 2 cm.
When you draw a net, you have to draw the lengths accurately.
You may have to use a scale for your drawing.
Choose a scale so that the net fits on your page and it's not too small.

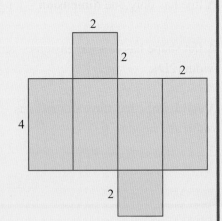

This is how the net folds up to make a cuboid.

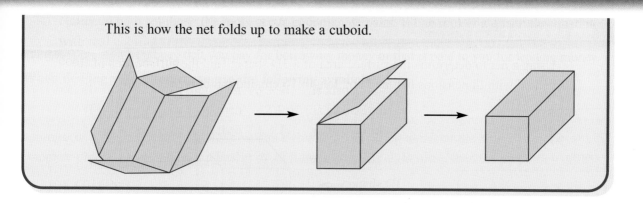

Naming parts of a 3D shape

Each flat surface is called a **face**. Two faces meet at an **edge**.
Edges of a shape meet at a corner, or point, called a **vertex**.
The plural of vertex is **vertices**.

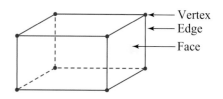

The cuboid has eight vertices (each marked with a •).
The cuboid has 12 edges (count each line, including dotted lines).
The cuboid has six faces. They are front and back (not indicated) plus top, base and sides.

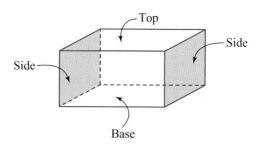

A net diagram indicates the faces clearly.

	Top	
	Back	
Side	Base	Side
	Front	

EXAMPLE

Using a net to determine the surface area of a 3D shape, find the surface area of the cuboid with dimensions height 7 cm, length 10 cm and width 6 cm.

Solution:

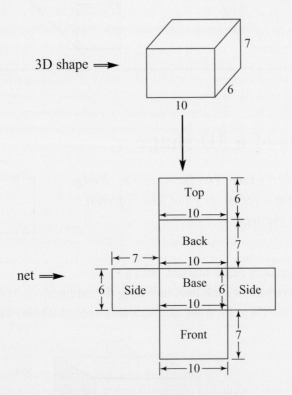

Surface area of a cuboid = The sum of the area of all six faces

= Sum of the area of all six faces of the net

= Area of (top + back + base + front + side + side)

= Area of ((top + base) + (back + front) + (side + side))

= 2(top) + 2(back) + 2(side)

= 2(10 × 6) + 2(10 × 7) + 2(6 × 7)

= 120 + 140 + 84

= 344 cm²

Note: We can write a formula for the surface area of a cuboid as $2lb + 2lh + 2bh$.

Examples of 3D shapes (or solids)

These are all examples of 3D shapes.

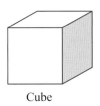

Cube

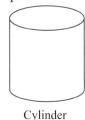

Cylinder

Pyramid with square base

Sphere

Can you name some other 3D shapes?

These 3D shapes are called prisms.

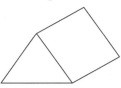 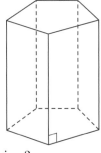 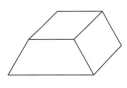

What do prisms have in common?

Can you draw another 3D shape that is a prism?

EXAMPLE

This prism is 8 cm long.
The ends are equilateral triangles with sides of 4 cm.
Draw an accurate net of the prism.

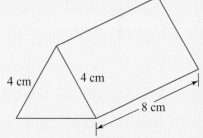

Solution:

Step 1: Draw the rectangular faces of the prism.
Each rectangle is 8 cm long and 4 cm wide.

Step 2: The ends of the prism are equilateral triangles.
The length of each side of the triangles is 4 cm.
Use your compass to construct the equilateral triangles.

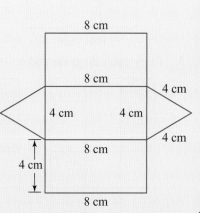

Exercise 5.11

1.

	1	2	3	4	5	6
Net						
	A	B	C	D	E	F
3D shape						

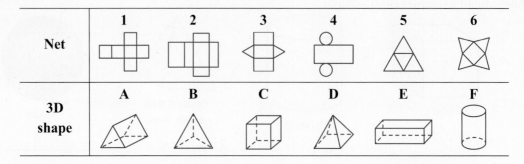

The table shows six nets numbered 1, 2, 3, 4, 5, 6 and six 3D shapes labelled A, B, C, D, E, F. Match each net to its correct 3D shape. The first one is done for you: (1, C).

2. Sam made this shape using multilink cubes. Four cubes are purple. The other six are white.

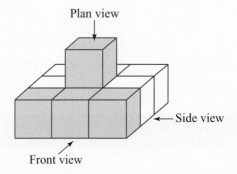

Plan view

Side view

Front view

Copy and complete each view of the shape by colouring in the squares that are purple.

(i)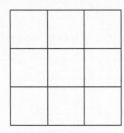

Plan view

(ii)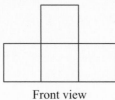

Front view

(iii)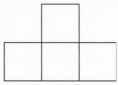

Side view

3. Copy each diagram and colour in two extra squares to give you the net of a cube.

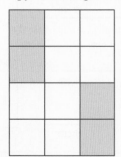 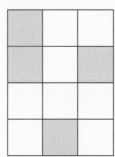 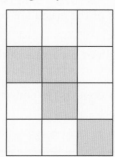

4. Draw an accurate net for each of these 3D shapes.

(i)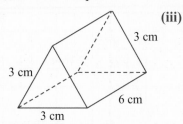

(ii)

(iii)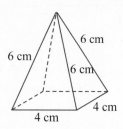

5. Here is the net of a triangular prism with dimensions in cm.

    (i) State the number of faces for this prism.

   (ii) How many vertices does the prism have?

  (iii) Find **(a)** the surface area of the prism **(b)** the volume of the prism.

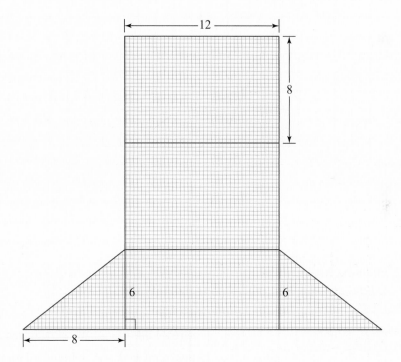

6. The nets of these shapes have reflection symmetry. Complete the nets and name the two shapes.

(i)

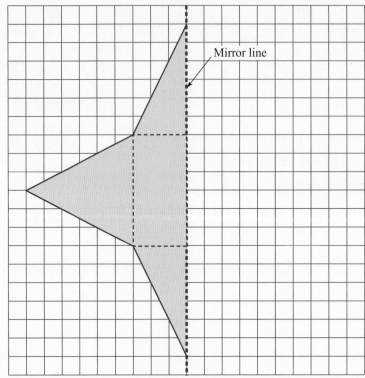

Mirror line

(ii)

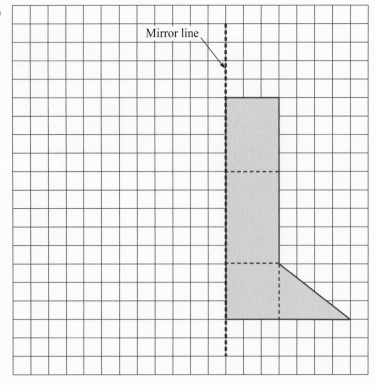

Mirror line

7. **(i)** A metal box with no lid is shown. Draw a net of the box.

    (ii) Hence or otherwise, find the area of the metal required to make this box. Give your answers in **(a)** cm^2 **(b)** m^2.

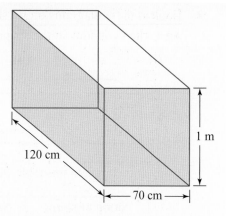

8. A rectangular sheet of metal measures 2 m by $1\frac{1}{2}$ m. A square of side 30 cm is removed from each corner. The remaining piece of metal is folded along the dotted lines to form an open box as shown.

    (i) Find the surface area of the net used to construct the box.

    (ii) Find the volume of the box in **(a)** cm^3 **(b)** m^3 **(c)** litres.

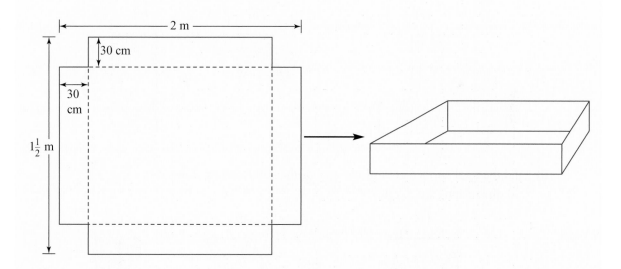

9. Look at these diagrams of 3D shapes. Dotted lines are used to show the edges that cannot be seen when you look at the shape from one side.

   (i)   **(ii)**   **(iii)**   **(iv)**

  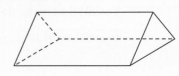

Copy and complete this table.

	Name of shape	Number of faces	Number of vertices	Number of edges
(i)				
(ii)				
(iii)				
(iv)				

10. **(i)** Which 3D solids could be made from the following nets?

          (a)   **(b)**   **(c)**

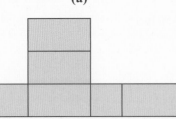 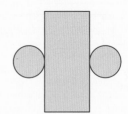

(ii) Find the total surface area of the nets of the solids below. Take $\pi = \dfrac{22}{7}$. (All dimensions are in cm.)

          (a)   **(b)**   **(c)**

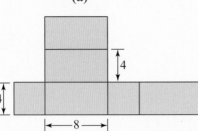 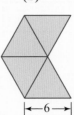 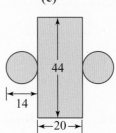

(iii) Find the volume of the solids in **(ii) (a)** and **(ii) (c)**, taking $\pi = \dfrac{22}{7}$.

11. The following net has a 3D shape with a volume of 2,512 cm³.

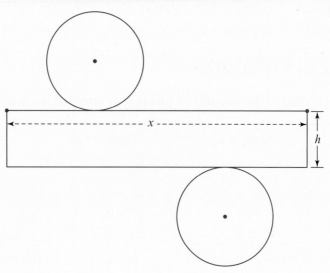

   (i) Name the 3D shape.

  (ii) Taking $\pi = 3 \cdot 14$ and given both identical circles have a diameter of 20 cm, calculate h and x, the dimensions of the rectangle.

 (iii) Can a similar 3D solid be made from the net shown on the right? Justify your answer.

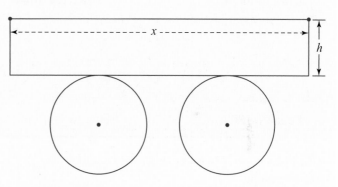

12. Find the volume of the prism associated with the given net. (All dimensions are in cm.)

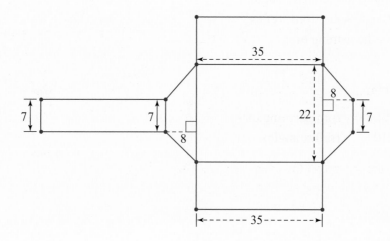

Types and names of angles

Angles are named according to the amount of turning, or rotation, measured in degrees.

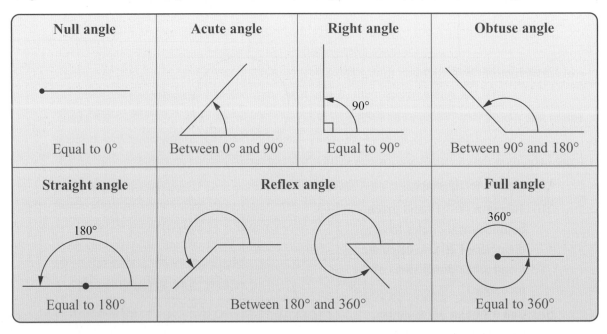

Null angle	Acute angle	Right angle	Obtuse angle
Equal to 0°	Between 0° and 90°	Equal to 90°	Between 90° and 180°

Straight angle	Reflex angle	Full angle
Equal to 180°	Between 180° and 360°	Equal to 360°

Ordinary angle

An **ordinary angle** is an angle between 0° and 180°. When naming an angle, it is **always** assumed that we are referring to the ordinary angle (non-reflex angle), unless the word 'reflex' precedes or follows the naming of an angle.

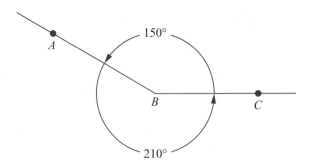

Consider the diagram.

$$|\angle ABC| = 150° \qquad \text{(ordinary angle)}$$
$$|\text{reflex } \angle ABC| = 210° \qquad \text{(reflex angle)}$$

Properties of angles

It is important to know the following properties of angles.

Vertically opposite angles (angles formed by two lines)	Complementary angles (angles in a right angle)	Supplementary angles (angles in a straight line)
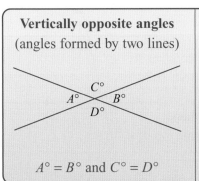 $A° = B°$ and $C° = D°$	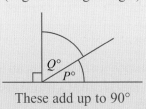 These add up to 90° $P° + Q° = 90°$	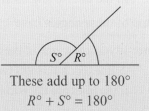 These add up to 180° $R° + S° = 180°$

Interior angles

Interior angles add up to 180°. A pair of interior angles is marked on each of the diagrams. Interior angles are always on the **same** side of the transversal.

$$|\angle 4| + |\angle 5| = 180° \qquad |\angle 3| + |\angle 6| = 180°$$

Looking for a ⌐ or ¬ shape can help you to spot interior angles.

In short:

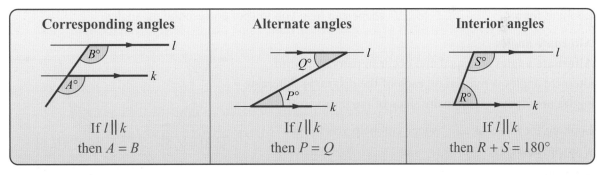

Corresponding angles	Alternate angles	Interior angles
If $l \parallel k$ then $A = B$	If $l \parallel k$ then $P = Q$	If $l \parallel k$ then $R + S = 180°$

The converses are also true:

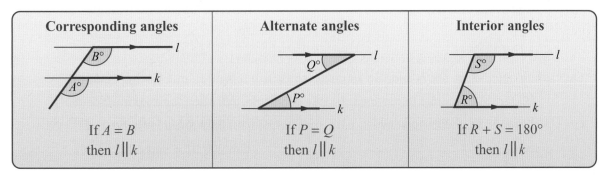

Corresponding angles	Alternate angles	Interior angles
If $A = B$ then $l \parallel k$	If $P = Q$ then $l \parallel k$	If $R + S = 180°$ then $l \parallel k$

Angles and parallel lines

When a line cuts a pair of parallel lines, eight angles are formed in such a way that:

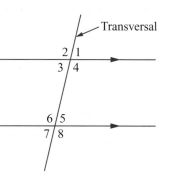

1. All the acute angles are equal.

2. All the obtuse angles are equal.

Some of these angles have special names.

Note: If you know one of these angles, then you can work out all the others.

A line that intersects two or more lines is called a **transversal**, even if the lines are not parallel.

Corresponding angles

Corresponding angles are equal and occur in pairs. A pair of corresponding angles is marked on each of the diagrams. Corresponding angles are always on the **same** side of the transversal.

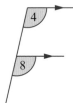

$$|\angle 4| = |\angle 8|$$

$$|\angle 3| = |\angle 7|$$

$$|\angle 2| = |\angle 6|$$

$$|\angle 1| = |\angle 5|$$

Looking for a F, $\daleth$, E or $\lrcorner$ shape can help you to spot corresponding angles.

Alternate angles

Alternate angles are equal and occur in pairs. A pair of alternate angles is marked on each of the diagrams. Alternate angles are always on **opposite** sides of the transversal.

Looking for a $\urcorner$ or $\lrcorner$ shape can help you to spot alternate angles.

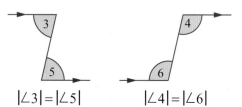

$$|\angle 3| = |\angle 5| \qquad |\angle 4| = |\angle 6|$$

Triangles

Angle sum of a triangle	Exterior angle of a triangle
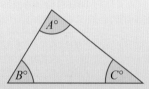	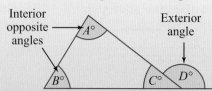
The three angles of a triangle add up to 180°.	If one side is produced, the exterior angle is equal to the sum of the two interior opposite angles.
$A° + B° + C° = 180°$	$D° = A° + B°$

Special triangles

Equilateral triangle	Isosceles triangle	Right-angled triangle
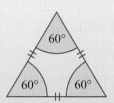	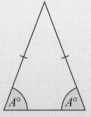	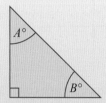
Three sides equal	Two sides equal	One angle is 90°
Three equal angles	Base angles are equal	The other two angles add
All angles are equal to 60°	(base angles are the angles	up to 90°.
	opposite the equal sides)	$A° + B° = 90°$

Notes:

1. **Scalene triangles** have no equal sides and no equal angles.
2. **Acute-angled triangles** have three acute angles.
3. **Obtuse-angled triangles** have one obtuse angle and two acute angles.
4. The tick marks on the sides of the triangle indicate sides of equal length.
5. In a triangle, the largest angle is always opposite the largest side and the smallest angle is opposite the smallest side.
6. If two sides are of unequal length, then the angles opposite these sides are also unequal.
7. The length of any two sides added together is always greater than the length of the third side.

Quadrilaterals

A **quadrilateral** is a figure that has four sides and four vertices. It has two diagonals that join the opposite vertices.

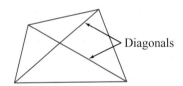

Diagonals

The four angles of a quadrilateral add up to 360°.

$A° + B° + C° + D° = 360°$

(This is because a quadrilateral can be divided up into two triangles.)

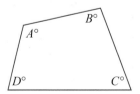

Note: *A* and *C* are called opposite angles, and *B* and *D* are also called opposite angles. Some quadrilaterals have special names and special properties.

Square properties

1. Opposite sides are parallel

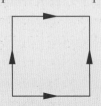

2. All sides are equal

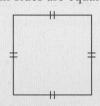

3. All angles are right angles

4. Diagonals are equal and bisect each other

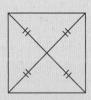

5. Diagonals intersect at right angles

6. Diagonals bisect each angle

Rectangle properties

1. Opposite sides are parallel

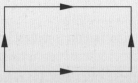

2. Opposite sides are equal

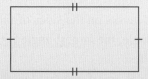

3. All angles are right angles

4. Diagonals are equal and bisect each other

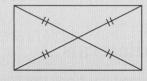

Parallelogram properties

1. Opposite sides are parallel

2. Opposite sides are equal

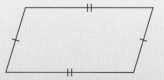

3. Opposite angles are equal

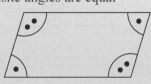

4. Diagonals bisect each other

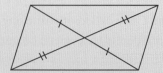

Converse: If the diagonals of a quadrilateral bisect each other, then the quadrilateral is a parallelogram.

Rhombus

1. Opposite sides are parallel

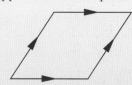

2. All sides are equal

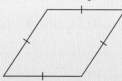

3. Opposite angles are equal

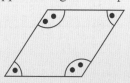

4. Diagonals bisect each other

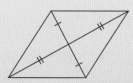

5. Diagonals intersect at right angles

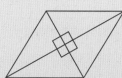

6. Diagonals bisect opposite angles

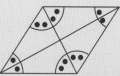

EXAMPLE 1

Calculate the value of:

(i) x **(ii)** y

In each case, give a reason for your answer.

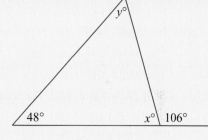

Solution:

(i) $x° + 106° = 180°$ (straight angle)

∴ $x + 106 = 180$

$x = 74$ (subtract 106 from both sides)

(ii) $x° + y° + 48° = 180°$ (three angles in a triangle)

∴ $x + y + 48 = 180$

∴ $74 + y + 48 = 180$ (put in $x = 74$)

$y + 122 = 180$

$y = 58$ (subtract 122 from both sides)

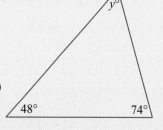

EXAMPLE 2

In the diagram, $|AB| = |AC|$ and $|\angle BAC| = 68°$.

(i) What type of triangle is $\triangle ABC$?

(ii) Calculate $|\angle ABC|$. Give a reason for your answer.

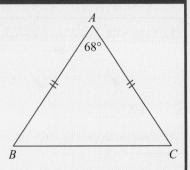

Solution:

(i) As $|AB| = |AC|$, $\triangle ABC$ is an isosceles triangle.

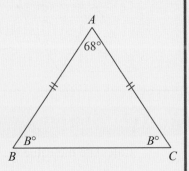

(ii) Let $\angle ABC = B°$.

The triangle is isosceles.

Therefore, the two base angles are equal.

$B° + B° + 68° = 180°$ (three angles in a triangle)

$B + B + 68 = 180$

$2B + 68 = 180$

$2B = 112$ (subtract 68 from both sides)

$B = 56$ (divide both sides by 2)

$\therefore |\angle ABC| = 56°$

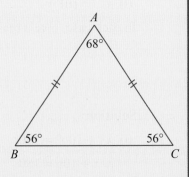

EXAMPLE 3

$ABCD$ is a parallelogram, with $|\angle BAD| = 115°$ and $|\angle CBD| = 30°$.

Find: (i) $|\angle BCD|$ (ii) $|\angle ADB|$ (iii) $|\angle ABD|$

(iv) $|\angle CDB|$

In each case, give a reason for your answer.

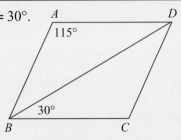

Solution:

(i)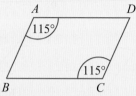

$$|\angle BCD| = |\angle BAD| = 115°$$
opposite angles of the parallelogram

(ii)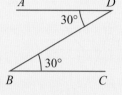

$$|\angle ADB| = |\angle CBD| = 30°$$
alternate angles

(iii)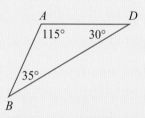

$$|\angle ABD| + |\angle BAD| + |\angle ADB| = 180°$$
Three angles in a triangle add to 180°.
$$|\angle ABD| + 115° + 30° = 180°$$
$$|\angle ABD| + 145° = 180°$$
$$|\angle ABD| = 35°$$

(iv)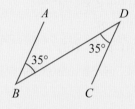

$$|\angle CDB| = |\angle ABD| = 35°$$
alternate angles

Exercise 6.1

Calculate the value of the letter representing the angle in each of the diagrams in questions 1–9. In each case, give a reason.

1.

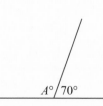

2.

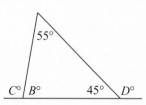

3.

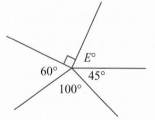

4.

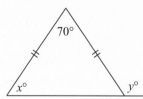

5.

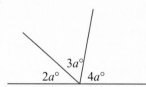

6.

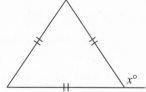

In questions 7–9, parallel lines are indicated with arrows.

7.

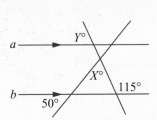

8.

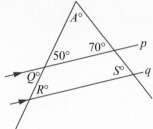

9.

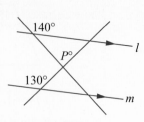

10. In the diagram, $|PQ| = |PR|$.

Find the value of:

(i) x (ii) y (iii) z

In each case, give a reason for your answer.

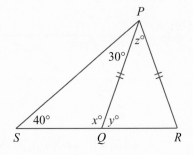

11. The diagram shows a parallelogram $PQRS$ with diagonal $[PR]$ and $|\angle PRS| = 45°$. T is a point on the ray $[PS$ such that $|\angle RST| = 130°$.

Find the measure of the following.

(i) $|\angle PSR|$ (ii) $|\angle PQR|$

(iii) $|\angle PRQ|$ (iv) $|\angle QPR|$

In each case, justify your answer.

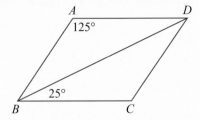

12. $ABCD$ is a parallelogram with $|\angle BAD| = 125°$ and $|\angle CBD| = 25°$.

Find: (i) $|\angle BCD|$ (ii) $|\angle ADB|$ (iii) $|\angle ABD|$

(iv) $|\angle CDB|$

In each case, give a reason for your answer.

13. $|PR| = |QR| = |RS|$ and $|\angle PRQ| = 48°$.

Find: (i) $|\angle PQR|$ (ii) $|\angle PSR|$

In each case, give a reason for your answer.

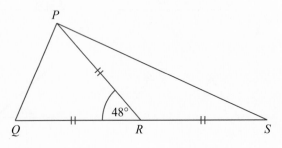

14. A paddle wheel has nine equally spaced arms, as shown. Showing all your work, calculate the angle between any two adjacent arms.

15. Three shapes *A*, *B* and *C* with angles 28°, 101° and 49°, respectively, fit together at the point *P*. Will they make a straight line? Justify your answer.

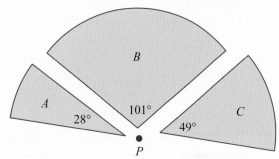

16. An isosceles triangle is always an obtuse-angled triangle. Is this statement true or false? Justify your answer.

17. In a right-angled triangle, one of the angles is obtuse. Is this statement true or false? Give a reason for your answer.

18. An equilateral triangle is also an acute-angled triangle. Is this statement true or false? Justify your answer.

19. In the diagram, $|PQ| = |QR|$ and $|PS| = |PR| = |RS|$.
    Find: **(i)** $|\angle QPR|$ **(ii)** $|\angle PSR|$ **(iii)** $|\angle QPS|$
    In each case, give a reason for your answer.

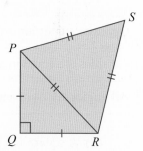

20. In the diagram, $|\angle QPR| = 2x°$ and $|\angle PQR| = (90 - x)°$. Prove that $|PQ| = |PR|$.

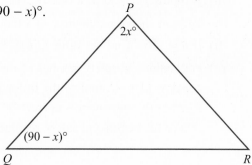

21. In the diagram, $PQ \perp QR$ and $|\angle APB| = |\angle CRQ| = 75°$.

Prove that $PS \perp RS$.

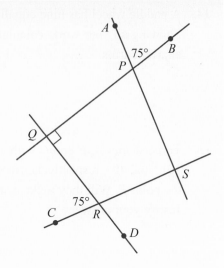

22. The diagram shows a square, A, a rectangle, B, a parallelogram, C, and a rhombus, D.

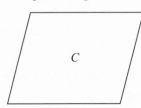

(i) Complete the following tables.

Opposite angles are equal in measure.	
All sides are equal in length.	
All angles are right angles.	

Diagonals intersect at right angles.	
Diagonals bisect each other.	
Diagonals are equal in length.	A, B

(ii) A square is a rectangle. True or false? Justify your answer.

(iii) A rhombus could be a square. True or false? Justify your answer.

23. The diagram shows a side view of a flat folding seat.

(i) If $A = 110°$, find the value of (a) B (b) C.

(ii) For health and safety reasons, A must be greater than or equal to 110°. Complete the following table, indicating whether the statement is correct (✓) or incorrect (✗) to satisfy the health and safety regulations.

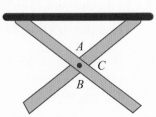

	Statement	✓ or ✗	Reason
(i)	$C > 70°$		
(ii)	$C \leq 70°$		
(iii)	$B > 110°$		
(iv)	$(A + B) < 220°$		

24. The line l bisects $\angle ABD$ and the line k bisects $\angle CBD$. Prove that $l \perp k$.

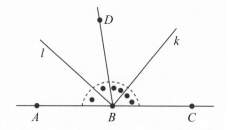

Angle-side relationship in a triangle and triangle inequality

Angle-side relationship in a triangle

> In a triangle, the angle opposite the greater of two sides is greater than the angle opposite the lesser side.

In $\triangle ABC$,

if $|AC| > |AB|$

then $|\angle B| > |\angle C|$.

Conversely,

if $|\angle B| > |\angle C|$

then $|AC| > |AB|$.

In other words, the greatest angle is opposite the longest side and the smallest angle is opposite the shortest side and vice versa. What can you say about the other angle and the other side?

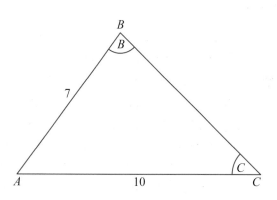

225

EXAMPLE

In $\triangle ABC$, $|AB| = 10$, $|AC| = 8$ and $|BC| = 7$.

   (i) Which angle is the greatest?

   (ii) Which angle is the smallest?

   (iii) What can you say about the remaining angle?

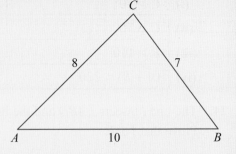

Solution:

Label angles A, B and C.

   (i) $\angle C$ is the greatest angle because it is opposite the longest side.

   (ii) $\angle A$ is the smallest angle because it is opposite the shortest side.

   (iii) $\angle B$ is less than $\angle C$ and $\angle B$ is greater than $\angle A$.

   Alternatively, $|\angle C| < |\angle B| < |\angle A|$.

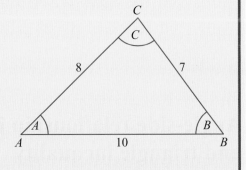

Triangle inequality

> The lengths of any two sides of a triangle added together are **always** greater than the length of the third side.

The converse is also true:

> If two lengths added together are less than or equal to a third length, then the three lengths **cannot** form a triangle.

Quick check: The two shorter sides added together must be greater than the longest side, otherwise a triangle **cannot** be drawn.

For the triangle on the right:

$$a + b > c$$
$$a + c > b$$
$$b + c > a$$

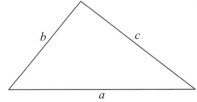

EXAMPLE

Find the range of values of k for which $\triangle ABC$ can be constructed.

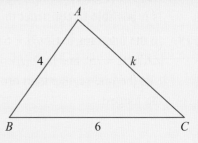

Solution:

The triangle inequality gives us three separate inequalities to solve.

1. $k + 4 > 6$	**2.** $k + 6 > 4$	**3.** $6 + 4 > k$
$k > 2$	$k > -2$	$10 > k$
	(length can't be negative)	$k < 10$

Combining 1 and 3: $2 < k < 10$.

The length k is greater than 2 and less than 10.

Exercise 6.2

1. **Fill in the blanks.**

    (i) If one side of a triangle is longer than a second side, then the larger angle is opposite the _____ side.

    (ii) The sum of the lengths of any two sides of a triangle is _____ than the length of the third side.

2. In $\triangle PQR$, $|PQ| = 8$, $|QR| = 5$ and $|PR| = 4$. Name the largest angle. Give a reason for your answer.

3. In $\triangle ABC$, $|\angle BAC| = 56°$ and $|\angle ABC| = 72°$. Which is the shortest side? Justify your answer.

4. In $\triangle DEF$, an exterior angle at D measures $110°$ and $|\angle DEF| = 65°$. Name the longest side of the triangle. Give a reason for your answer.

5. In $\triangle PQR$, $|\angle RPQ| = 54°$ and $|\angle RPQ| > |\angle PQR|$. Name the shortest side. Justify your answer.

Is it possible for a triangle to have the sides with the given lengths indicated in questions 6–17? In each case, justify your answer.

6. 3, 4, 5	7. 2, 6, 7	8. 2, 3, 7
9. 5, 12, 8	10. 6, 8, 11	11. 2, 3, 5
12. 13, 8, 9	13. 6, 7, 8	14. 9, 6, 2
15. 9, 8, 7	16. 1, 1, 3	17. 4, 21, 17

18. A woman wants to build a triangular-shaped rockery in her back garden. To fit in with the rest of her garden, she wants the measurements of the rockery to be 6 m by 10 m by 3 m. Is it possible to construct this rockery to the given dimensions? Justify your answer.

19. In the diagram, $|\angle CDB| = 65°$, $|\angle ADB| = 32°$, $|\angle CBD| = 75°$ and $|\angle DAB| = 84°$.
   List the line segments in order from the shortest to the longest.

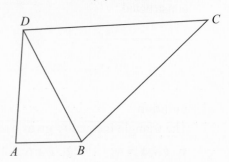

20. Two sides of an isosceles triangle measure 3 cm and 10 cm. What is the length of the third side? Justify your answer.

21. Two sides of an isosceles triangle measure 4 cm and 9 cm. What is the length of the third side? Justify your answer.

22. In each of the following, find the range of values of k for which the triangle can be constructed.

   (i)

   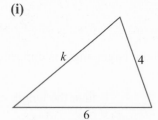

   (ii)

   (iii)

   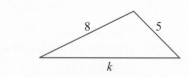

23. Two sides of a triangle have lengths 8 cm and 10 cm. The length of the third side can be any length between a cm and b cm. Find the value of a and the value of b. If the third side must be a whole number, find the minimum value and the maximum value.

24. You live 6 km from the shopping centre, S, and 4 km from your friend's house, F. The distance from your friend's house to the shopping centre is x km.

   (i) Write an inequality in terms of x that describes the distance between the shopping centre and your friend's house.

   (ii) Write an inequality that describes the distance, d, that you travel if you go to your friend's house first and then to the shopping centre.

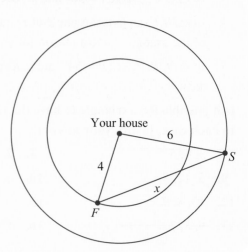

Pythagoras' theorem

The longest side of a right-angled triangle is always opposite the right angle and is called the **hypotenuse**.

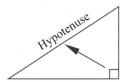

Pythagoras' theorem states that in a right-angled triangle:

The square on the hypotenuse is equal to the sum of the squares on the other two sides.

$$(\text{hypotenuse})^2 = (\text{side 1})^2 + (\text{side 2})^2$$

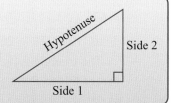

This equation can be written algebraically:

$$c^2 = a^2 + b^2$$

The converse (opposite) also applies:
if $c^2 = a^2 + b^2$, then the triangle must be right-angled.

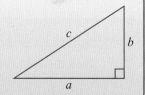

Note: Pythagoras' theorem applies only to right-angled triangles.

We can use Pythagoras' theorem to find the missing length of a side in a right-angled triangle if we know the lengths of the other two sides.

Pythagoras' theorem can also be written as:

$$|AB|^2 = |AC|^2 + |BC|^2$$

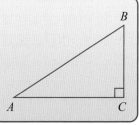

EXAMPLE 1

Prove that the triangle with sides of lengths 10 units, 24 units and 26 units is right-angled.

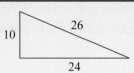

Solution:

$$10^2 + 24^2 \qquad\qquad 26^2$$
$$= 100 + 576 \qquad = 676$$
$$= 676$$

Thus, $10^2 + 24^2 = 26^2$

∴ The triangle is right-angled
(according to Pythagoras' theorem).

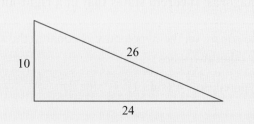

EXAMPLE 2

Find the value of **(i)** x and **(ii)** y, correct to two decimal places.

(i)

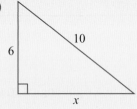

(ii)

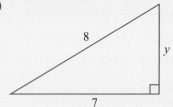

Solution:

(i) $x^2 + 6^2 = 10^2$

$x^2 + 36 = 100$

$x^2 = 64$

$x = \sqrt{64}$

$x = 8$

(ii) $y^2 + 7^2 = 8^2$

$y^2 + 49 = 64$

$y^2 = 15$

$y = \sqrt{15}$

$y = 3\cdot872983346$

$y = 3\cdot87$

(correct to two decimal places)

Note: If a question requires an answer in surd form, then leave the square root in the answer. In part **(ii)** above, you would leave the answer as $y = \sqrt{15}$ (surd form).

EXAMPLE 3

The diagonal of a square is $\sqrt{18}$. Calculate the length of the side.

Solution:

Draw a square.

Let x = the length of a side.

The diagonal bisects the square to create two right-angled triangles.

Therefore, we can apply Pythagoras' theorem.

$$a^2 + b^2 = h^2 \qquad \text{(Pythagoras' theorem)}$$
$$x^2 + x^2 = \left(\sqrt{18}\right)^2$$
$$2x^2 = 18$$
$$x^2 = 9 \qquad \text{(divide both sides by 2)}$$
$$x = \sqrt{9} \qquad \text{(take the square root of both sides)}$$
$$x = 3$$

Therefore, the length of a side of the square is 3.

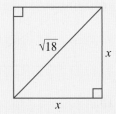

Note: $\left(\sqrt{a}\right)^2 = a$. For example, $\left(\sqrt{20}\right)^2 = 20$, $\left(\sqrt{50}\right)^2 = 50$.

Exercise 6.3

1. Complete the table.

a	b	c	a^2	b^2	c^2
3	4				
	8	10			
8		17			
			144		169
			49	576	
		50		900	
	7		576		
				2·25	6·25

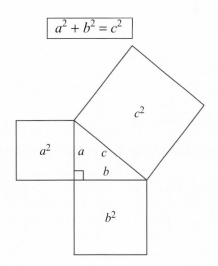

$a^2 + b^2 = c^2$

Use Pythagoras' theorem to find the length of the side indicated by a letter in each of the diagrams in questions 2–25.

2.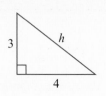

3.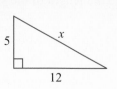

4.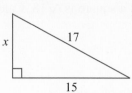

5.

6.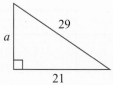

7.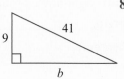

8.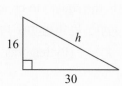

9.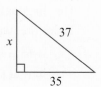

10.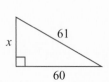

11.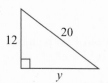

12.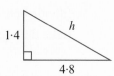

13.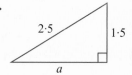

In questions 14–17, remember that $\left(\sqrt{x}\right)^2 = x$. For example, $\left(\sqrt{5}\right)^2 = 5$, $\left(\sqrt{8}\right)^2 = 8$.

14.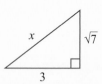

15.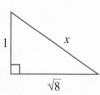

16.

17.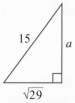

In questions 18–21, leave your answer in square root (surd) form.

18.

19.

20.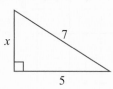

21.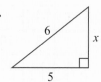

In questions 22–25, the diagrams represent squares.

22.

23.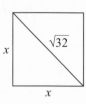

24.

25.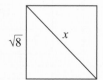

26. Prove that the triangle with sides of lengths 7 units, 24 units and 25 units is right-angled.

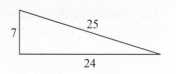

27. Using Pythagoras' theorem, investigate which triangles are right-angled and which are not.

(i)

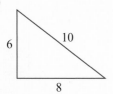

(ii)

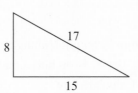

(iii)

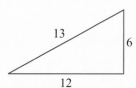

(iv)

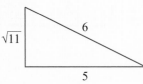

(v)

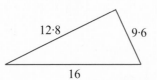

(vi)

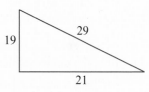

28. *ABCD* is a parallelogram. $AE \perp BC$,
$|AB| = 5, |AD| = 8$ and $|BE| = 3$.
Calculate:

   (i) $|AE|$

   (ii) The area of the parallelogram *ABCD*

In questions 29–31, use Pythagoras' theorem (i) to find the perpendicular height, *h* cm, and then (ii) find the area of the parallelogram.

29.

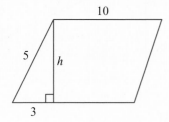

30.

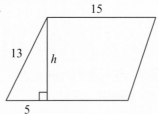

31.

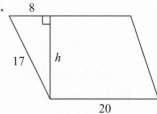

32. Find the area of the squares marked A and B in the following diagrams.

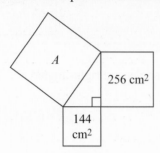

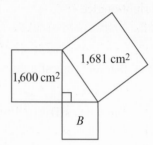

33. The diagram shows a ladder 6 m in length leaning against a vertical wall. The foot of the ladder is on horizontal ground, 3·6 m from the wall. Calculate how far up the wall the ladder reaches.

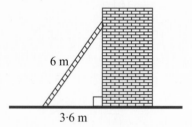

34. O is the centre of the circle.

$|AC| = 16$ cm and $|BC| = 12$ cm.

   (i) Calculate $|\angle ACB|$. Give a reason for your answer.

   (ii) Calculate the radius of the circle.

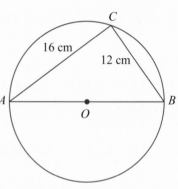

35. Find the values of x and y.

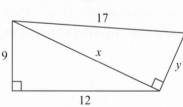

36. In the diagram, $|PR| = \sqrt{97}$ cm, $|PQ| = 4$ cm and $|PT| = |TS| = 5$ cm. $PQ \perp RT$ and $RT \perp TS$.

Calculate: **(i)** $|QT|$ **(ii)** $|QR|$ **(iii)** $|RT|$ **(iv)** $|RS|$

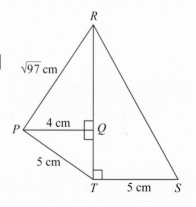

37. The diagram shows the side view of a wedge. The wedge is 112 mm long and 30 mm high. The top part of the wedge is 40 mm long. Calculate the length of the sloping part of the wedge.

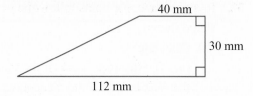

38. A mast is held in position by two wires. Both wires are 30 m in length. The first is attached to the ground at 24 m from the base of the mast and the second is attached to the ground 28·8 m from the base of the mast. Calculate h m, the distance between the two points where the wire joins the mast.

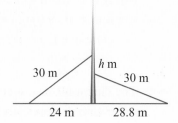

39. In the diagram, the length of the larger square is 31 cm. Calculate **(i)** the perimeter and **(ii)** the area of the smaller square.

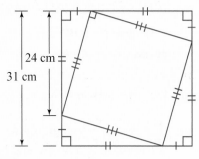

40. Andrew and Brian are in the All-Ireland conkers competition in Freshford, Co. Kilkenny. Andrew's conker, C, is tied to the end of a string 34 cm in length. He pulls it back from its vertical position until it is 30 cm horizontal from its original position. Calculate h, the vertical distance that the conker has risen.

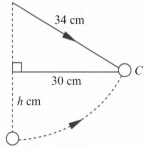

41. A girl takes a shortcut along a path across a field from the gate to the bus stop.

(i) Calculate how much further she would have walked if she walked around the perimeter of the field.

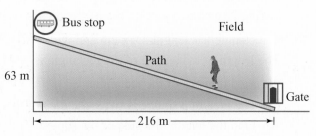

(ii) She can walk at 2 m/s on the perimeter of the field and 1·5 m/s across the field. Calculate the quickest route and the time saved.

42. In a boat race, the boats follow the triangular shape shown.
    (i) Calculate:
        (a) The distance between the buoys
        (b) The length of the racecourse
    (ii) A boat can travel at an average speed of 8 m/s. How long will it take this boat to complete the race? Give your answer in:
        (a) Seconds   (b) Minutes   (c) Hours

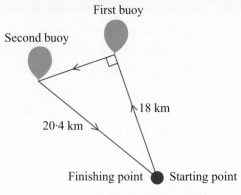

43. The diagram shows a cuboid wooden model of a room with diagonal struts $[QW]$, $[PV]$ and $[PW]$. $|PQ| = 9$ cm, $|QV| = 12$ cm and $|WV| = 5$ cm.

    Calculate (i) $|QW|$ (ii) $|PV|$ (iii) $|PW|$ correct to two decimal places.

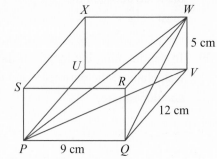

44. The isosceles triangle shown in the diagram has a base of length 40 cm and the other two sides are each 29 cm in length. Find h, the perpendicular height of the triangle.

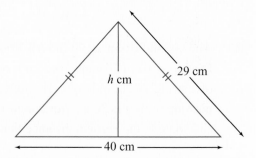

45. The lengths of the sides of an isosceles triangle are $\sqrt{x^2 + 1}$, $\sqrt{x^2 + 1}$ and $2x$. Taking $2x$ as the base, find the perpendicular height of the triangle.

46. A rectangle has length $2\sqrt{x}$ cm and width $\sqrt{x}$ cm. The length of a diagonal of the rectangle is $\sqrt{45}$ cm.

    (i) Find the area of the rectangle.
    (ii) The area of a square is twice the area of the rectangle. Find the length of a side of the square.

47. The lengths of the sides of a triangle are $4\sqrt{x}$, $(x - 4)$ and $(x + 4)$, where $x > 4$. Prove that the triangle is right-angled.

48. A team suspected that their pitch did not
have 90° corners. Suggest a method that the
team members could use to check the
problem using only a metre stick.

49. Consider $\triangle ABC$. Using **acute angle**, **right angle**
or **obtuse angle**, name the type of angle that
$\angle ACB$ makes if:

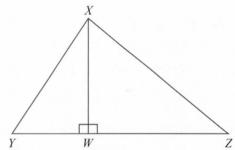

   (i) $c^2 = a^2 + b^2$
   (ii) $c^2 > a^2 + b^2$
   (iii) $c^2 < a^2 + b^2$

   In each case, explain your answer.

In questions 50–53, a proof is required.

50. In $\triangle XYZ$, $XW \perp YZ$. Show that:

   (i) $|XW|^2 = |XY|^2 - |WY|^2$
   (ii) $|XW|^2 = |XZ|^2 - |WZ|^2$
   (iii) $|XY|^2 + |WZ|^2 = |XZ|^2 + |WY|^2$

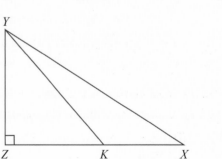

51. In $\triangle XYZ$, $|\angle XZY| = 90°$.
   K is a point on $[XZ]$. Show that:
   (i) $|YZ|^2 = |XY|^2 - |XZ|^2$
   (ii) $|YZ|^2 = |KY|^2 - |KZ|^2$
   (iii) $|XY|^2 + |KZ|^2 = |KY|^2 + |XZ|^2$

52. *ABCD* is a quadrilateral in which
   AC is perpendicular to *BD*.
   (i) Why is $|AB|^2 = |AM|^2 + |BM|^2$?
   (ii) Hence, prove that $|AB|^2 + |CD|^2 = |AD|^2 + |BC|^2$.

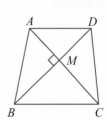

53. *PQRS* is a square. The diagonals meet at *T*.
Prove that $|QR|^2 = 2|PT|^2$.

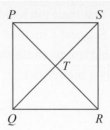

Area of a triangle and a parallelogram

Triangle (three cases)

1.   **2.**   **3.**

$$A = \tfrac{1}{2}\,bh$$

b = base h = perpendicular height

Notes: In case 1, the perpendicular height is inside the triangle.
          In case 2, a right-angled triangle, the perpendicular height is one of the sides.
          In case 3, the perpendicular height is outside the triangle.
In each case, the perpendicular height, h, is at right angles to the base, b.

Any side can be chosen as the **base**. However, the **height** must always be measured at right angles to the base chosen from the vertex opposite the side. This is shown in the diagrams on the next page.

Note: The perpendicular height of a triangle is often called the **altitude** of the triangle.

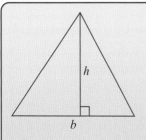 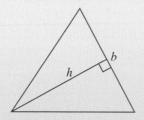 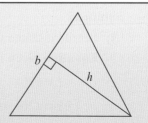

In each case, $A = \frac{1}{2} bh$ will give the same answer.

Note: The mathematical tables booklet uses a instead of b.

EXAMPLE 1

Find the area of each of the following triangles (all dimensions are in centimetres).

(i)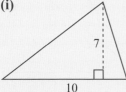

(ii)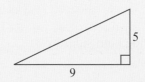

(iii)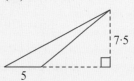

Solution:

(i) $A = \frac{1}{2} bh$

$= \frac{1}{2}(10)(7)$

$= 35$ cm^2

(ii) $A = \frac{1}{2} bh$

$= \frac{1}{2}(9)(5)$

$= 22\cdot5$ cm^2

(iii) $A = \frac{1}{2} bh$

$A = \frac{1}{2}(5)(7\cdot5)$

$= 18\cdot75$ cm^2

EXAMPLE 2

The area of $\triangle ABC$ is 120 cm^2.

$|BC| = 20$ cm and the distance from B to AC is 16 cm. Calculate:

(i) The distance from A to BC

(ii) $|AC|$

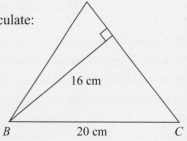

Solution:

(i) Let the distance from A to BC be h cm.

Equation given in disguise:

$A = 120$

$\frac{1}{2} bh = 120$

$\frac{1}{2} (20)h = 120$ (put in $b = 20$)

$10 h = 120$

$h = 12$ (divide both sides by 10)

∴ The distance from A to BC is 12 cm.

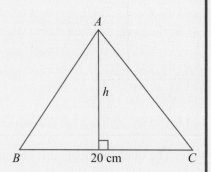

(ii) Let $|AC| = b$ cm.

Equation given in disguise:

$A = 120$

$\frac{1}{2} bh = 120$

$\frac{1}{2} b(16) = 120$ (put in $h = 16$)

$8b = 120$

$b = 15$ (divide both sides by 8)

∴ $|AC| = 15$ cm

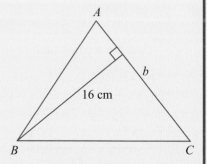

Note: $\frac{1}{2}(20)(12) = \frac{1}{2}(15)(16) = 120$ cm^2

Area of a parallelogram

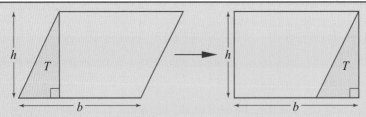

The area of a parallelogram of base b and height h has the same area as a rectangle of length b and width h. This can be seen by cutting out the triangle T in the parallelogram and placing it at the other end to form a rectangle. Thus, this parallelogram has the same area as the rectangle. The area of the rectangle is bh.

A parallelogram of base b and height h has area A given by $A = bh$.

Note: The mathematical tables booklet uses a instead of b.

Any side can be taken as the **base**. It does not need to be at the bottom of the parallelogram. The height must always be perpendicular to the side chosen as the base.

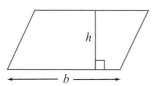

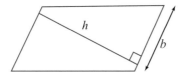

b = length of base
h = parallelogram height
$A = b \times h$

In a parallelogram, therefore, there are two possible values for its base. Each of these **base lengths** has a corresponding **perpendicular height**.

Therefore, there are two possible ways to calculate the area of a parallelogram. It depends on the base length and perpendicular height that is known. In some questions we have to use Pythagoras' theorem to find the perpendicular height.

Diagonals and area

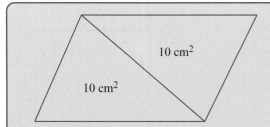

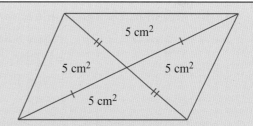

A diagonal divides a parallelogram into two triangles, each of equal area.

If the area of the parallelogram is 20 cm², then the area of each triangle is 10 cm².

Two diagonals divide a parallelogram into four triangles, each of equal area.

If the area of the parallelogram is 20 cm², then the area of each triangle is 5 cm².

Note: The diagonals of a parallelogram bisect each other.

Converse: If the diagonals of a quadrilateral bisect each other, then the quadrilateral is a parallelogram.

EXAMPLE

$ABCD$ is a parallelogram.
$AE \perp BC, |AB| = 17, |AD| = 34$ and $|BE| = 8$.

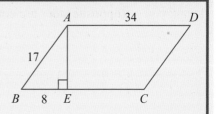

Calculate the following.

(i) $|AE|$

(ii) The area of the parallelogram $ABCD$

(iii) The length of the perpendicular from $[AB]$ to $[CD]$

(iv) The perimeter of the parallelogram $ABCD$

Solution:

(i) $\triangle ABE$ is a right-angled triangle.

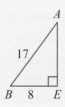

Using Pythagoras' theorem:
$$|AE|^2 + |BE|^2 = |AB|^2$$
$$|AE|^2 + 8^2 = 17^2$$
$$|AE|^2 + 64 = 289$$
$$|AE|^2 = 225$$
$$|AE| = \sqrt{225} = 15$$

(ii) Area of parallelogram $ABCD$

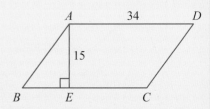

$$= \text{base} \times \text{height}$$
$$= |AD| \times |AE|$$
$$= 34 \times 15$$
$$= 510$$

(iii) Let the length of the perpendicular from $[AB]$ to $[CD] = h$.

Equation given in disguise:

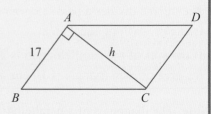

area of parallelogram $= 510$
$$\text{base} \times \text{height} = 510$$
$$|AB| \times h = 510$$
$$17 \times h = 510$$
$$h = 30$$

Therefore, the length of the perpendicular from $[AB]$ to $[CD]$ is 30.

(Notice that $15 \times 34 = 17 \times 30$. Both are equal to 510.)

(iv) Perimeter of the parallelogram
(opposite sides are equal in length)

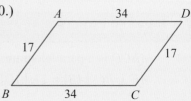

$$= 17 + 34 + 17 + 34$$
$$= 102$$

Exercise 6.4

Find the area of each of the following triangles for questions 1–6 (all dimensions are in centimetres).

1.
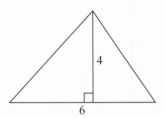

2.
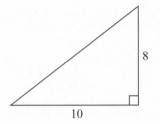

3.
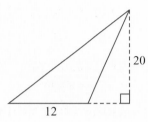

4.
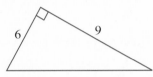

5.
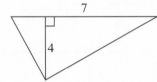

6.
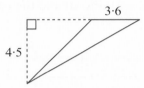

In questions 7–9, calculate the perpendicular height, h cm, where the area, A cm², is given.

7.
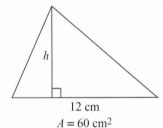

12 cm
$A = 60$ cm²

8.
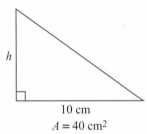

10 cm
$A = 40$ cm²

9.
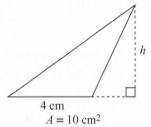

4 cm
$A = 10$ cm²

In questions 10–15, calculate (i) the perimeter and (ii) the area of each of the following parallelograms (all dimensions are in centimetres).

10.
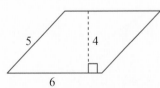

11.
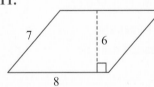

12.
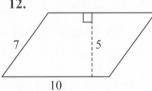

13.
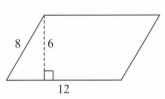

14.
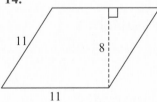

15.
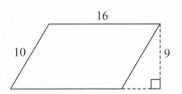

243

In questions 16–18, calculate the perpendicular height, h cm, where the area, A cm^2, is given.

16.

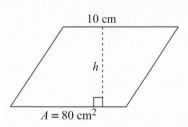

17.

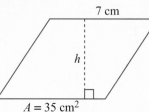

18.

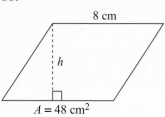

In questions 19–21, use Pythagoras' theorem to find (i) the perpendicular height, h cm, and then (ii) the area of the parallelogram.

19.

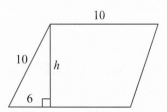

20.

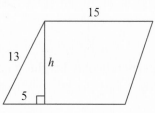

21.

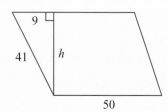

22. The triangle and rectangle have equal area. Calculate h.

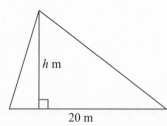

23. The diagram shows a rectangle of length 42 cm. The area of the rectangle is 966 cm^2.

  (i) Find the height of the rectangle.

  (ii) Find the area of the shaded triangle.

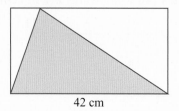

24. $ABCD$ is a parallelogram.

$AE \perp BC, |AB| = 5, |AD| = 8$ and $|BE| = 3$.

Calculate the following.

  (i) $|AE|$

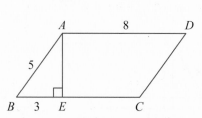

  (ii) The area of the parallelogram $ABCD$

  (iii) The length of the perpendicular from $[AB]$ to $[CD]$

  (iv) The perimeter of the parallelogram $ABCD$

25. A 4 m-wide crosswalk diagonally crosses a street, as shown. The curbs are 8 m apart. The crosswalk intersects the opposite curb with a 6 m displacement. Find the area of the crosswalk.

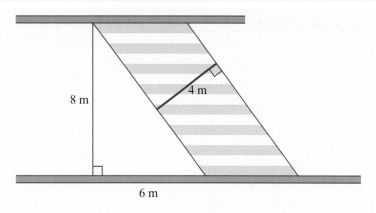

26. The area of *ABDE* is 120 cm². *AC* ⊥ *BC*, |*AE*| = 2|*BC*| = 12 cm. Calculate |*AC*|.

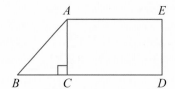

27. In the diagram, *ABCF*, *ABFE* and *ACDE* are parallelograms. The area of △ *AFE* is 15 square units.

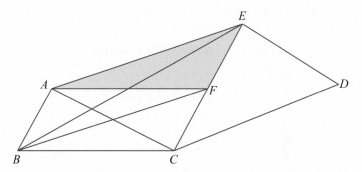

   (i) State clearly why the area of △ *AFB* must also be 15 square units.

   (ii) Find the area of the whole figure *ABCDE*. Show your work.

   (iii) If the perpendicular distance from *D* to the line *EC* is 6, find |*AB*|. Show your work.

Using the formula area of a triangle, $A = \sqrt{s(s - a)(s - b)(s - c)}$, where $s = \dfrac{a + b + c}{2}$, calculate the area of the triangles in questions 28–30.

28.

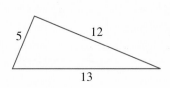

29.

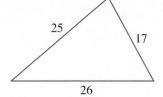

30.

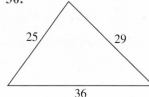

245

31. The great pyramid of Giza has a square base and four congruent triangular faces. The base of the pyramid is of side 240 m and each slanted edge has length 150 m. Calculate the total area of the four triangular faces of the pyramid, assuming they are smooth, flat surfaces.

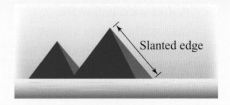

Slanted edge

32. In $\triangle ABC$, $|AC| = 13$, $|BC| = 12$ and $AB \perp CB$.

   (i) Calculate: (a) $|AB|$ (b) $\sin C$

   (ii) Calculate the area of $\triangle ABC$ using:

   (a) $\frac{1}{2} bh$ (b) $\frac{1}{2} ab \sin C$

   (c) $\sqrt{s(s-a)(s-b)(s-c)}$, where $s = \dfrac{a+b+c}{2}$

   (iii) Comment on your answers to part (ii).

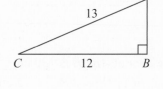

33. In $\triangle PQR$, $|QR| = 16$, $|PQ| = 10$ and $|\angle PQR| = |\angle PRQ|$.

   (i) Write down the value of $|PR|$. Justify your answer.

   (ii) Calculate the perpendicular distance from P to QR.

   (iii) Hence, write down the ratio $\sin Q$.

   (iv) Calculate the area of $\triangle PQR$ using:

   (a) $\frac{1}{2} bh$ (b) $\frac{1}{2} pq \sin R$

   (c) $\sqrt{s(s-p)(s-q)(s-r)}$, where $s = \dfrac{p+q+r}{2}$

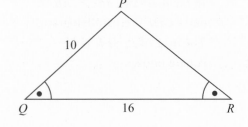

34. In $\triangle ABC$, $|BC| = 21$ cm, $|AB| = 17$ cm and $|AC| = 10$ cm.

   (i) Using the formula area $= \sqrt{s(s-a)(s-b)(s-c)}$, where $s = \dfrac{a+b+c}{2}$, show that the area of $\triangle ABC = 84$ cm^2.

   (ii) Hence or otherwise, calculate h, the distance from A to BC.

   (iii) Write down: (a) $\sin C$ (b) $\sin B$

   (iv) Verify that $\frac{1}{2} ab \sin C = \frac{1}{2} ac \sin B = 84$.

   (v) Calculate the distance from B to AC.

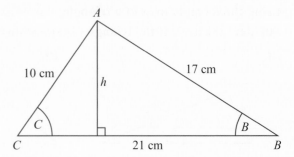

Transversal intersecting three parallel lines

> If three parallel lines cut off equal segments on some transversal, then they will cut off equal segments on any other transversal.

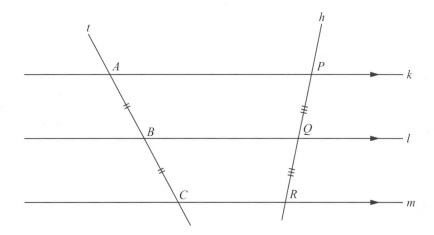

In the diagram, $k \parallel l \parallel m$, three parallel lines. t is a transversal that meets the lines k, l and m, respectively, at points A, B and C such that $|AB| = |BC|$.

Draw any other transversal, h, to meet the lines k, l and m, respectively, at P, Q and R.

Then $|PQ| = |QR|$.

This is true for any other transversal that meets the parallel lines k, l and m.

EXAMPLE

In the diagram, l, m and n are parallel lines that cut equal segments on the transversal, h. $|AB| = 10$, $|DE| = 12$ and $|EF| = 3x$.

(i) Find $|BC|$. Justify your answer.

(ii) Calculate x, giving a reason for your answer.

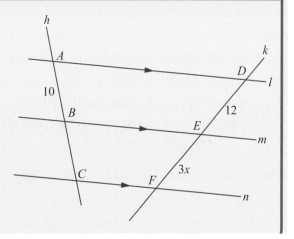

Solution:

(i) $|BC| = |AB|$ (given)

     but $|AB| = 10$

     $\therefore |BC| = 10$

(ii) $|EF| = |DE|$

     Equal segments are cut on any other transversal

     $\therefore 3x = 12$

        $x = 4$

Exercise 6.5

In the diagrams for questions 1–4, *l*, *m* and *n* are parallel lines. They cut equal intercepts on the transversal. In each case, calculate the value of the variables *x*, *y*, *a* and *b*.

1.

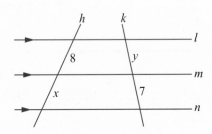

2.

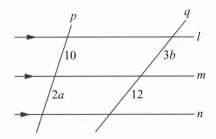

3.

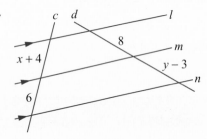

4.

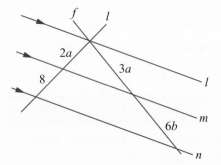

5. In the diagram, *l*, *m* and *n* are parallel lines. They make equal intercepts on the line *h*. $AB \parallel h$.

    (i) What are the lines *h* and *k* called?

    (ii) Giving a reason in each case, calculate:

       (a) $|AB|$ **(b)** $|AC|$

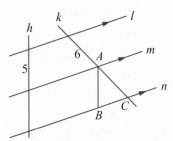

6. In the diagram, p, q and r are parallel lines.
They make equal intercepts on the
perpendicular transversal, t.

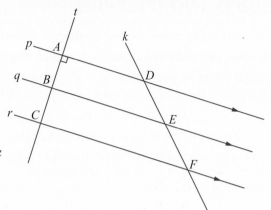

   (i) If $|AC| = 14$ cm,
      calculate $|AB|$.

  (ii) If $|AC| + |DF| = 30$,
      calculate $|EF|$.

 (iii) $ACGD$ is a rectangle. Indicate the point G
      on the diagram. Calculate the area of
      rectangle $ACGD$ if $|AD| = |DF|$.

7. $ABCD$ is a rectangular-shaped
steel gate.
$AB \parallel PQ \parallel RS \parallel DC$ and
$|AP| = |PR| = |RD|$.
$|AB| = 2 \cdot 4$ m and $|BC| = 1 \cdot 8$.

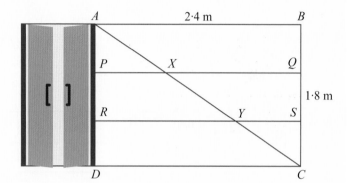

   (i) Calculate:

     (a) $|AP|$. Justify your answer.

     (b) $|XY|$. Give a reason for
        your answer.

  (ii) (a) $RAXZ$ is a parallelogram. Indicate the point Z on the diagram.

     (b) Calculate the area of the parallelogram $RAXZ$.

8. l, m and n are parallel lines.
They cut equal intercepts on
the line p, where $p \perp l$.

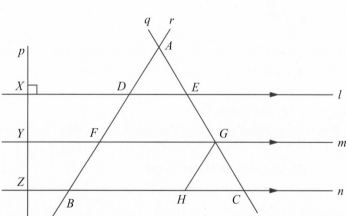

   (i) Describe the line p.

  (ii) Is $p \perp m$? Explain your
     answer.

 (iii) If $|XZ| = 20$ cm,
     calculate $|YZ|$.

 (iv) If $|XZ| + |DB| = 44$ cm,
     calculate $|FB|$.

  (v) If $|FG| = 30$ cm and
     $FB \parallel GH$, calculate the area of the parallelogram $BFGH$.

 (vi) Hence, calculate the distance between the parallel lines FB and GH.

Congruent triangles

The word '**congruent**' means '**identical**'. Two triangles are said to be congruent if they have exactly the same size and shape. They have **equal length of sides, equal angles and equal areas**. One triangle could be placed on top of the other so as to cover it exactly. Sometimes it is necessary to turn one of the triangles over to get an exact copy. The symbol for congruence is ≡. The fact that △*ABC* is congruent to △*PQR* is written as △*ABC* ≡ △*PQR*. When naming congruent triangles, it is important that the order of the letters is correct when stating whether two triangles are congruent. In other words, the points *ABC* correspond to the points *PQR* in that order.

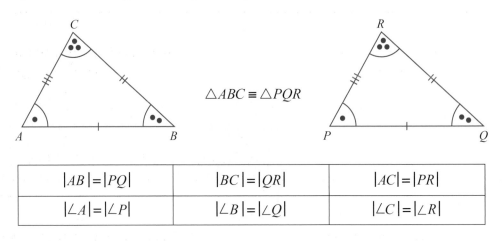

$$\triangle ABC \equiv \triangle PQR$$

$|AB|=|PQ|$	$|BC|=|QR|$	$|AC|=|PR|$
$|\angle A|=|\angle P|$	$|\angle B|=|\angle Q|$	$|\angle C|=|\angle R|$

For two triangles to be congruent (identical), the three sides and the three angles of one triangle must be equal to the three sides and three angles of the other triangle. However, it is not necessary to prove all six equalities to show that two triangles are congruent. There are four standard minimum tests that can be used to determine whether two triangles are congruent. Any one of the four tests is sufficient to prove that two triangles are congruent. However, each of these tests must include the fact that the length of at least one of the sides is equal in both triangles.

Four tests for congruency

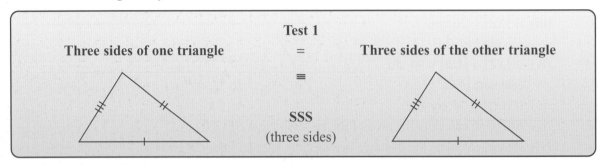

Test 1

Three sides of one triangle = Three sides of the other triangle

SSS
(three sides)

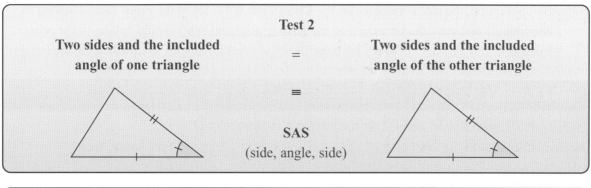

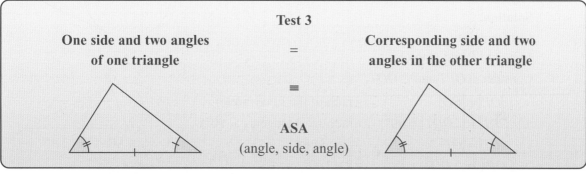

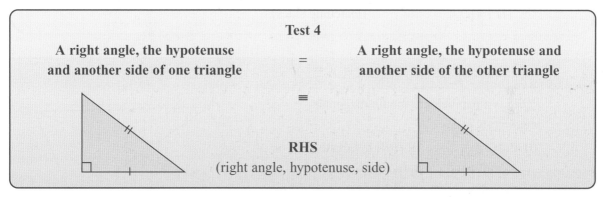

Note: Consider test 3. If any two pairs of angles are equal, then the third pair must also be equal. What is essential is that the equal sides correspond to each other.

A proof using congruent triangles contains three steps.

1. Identify the two triangles that are being used in the proof.
2. Name the three pairs of equal sides and/or angles.
   Always give reasons why the angles used are equal, e.g. alternate angles.
   Always give reasons why the lengths of the sides used are equal, e.g. opposite sides of a parallelogram.
3. Name the congruent triangles in matching order.
   State the congruence test used, i.e. SSS, SAS, ASA or RHS.

Note: By convention, the sides or angles on the LHS (left-hand side) of the proof should belong to one triangle and the sides or angles on the RHS (right-hand side) should belong to the other triangle. It can also help in a test for congruency to label the angles used with a number.

EXAMPLE 1

In the diagram, TP and TQ are tangents to a circle, centre O.
Prove that $|TP| = |TQ|$.

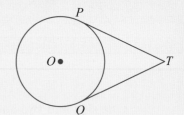

Solution:

Construction:

Join O to P and O to Q.

Consider $\triangle OPT$ and $\triangle OQT$.

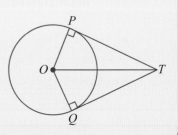

$|OP| = |OQ|$	(radii of the same circle)
$|\angle OPT| = |\angle OQT| = 90°$	(radii meet tangents at 90°)
$|OT| = |OT|$	(common)
$\therefore \triangle OPT \equiv \triangle OQT$	(RHS)
$\therefore \quad |TP| = |TQ|$	(matching sides)

EXAMPLE 2

$PQRS$ is a parallelogram with diagonals intersecting at T.

(i) Prove that diagonal $[PR]$ bisects the area of parallelogram $PQRS$.

(ii) Prove that $|QT| = |ST|$.

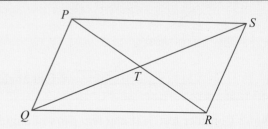

Solution:

(i) **Construction:**

Redraw $\triangle PQR$ and $\triangle PSR$ separately.

In $\triangle PQR$ and $\triangle PSR$:

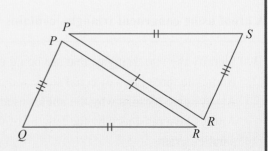

$|PQ| = |RS|$	(opposite sides)
$|QR| = |SP|$	(opposite sides)
$|PR| = |PR|$	(common)
$\therefore \qquad \triangle PQR \equiv \triangle RSP$	(SSS)

$\therefore$ Area of $\triangle PQR$ = area of $\triangle RSP$

$\therefore$ Diagonal $[PR]$ bisects the area of the parallelogram $PQRS$.

(ii) **Construction:**
Redraw △PTS and △RTQ separately.
Label angles 1, 2, 3 and 4.
In △PTS and △RTQ:

$\lvert\angle 1\rvert=\lvert\angle 3\rvert$	(alternate angles)
$\lvert PS\rvert=\lvert RQ\rvert$	(opposite sides)
$\lvert\angle 2\rvert=\lvert\angle 4\rvert$	(alternate angles)
$\therefore \triangle PTS \equiv \triangle RTQ$	(ASA)
$\therefore \ \lvert QT\rvert=\lvert ST\rvert$	(matching sides)

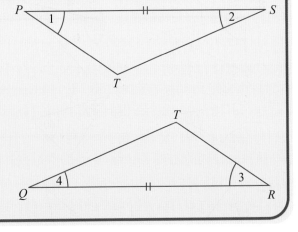

Note: It should be noted that in many situations, more than one test of congruency can be used.
Under a translation, axial symmetry or central symmetry, the shape and size of a figure remain **exactly the same**. Therefore, when these transformations are applied to a figure, the image is **always congruent** to the original figure.

Exercise 6.6

1. State the four tests for triangles to be congruent.

Write down the test required for each of the pairs of triangles in questions 2–13 to be congruent (all dimensions are in centimetres; diagrams are not drawn to scale).

2.
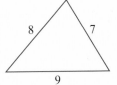

3.
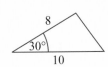

4.
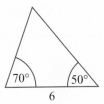

5.
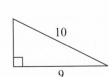
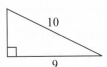

6.
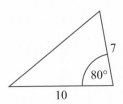
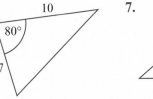

7.
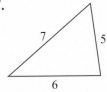
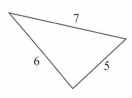

8.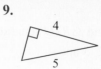

9.

10.

11.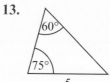

12.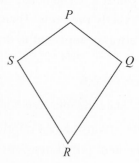

13.

14. The diagram shows the kite $PQRS$.
$|PQ| = |PS|$ and $|RQ| = |RS|$.
Prove that $\triangle PQR$ and $\triangle PSR$ are congruent.

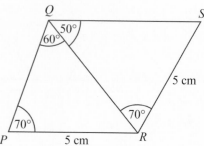

15. Is $\triangle PQR$ congruent to $\triangle QRS$?
Justify your answer.

16. A person is walking on stilts that always remain parallel.
The braces $[PS]$ and $[QR]$ are joined at T.
T is the midpoint of both braces.
Prove that $\triangle PQT \equiv \triangle SRT$.

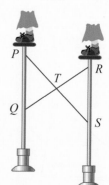

17. Two congruent triangular trusses are needed for the roof of an extension on a house. The diagram shows two trusses. Are they congruent? Justify your answer.

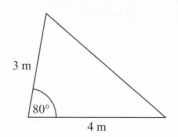 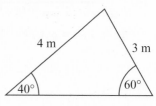

18. The diagram shows the rectangular frame, *ABCD*, of a door with diagonal brace [*DB*]. Prove that △*ABD* and △*DCB* are congruent.

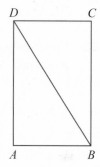

19. In the diagram, $|PS| = |RS|$ and $|\angle PSQ| = |\angle RSQ|$.

   (i) Prove that $\triangle PQS \equiv \triangle RQS$.

   (ii) Hence, show that $\triangle PQR$ is isosceles.

   (iii) Prove that $PR \perp QS$.

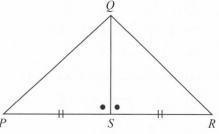

20. (i)

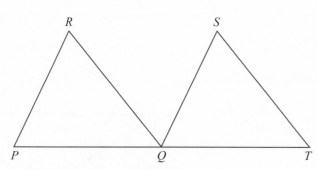

   $PR \parallel QS$, $RQ \parallel ST$ and $|PQ| = |QT|$.
   Prove that $|PR| = |QS|$.

   (ii)

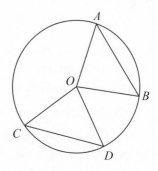

   O is the centre of the circle and $|AB| = |CD|$.
   Prove that $|\angle AOB| = |\angle COD|$

21. Lines AD and CB intersect at the point E.
    $|AE| = |CE|$ and $|BE| = |DE|$.
    Is $\triangle ABE \equiv \triangle CDE$? Justify your answer.

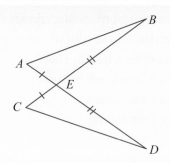

22. In the diagram, $PQ \parallel ST$ and $|PR| = |TR|$.
    Prove that $\triangle PQR \equiv \triangle TSR$.

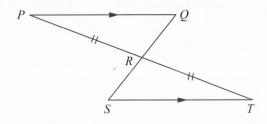

23. The diagram shows $\triangle XYZ$ in which $|XY| = |ZY|$
    and YW bisects $[XZ]$.

    (i) Prove that $\triangle YXW \equiv \triangle YZW$.

    (ii) Hence, prove that $YW \perp XZ$.

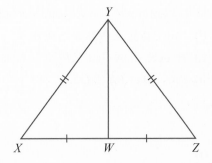

24. $ABCD$ is a cyclic quadrilateral (all four vertices
    are on the circle).
    $|AB| = |AD|$ and $[AC]$ is a diameter of the circle.

    (i) Prove that $\triangle ABC \equiv \triangle ADC$.

    (ii) Hence, show that $|\angle BAC| = |\angle DAC|$.

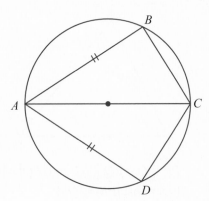

25. If two sectors, each with equal angles at the centre, were cut from a circle, would you be able to place one sector **exactly** on the other? Justify your answer.

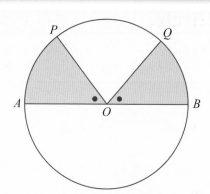

26. (i) Is △ABC ≡ △PQR? Explain your answer.

(ii) If the triangles are not congruent, write down one extra piece of information you would need to be given for the triangles to be congruent.

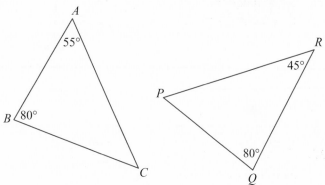

27. The diagram shows the end frame of a child's swing. |∠ADF| = |∠CDF| and |DE| = |DG|.

(i) Prove that △DEF ≡ △DGF.

(ii) Prove that |EF| = |GF|.

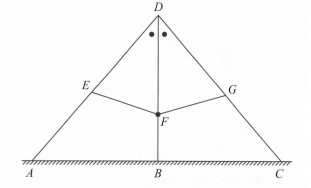

28. ABCD is a parallelogram. [AD] is extended to E such that |AD| = |DE|. DC intersects EB at the point F. Prove that |DF| = |FC|.

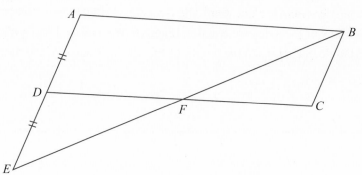

Circle

The diagrams below show some of the terms we use when dealing with a circle.

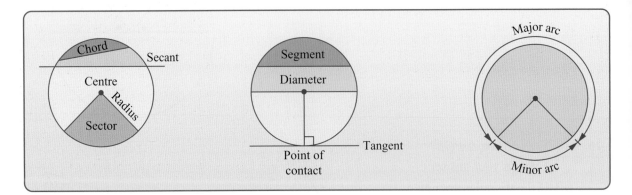

Angle in a semicircle

A **diameter** divides a circle into two **semicircles**.

> Each angle in a semicircle is a right angle.

The converse is also true.

> If the angle standing on a chord at a point on the
> circle is a right angle, then the chord is a diameter.

If $|\angle BAC| = 90°$, then $[BC]$ is a diameter and vice versa.

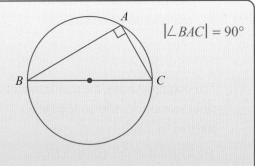

$|\angle BAC| = 90°$

Isosceles triangle

When dealing with a circle, look out for the isosceles and equilateral
triangle within the question. The isosceles triangle occurs when the
lengths of the sides are equal in length to the radius. The equilateral
triangle occurs when the length of the chord is equal to the radius.

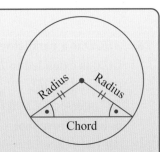

Tangent and radius are perpendicular to each other at the point of contact

(i) Each tangent is perpendicular to the radius at the point of contact.

$$OP \perp t, \ OQ \perp u \text{ and } OR \perp v$$

(ii) Converse:

If a point P is on a circle and a line t is perpendicular to the radius at P, then line t is a tangent to the circle.

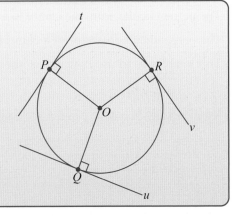

From a point outside a circle, two tangents can be drawn

Two tangents can be drawn to a circle from a point outside the circle. Three properties emerge:

1. $|PT| = |PS|$

2. $|\angle TPO| = |\angle SPO|$

3. $|\angle POT| = |\angle POS|$

These can be proved using **congruent triangle**.

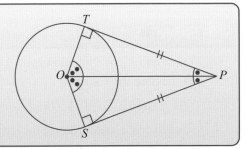

Touching circles

If two circles intersect at one point only, then the two centres and the point of contact are collinear (on the same straight line).

Two circles are said to be **touching** if they have only one point of intersection. To investigate whether two circles touch, we compare the distance between their centres with the sum or difference of their radii.

Consider two circles of radius r_1 and r_2 (where $r_1 > r_2$) and let d be the distance between their centres.

  1. Circles touch externally   **2. Circles touch internally**

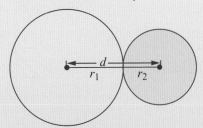   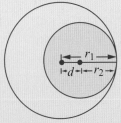

          $d = r_1 + r_2$ $d = r_1 - r_2$

  Distance between their centres   Distance between their centres

      = sum of their radii   = difference of their radii

Chord bisector

The perpendicular from the centre to a chord bisects the chord.

The perpendicular bisector of a chord passes through the centre.

This enables us to use Pythagoras' theorem.

$$x^2 + y^2 = r^2$$

Knowing any two of x, y and r, we can find the third.

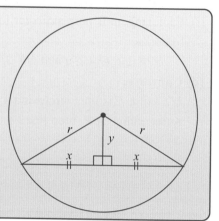

EXAMPLE 1

A, B and C are three points on a circle of centre O.
Calculate the value of:

(i) $|\angle COB|$ **(ii)** $|\angle OBC|$ **(iii)** $|\angle OBA|$

Justify your answer in each case.

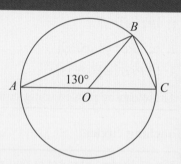

Solution:

Let

$x° = |\angle COB|$
$y° = |\angle OBC|$
$z° = |\angle OBA|$

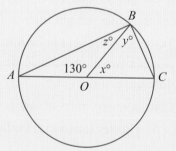

(i) $x° + 130° = 180°$ (straight angle)

$x + 130 = 180$

$x = 50$ (subtract 130 from both sides)

$\therefore |\angle COB| = 50°$

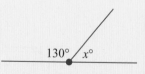

(ii) $\triangle OBC$ is isosceles, as $|OB| = |OC| =$ radius of the circle.

Therefore, the two base angles are equal to $y°$.

$y° + y° + 50° = 180°$ (three angles in a triangle add up to 180°)

$y + y + 50 = 180$

$2y + 50 = 180$

$2y = 130$ (subtract 50 from both sides)

$y = 65$ (divide both sides by 2)

$\therefore |\angle OBC| = 65°$

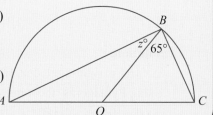

(iii) $z° + y° = 90°$ (angle in a semicircle is 90°)

$z + y = 90$

$z + 65 = 90$ (put in $y = 65$)

$z = 25$ (subtract 65 from both sides)

$\therefore |\angle OBA| = 25°$

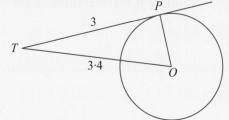

EXAMPLE 2

The point P lies on a circle of centre O.

PT is a tangent to the circle.

$|OT| = 3\cdot4$ and $|PT| = 3$.

(i) Write down $|\angle OPT|$, giving a reason for your answer.

(ii) Calculate the length of the radius of the circle.

Solution:

(i) $|\angle OPT| = 90°$

Tangent and a radius are perpendicular to each other at the point of contact.

(ii) $\triangle OPT$ is a right-angled triangle and $|OP| =$ radius $= r$.

Using Pythagoras' theorem:

$r^2 + 3^2 = 3\cdot4^2$

$r^2 + 9 = 11\cdot56$

$r^2 = 2\cdot56$

$r = \sqrt{2\cdot56}$

$r = 1\cdot6$ cm

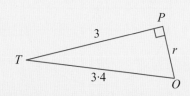

EXAMPLE 3

O is the centre of the circle c and $OM \perp AB$.

$|OM| = 5$ cm and the radius is 13 cm.

Find $|AB|$.

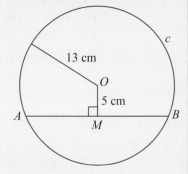

Solution:

$\triangle AMO$ is right-angled at M.

Using Pythagoras' theorem:

$|AM|^2 + |MO|^2 = |OA|^2$

$\quad |AM|^2 + 5^2 = 13^2$

$\quad |AM|^2 + 25 = 169$

$\quad\quad |AM|^2 = 144$

$\quad\quad\; |AM| = \sqrt{144} = 12$

$|AB| = 2|AM| = 2(12) = 24$ cm

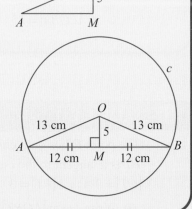

Exercise 6.7

Calculate the value of the letter representing the angle in each of the diagrams in questions 1–9, where O is the centre of the circle. In each case, give a reason for your answer.

1.

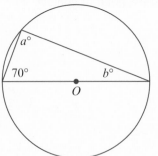

2.

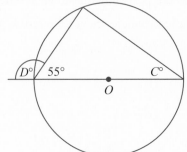

3.

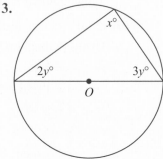

In questions 4–6, look for the isosceles triangles and equilateral triangles in the diagrams.

4.

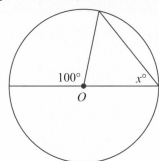

5.

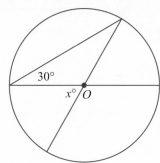

6.

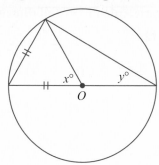

In questions 7–9, *TP* and *TQ* are tangents.

7.

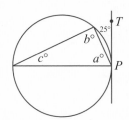

8.

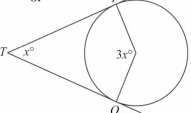

9.

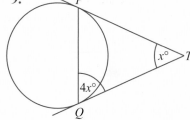

10. In the diagram, *BR* and *BK* are tangents to the circle at *R* and *K*, respectively. *Q* is a point on the circle and *T* is a point on *BR*, as shown. Find:

   (i) $|\angle BKR|$

   (ii) $|\angle QRT|$

   (iii) $|\angle QKR|$

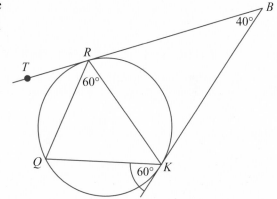

11. *A*, *B* and *C* are points on the circle *k*. *O* is the centre of the circle and $|\angle OBA| = 15°$. $|AB| = |AC|$ and $|OB| = |OC| = |BC|$.

   (i) Calculate $|\angle OBC|$. Give a reason for your answer.

   (ii) Calculate $|\angle ABC|$.

   (iii) Prove that $|\angle BOC| = 2\,|\angle BAC|$.

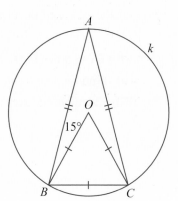

In questions 12–14, *TP* is a tangent to the circle of centre *O*. *P* is a point on the circle. In each case, calculate *x* (all dimensions are in centimetres).

12.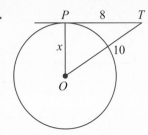

13.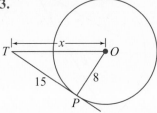

14.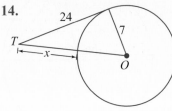

15. *B* is the centre of the circle of radius 4·5 cm.
    PT is a tangent and *T* is a point on the circle.
    If $|PA| = 3$ cm, calculate $|PT|$.

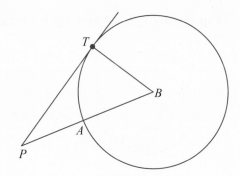

16. A circle, centre *O*, has a chord [*AB*] of length 30 cm.
    M is a point on [*AB*] and $OM \perp AB$. $|OM| = 8$ cm.

    (i) Calculate the length of [*AM*], giving a reason
    for your answer.

    (ii) Calculate the length of the radius of the circle.

    (iii) Calculate the area of $\triangle OAB$.

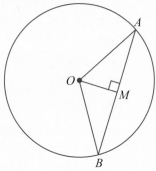

17. *O* is the centre of the circle and $OM \perp AB$.
    $|OM| = 7$ cm and $|AB| = 48$ cm.

    (i) Write down $|AM|$, giving a reason for your answer.

    (ii) Find the length of the radius.

    (iii) Calculate the area of $\triangle OAB$.

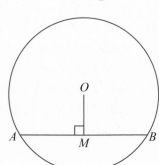

18. *O* is the centre of the circle of radius 29 cm.
    OR ⊥ *PQ* and |*PQ*| = 42 cm.
    (i) Calculate |*SR*|.
    (ii) Explain why the quadrilateral *OPRQ* is called a kite.
    (iii) Calculate the area of the kite.

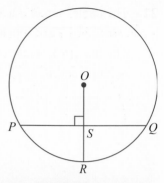

19. The diagram shows the cross-section of a road
    tunnel. The tunnel is part of a circle of radius
    5 m. The width of the tunnel at road level is 9·6 m.
    (i) Calculate its height, *h* m.
    (ii) An extra-wide vehicle 6·8 m wide and 4·4 m
    high wants to enter the tunnel. Would this
    vehicle be able to enter the tunnel? Justify your
    answer. If this was a two-way tunnel, what
    precautions would be required for a wide
    vehicle to enter the tunnel?

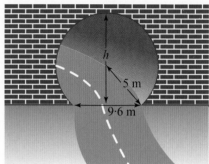

20. The diagram shows a piece of metal that has broken
    off from a disc, where *PRQ* is part of the original circle
    of centre *T*.
    RT ⊥ *PQ*, |*RS*| = 12 cm and |*ST*| = 4|*RS*|.
    (i) Write down the radius of the disc.
    (ii) Calculate |*PQ*|.
    (iii) Calculate the area of the quadrilateral *PRQT*.
    (iv) Assuming π = 3·14, express the area of the quadrilateral *PRQT* as a percentage of the
    area of the circle, correct to two decimal places.

21. A circle, centre *X*, of radius 12 cm, touches another
    circle, centre *Y*, of radius 3 cm, at the point *W*. The circles
    also touch the sides of a rectangle at the points *P*, *Q*, *R*, *S*
    and *T*, as shown, and *YZ* ∥ *QP*. Calculate the following.
    (i) |*XY*|
    (ii) |*XZ*|
    (iii) |*ZY*|
    (iv) The area of the outer rectangle
    (v) Is |∠*ZXY*| > |∠*ZYX*|? Justify your answer.

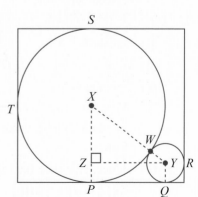

22. The circles p and q have radii of 18 cm and 8 cm, respectively, and touch externally, as shown. The line AB is a tangent to both circles at points A and B, respectively. Calculate $|AB|$.

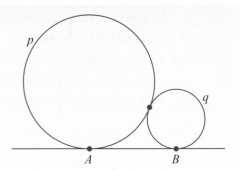

23. Three circles, a, b and c, have radii of 24 cm, 10 cm and 6 cm and centres P, Q and R, respectively. They also touch each other externally, as shown. Show that $\triangle PQR$ is a right-angled triangle.

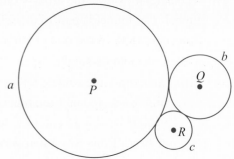

24. The diagram shows two circles, h and k, intersecting externally at one point. The radius of h is 6 cm and the radius of k is 4 cm. P is any point on h and Q is any point on k.
   (i) Calculate the maximum value of $|PQ|$.
   (ii) If the circles touched at one point internally, calculate the maximum value of $|PQ|$.

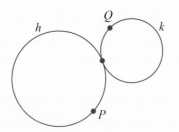

25. PA and PB are tangents to a circle, centre O. PO intersects the circle at C and D. $|OA| = 5$ and $|PC| = 8$.
   (i) Calculate $|OP|$.
   (ii) Give a reason why $|\angle OAP| = 90°$.
   (iii) Calculate $|AP|$.
   (iv) Write $\tan \angle OPA$ as a fraction and calculate $|\angle OPA|$, correct to the nearest degree.
   (v) Hence, calculate the following, correct to the nearest degree.
       (a) $|\angle AOP|$ (b) $|\angle ADP|$

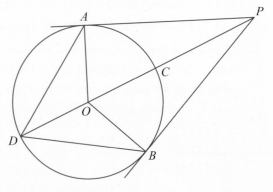

26. **(i)** *A*, *B* and *C* are points on circle *k*. *O* is the centre of the circle. Give a reason why:

   (a) $|OA|=|OB|=|OC|$
   (b) $|\angle OAB|=|\angle OBA|$
   (c) $|\angle OBC|=|\angle OCB|$

(ii) Let $|\angle OAB|=x°$ and $|\angle OBC|=y°$.
   Calculate the following and give a reason for your answer.

   (a) $2x+2y$
   (b) $x+y$
   (c) $|\angle ABC|$

(iii) What angle, therefore, must be a semicircle?

Questions 27–31 require a proof.

27. In the diagram, *PR* is a tangent to the circle of centre *O*, at *Q*. [*AB*] is a chord and $PQ \parallel AB$. Prove that $|QA|=|QB|$.

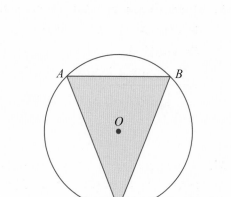

28. In the diagram, *PR* is a tangent to the circle at *Q*. [*QS*] is any chord. *X* and *Y* are points on the circle. *QX* bisects $\angle PQS$ and *QY* bisects $\angle RQS$. Prove that [*XY*] is a diameter of the circle.

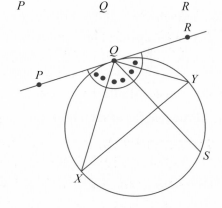

29. In the diagram, [*XY*] is a diameter of the circle of centre *O*. *ZT* is a tangent at *P* and $XZ \perp ZT$.
   Prove that:

   (i) $|\angle XPZ|=|\angle OPY|$
   (ii) $|\angle ZXP|=|\angle YPT|$

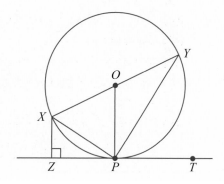

30. *P*, *T* and *U* are points on a circle *k*, centre *O*.
WT is the tangent at *T*. [*PT*] is a diameter.
Prove that $|\angle WTU| = |\angle TPU|$.

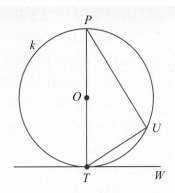

31. In the diagram, *PT* and *PS* are tangents to a circle of
centre *O* at *T* and *S*, respectively.

Prove the following.

(i) $\triangle OPT \equiv \triangle OPS$ **(ii)** $|PT| = |PS|$

(iii) $|\angle TPO| = |\angle SPO|$ **(iv)** $|\angle SPR| = 2|\angle SOP|$

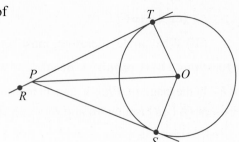

Similar triangles

Two triangles are similar if they have the same shape. One triangle can be obtained from the other by either an enlargement or a reduction (the reduction is also called an enlargement). The symbol for similarity is ||| or ~. The fact that $\triangle ABC$ is similar to $\triangle XYZ$ is written as $\triangle ABC \,|||\, \triangle XYZ$.

Four tests for similarity of triangles

1. If the lengths of matching sides are in proportion (same ratio), then the triangles are similar.

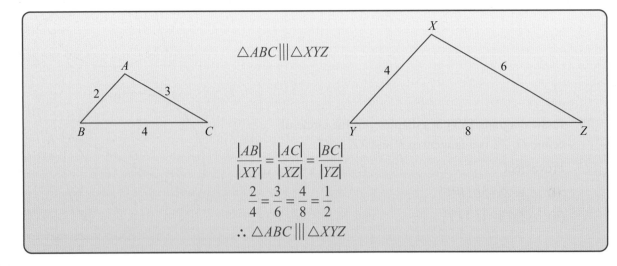

2. **If two pairs of matching angles are equal, then the triangles are similar.**

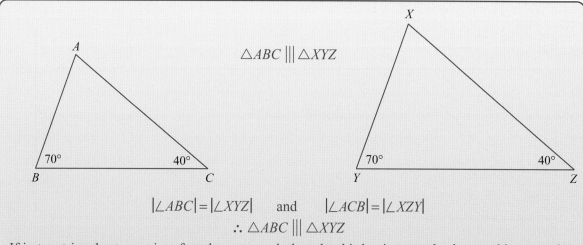

$\triangle ABC \,|||\, \triangle XYZ$

$$|\angle ABC| = |\angle XYZ| \quad \text{and} \quad |\angle ACB| = |\angle XZY|$$
$$\therefore \triangle ABC \,|||\, \triangle XYZ$$

If in two triangles two pairs of angles are equal, then the third pair must also be equal because the three angles in a triangle add up to 180°. Therefore, to prove that two triangles are similar, it is sufficient to show that two pairs of angles are equal.

3. **If the lengths of two sides are in proportion (same ratio) and the included angles are equal, then the triangles are similar.**

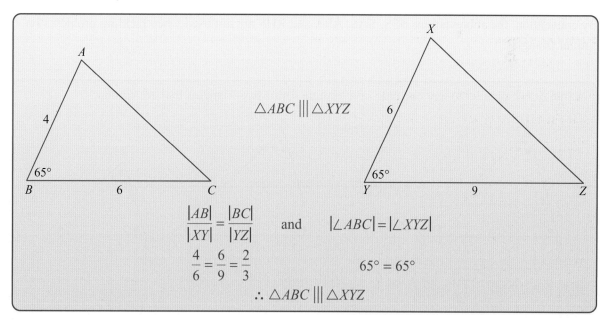

$\triangle ABC \,|||\, \triangle XYZ$

$$\frac{|AB|}{|XY|} = \frac{|BC|}{|YZ|} \quad \text{and} \quad |\angle ABC| = |\angle XYZ|$$
$$\frac{4}{6} = \frac{6}{9} = \frac{2}{3} \qquad 65° = 65°$$
$$\therefore \triangle ABC \,|||\, \triangle XYZ$$

4. **In a right-angled triangle, if the length of the hypotenuse and another side are in proportion (same ratio), then the triangles are similar.**

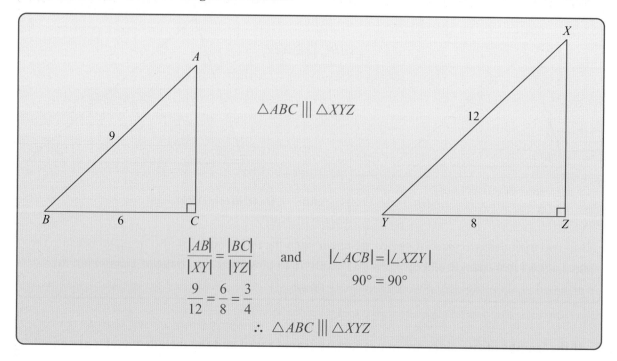

$$\triangle ABC \;|||\; \triangle XYZ$$

$$\frac{|AB|}{|XY|} = \frac{|BC|}{|YZ|} \quad \text{and} \quad |\angle ACB| = |\angle XZY|$$

$$\frac{9}{12} = \frac{6}{8} = \frac{3}{4} \qquad\qquad 90° = 90°$$

$$\therefore \; \triangle ABC \;|||\; \triangle XYZ$$

To prove that two triangles are similar, you only need to show one of the conditions for similarity. By convention, the abbreviations SSS, SAS, ASA and RHS are not used when tackling problems on similar triangles.

A line drawn parallel to any one side of a triangle forms two triangles that are similar.

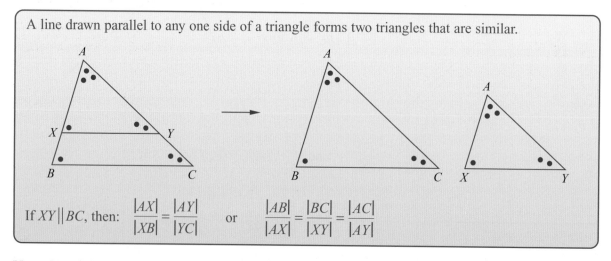

If $XY \| BC$, then: $\dfrac{|AX|}{|XB|} = \dfrac{|AY|}{|YC|}$ or $\dfrac{|AB|}{|AX|} = \dfrac{|BC|}{|XY|} = \dfrac{|AC|}{|AY|}$

Note: In solving problems on similar triangles, it helps if the two triangles are redrawn so that the corresponding sides or angles match each other. It is good practice to put the unknown length on the top of the first fraction.

EXAMPLE 1

Show that each pair of triangles are similar.

(i)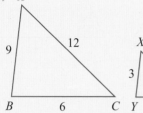

(ii)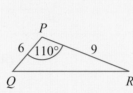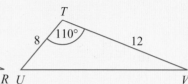

Solution:

(i) In △ABC and △XYZ:

$$\frac{|AB|}{|XY|} = \frac{9}{3} = 3$$

$$\frac{|BC|}{|YZ|} = \frac{6}{2} = 3$$

$$\frac{|AC|}{|XZ|} = \frac{12}{4} = 3$$

$$\therefore \triangle ABC \,|||\, \triangle XYZ$$

(three pairs of matching sides are in the same ratio)

(ii) In △PQR and △TUV:

$$\frac{|PQ|}{|TU|} = \frac{6}{8} = \frac{3}{4}$$

$$\frac{|PR|}{|TV|} = \frac{9}{12} = \frac{3}{4}$$

$$|\angle QPR| = |\angle UTV| = 110°$$

$$\therefore \triangle PQR \,|||\, \triangle TUV$$

(two pairs of matching sides are in the same ratio and the included angles are equal)

EXAMPLE 2

(i) Explain why △ABC and △PQR are similar.

Hence, calculate:

(ii) |AB| (iii) |PR|

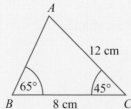 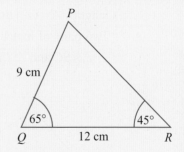

Solution:

(i) $|\angle ABC| = |\angle PQR| = 65°$ and $|\angle ACB| = |\angle PRQ| = 45°$.

Two pairs of matching angles are equal, therefore △ABC ||| △PQR.

Small triangle	Large triangle
$\lvert AB \rvert$	9
8	12
12	$\lvert PR \rvert$

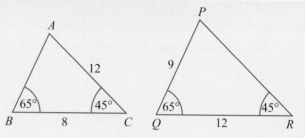

(ii) $\dfrac{\lvert AB \rvert}{9} = \dfrac{8}{12}$

$\lvert AB \rvert = \dfrac{9 \times 8}{12}$

(multiply both sides by 9)

$\lvert AB \rvert = \dfrac{72}{12} = 6$ cm

(iii) $\dfrac{\lvert PR \rvert}{12} = \dfrac{12}{8}$

$\lvert PR \rvert = \dfrac{12 \times 12}{8}$

(multiply both sides by 8)

$\lvert PR \rvert = \dfrac{144}{8} = 18$ cm

EXAMPLE 3

(i) In $\triangle ABC$, $XY \parallel BC$. Prove that $\triangle ABC$ and $\triangle AXY$ are similar.

(ii) If $\lvert AX \rvert = 4$ cm, $\lvert XB \rvert = 2$ cm, $\lvert AY \rvert = 6$ cm and $\lvert BC \rvert = 12$ cm, find **(a)** $\lvert YC \rvert$ and **(b)** $\lvert XY \rvert$.

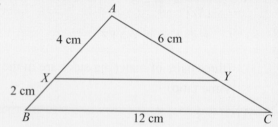

Solution:

(i) Redraw $\triangle ABC$ and $\triangle AXY$ separately. Label angles 1, 2, 3 and 4 and put in known lengths. As $XY \parallel BC$, $\lvert \angle 1 \rvert = \lvert \angle 2 \rvert$ and $\lvert \angle 3 \rvert = \lvert \angle 4 \rvert$, corresponding angles.

Two pairs of matching angles.

$\therefore$ $\triangle ABC$ and $\triangle AXY$ are similar.

Large triangle	Small triangle
6	4
$\lvert AC \rvert$	6
12	$\lvert XY \rvert$

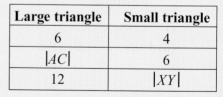

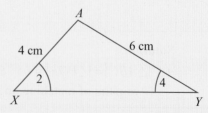

(ii) (a) $\dfrac{|AC|}{|AY|} = \dfrac{|AB|}{|AX|}$

$\dfrac{|AC|}{6} = \dfrac{6}{4}$

$|AC| = \dfrac{6 \times 6}{4}$

(multiply both sides by 6)

$|AC| = \dfrac{36}{4} = 9$ cm

$|YC| = |AC| - |AY| = 9 - 6 = 3$ cm

(b) $\dfrac{|XY|}{|BC|} = \dfrac{|AX|}{|AB|}$

$\dfrac{|XY|}{12} = \dfrac{4}{6}$

$|XY| = \dfrac{12 \times 4}{6}$

(multiply both sides by 12)

$|XY| = \dfrac{48}{6} = 8$ cm

Exercise 6.8

1. State the four tests for triangles to be similar.

In questions 2–9, verify that the triangles are similar and state the test used (all dimensions are in centimetres and diagrams are not drawn to scale).

2.

3.
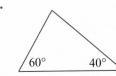

4.

5.

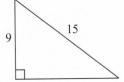

6.
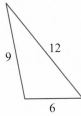

7.
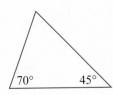

8.

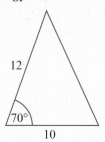

9.

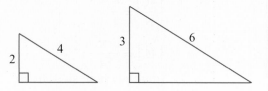

In questions 10–13, give one reason why each pair of triangles is not similar.

10.

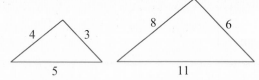

11.

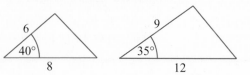

12.

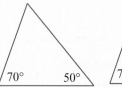

13.

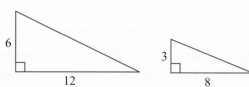

14. In the diagram, $PQ \parallel BC$.
Redraw $\triangle APQ$ and $\triangle ABC$
separately.

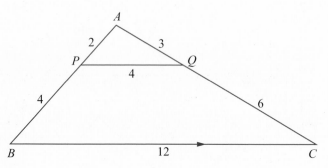

   (i) Are $\triangle APQ$ and $\triangle ABC$
   similar? Give a reason for
   your answer.

   (ii) Show that **(a)** $\dfrac{|AP|}{|AB|} = \dfrac{|AQ|}{|AC|} = \dfrac{|PQ|}{|BC|}$

   (b) $\dfrac{|AP|}{|PB|} = \dfrac{|AQ|}{|QC|}$

   (iii) Simplify: **(a)** $\dfrac{|CQ|}{|QA|}$　**(b)** $\dfrac{|BC|}{|PQ|}$　**(c)** $\dfrac{|AB|^2}{|AP|^2}$

In questions 15–24, the triangles are similar with equal angles marked. In each case, calculate the lengths p and q (all dimensions are in centimetres and diagrams are not drawn to scale).

15.
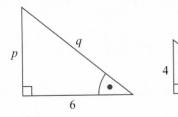

16.
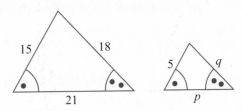

17.
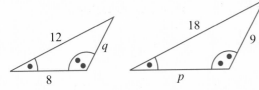

18.
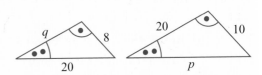

19.
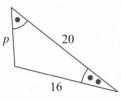

20.
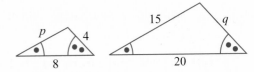

21.
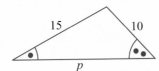

22.
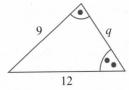
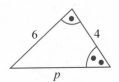

In questions 23 and 24, it may help to redraw the triangles so that the positions of corresponding angles or sides match each other.

23.
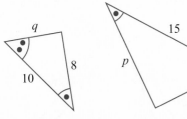

24.
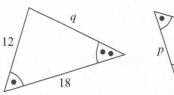

25. The quadrilaterals $PQRS$ and $ABCD$ are similar.

  (i) Calculate $|\angle ADC|$.

  (ii) Calculate:

    (a) $|PQ|$ **(b)** $|DC|$

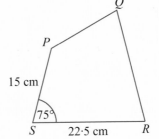

In questions 26–29, it may help to redraw the triangles separately.

26. In $\triangle PQR$, $ST \parallel QR$.

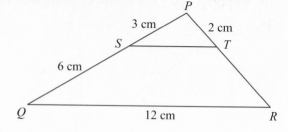

   (i) Are $\triangle PQR$ and $\triangle PST$ similar? Justify your answer.

   (ii) $|PS| = 3$ cm, $|PT| = 2$ cm, $|SQ| = 6$ cm and $|QR| = 12$ cm. Calculate $|PQ|$.

   (iii) Calculate (a) $|PR|$ (b) $|TR|$ (c) $|ST|$

27. In $\triangle ABC$, $XY \parallel BC$.

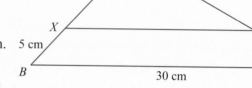

   (i) Are $\triangle ABC$ and $\triangle AXY$ similar? Give a reason for your answer.

   (ii) $|AX| = 10$ cm, $|AY| = 15$ cm, $|XB| = 5$ cm and $|BC| = 30$ cm. Calculate $|AB|$.

   (iii) Calculate: (a) $|AC|$ (b) $|YC|$ (c) $|XY|$

28. In $\triangle STR$, $XY \parallel ST$.

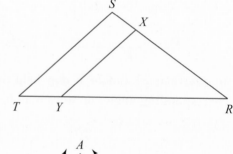

   (i) Explain why $\triangle STR$ and $\triangle XYR$ are similar.

   (ii) $|SX| = 4$ cm, $|RY| = 12$ cm and $|SR| = 12$ cm. Calculate $|XR|$.

   (iii) Calculate: (a) $|TR|$ (b) $|YT|$

   (iv) If $|XY| = 6$ cm, calculate $|ST|$.

29. In $\triangle ABC$, $XY \parallel BC$ and $|AX| = 3|XB|$. $|AB| = 20$ cm, $|AY| = 18$ cm and $|BC| = 36$ cm.

   Calculate the following.

   (i) $|AX|$ (ii) $|YC|$

   (iii) $|AC|$ (iv) $|XY|$

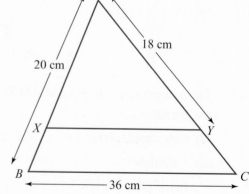

30. In the diagram,
$|\angle BAC| = |\angle DEC|$, $|AB| = 3$ cm,
$|BC| = 6$ cm, $|CD| = 4$ cm
and $|CE| = 5$ cm.

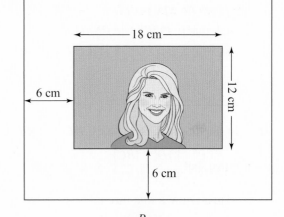

(i) Explain why $\triangle ABC$ and $\triangle EDC$
are similar.

(ii) Calculate: **(a)** $|DE|$ **(b)** $|AC|$

31. A rectangular photograph, 18 cm by 12 cm,
fits into a rectangular frame so that there is a
border 6 cm wide all the way around it.

Are the two rectangles similar? Justify your
answer.

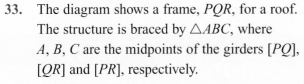

32. The diagram shows a cylindrical metal
drum fixed by cables on a horizontal
platform, where O is the centre of the drum.

(i) Prove that $\triangle PMR$ and $\triangle PMQ$ are similar.

(ii) Prove that $\triangle PMQ$ and $\triangle MQR$ are similar.

(iii) Hence, explain why $\triangle PMR$ and $\triangle MQR$
are similar.

(iv) Write down one other pair of similar
triangles. Justify your answer.

(v) If $|PS| = |MS|$, prove that $\triangle PSM$ and
$\triangle SMT$ are congruent.

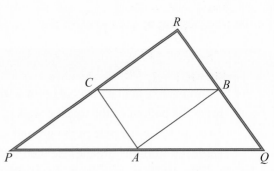

33. The diagram shows a frame, PQR, for a roof.
The structure is braced by $\triangle ABC$, where
A, B, C are the midpoints of the girders $[PQ]$,
$[QR]$ and $[PR]$, respectively.

(i) Prove that $\triangle PQR$ and $\triangle ABC$ are similar.

(ii) Explain why $\triangle PAC$ and $\triangle AQB$ are
congruent.

(iii) The area of $\triangle PQR$ is 20 m². Write down
the area of: **(a)** $\triangle RCB$ **(b)** Shape $PCBQ$

In questions 34–37, a proof is required.

34. *ABCD* is a rectangle with diagonal *AC*.
    XY ∥ *BC* and *XY* intersects *AC* at *Z*.

    Prove that: (i) $\dfrac{|AX|}{|XB|} = \dfrac{|AZ|}{|ZC|}$

    (ii) $\dfrac{|AX|}{|CY|} = \dfrac{|XZ|}{|YZ|}$

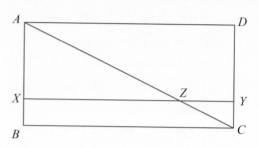

35. In △*PQR*, *MN* is drawn
    such that $|\angle PQR| = |\angle PNM|$.
    (i) Prove that △*PQR* and △*PNM* are similar.

    (ii) Prove that $\dfrac{|PQ|}{|PN|} = \dfrac{|PR|}{|PM|}$.

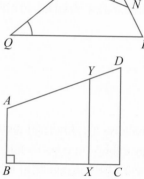

36. In the diagram, *AB* ∥ *YX* ∥ *DC* and *AB* ⊥ *BC*.

    Prove that $\dfrac{|AD|}{|AY|} = \dfrac{|BC|}{|BX|}$.

    (**Hint:** Draw a line through *A* parallel to *BC*.)

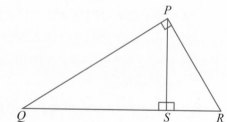

37. In △*PQR*, *QP* ⊥ *PR* and *PS* ⊥ *QR*. Show that:
    (i) △*PQR* is similar to △*SQP*
    (ii) △*PQR* is similar to △*SPR*
    (iii) $|PS|^2 = |QS| \times |RS|$

Using similar triangles to solve real-life problems

Similar triangles can be used to solve practical or real-life problems.

● **EXAMPLE**

Pat wants to calculate the height of a tree.
From the bottom of the tree, he walks
50 m and places a pole in the ground 2 m
vertically from the ground. He then walks
another 10 m. He notices that from this point on the ground, the top of the pole and the top
of the tree are in line. Calculate the height of the tree.

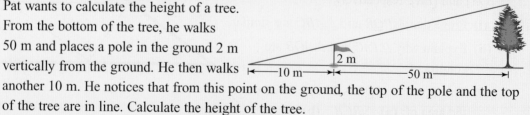

Solution:

Let the height of the tree be h m and represent the situation with two similar triangles.

$$\frac{h}{2} = \frac{60}{10}$$

$$h = \frac{60 \times 2}{10} \quad \text{(multiply both sides by 2)}$$

$$h = \frac{120}{10}$$

$$h = 12$$

Thus, the height of the tree is 12 m.

Exercise 6.9

1. A girl wants to calculate the height of a building. From the bottom of the building, she walks 35 m and places a pole in the ground 2 m vertically from the ground. She then walks another 5 m. She notices that from this point on the ground, the top of the pole and the top of the building are in line. Calculate the height of the building.

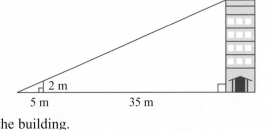

2. The diagram shows a building of height 48 m and another building of height h m. Paul paces out distances as shown so that the tops of each building are in line with each other. Calculate the height of the smaller building.

3. A conveyor belt of length 40 m carries bricks from the ground up to the top of a building. When the bricks have travelled a distance of 16 m on the conveyor belt, they are 6 m above the ground. Calculate the height of the building.

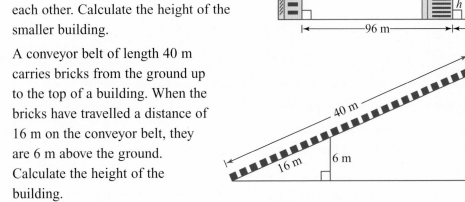

4. The rope on a pair of stepladders, as shown, stops the steps from opening too far. Using similar triangles, find the length of the rope.

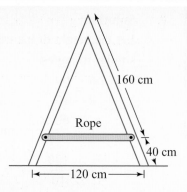

5. Frank estimated the width, w m, of a river by taking measurements as shown and then using similar triangles.

   (i) Find w.

   (ii) Explain why w is only an estimate.

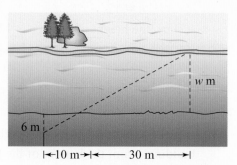

6. Two markers, P and Q, have been placed in a lake to indicate deep water. The owner of the lake wants to know how far apart the markers have been placed. She took measurements as shown, where $AB \parallel PQ$.

   (i) Calculate the distance between the markers.

   (ii) In your opinion, which of the measurements was the most difficult to obtain? Explain your answer.

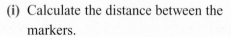
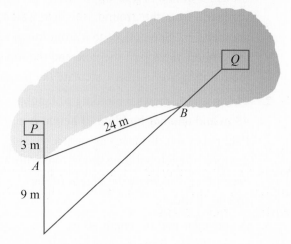

7. A 15 m ladder leans against a vertical wall. The foot of the ladder is 4.2 m from the base of the wall on level ground.

   (i) How far up the wall is the ladder?

   (ii) A person is two-thirds of the way up the ladder.

   (a) How far above the ground is the person?

   (b) How far away from the wall is the person?

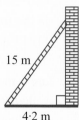

8. A swimming pool is being filled. Find the length, *l* m, of the surface of the water when the pool has been filled to a depth of 3 m.

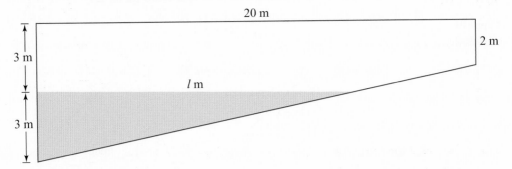

9. Joe wants to estimate the height, *h* m, of a tower on level ground. Describe in your own words a method that Joe could use to estimate the height of the tower.

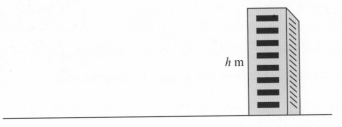

Enlargements

An **enlargement** changes the size of a shape to give a similar image. To enlarge a shape, we need:

1. A centre of enlargement. **2.** A scale factor.

When a shape is enlarged, all lengths are multiplied by the scale factor and all angles remain unchanged. A slide projector makes an enlargement of a shape. In this case, the light bulb is the **centre of enlargement**.

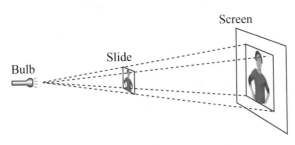

Ray method

In the diagram below, the triangle ABC is the **object** (the starting shape) and the triangle $A'B'C'$ is the **image** (the enlarged shape) under an enlargement, centre O and scale factor 2.

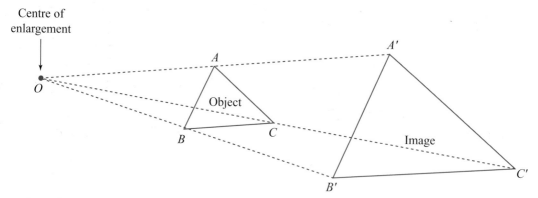

The rays have been drawn from the centre of enlargement, O, to each vertex and beyond. The distance from the centre of enlargement, O, to each vertex on triangle ABC was measured and multiplied by 2. Thus, $|OA'| = 2|OA|$, $|OB'| = 2|OB|$ and $|OC'| = 2|OC|$.

Note: All measurements are made from the centre of enlargement, O.

Properties of enlargements:

1. The shape of the image is the same as the shape of the object (only the size has changed).
2. The amount by which a figure is enlarged is called the **scale factor** and is denoted by k.
3. Image length $= k$(object length)   or $k = \dfrac{\text{image length}}{\text{object length}}$.
4. Area of image $= k^2$(area object)   or $k^2 = \dfrac{\text{area of image}}{\text{area of object}}$.

Notes:

1. The scale factor can be less than 1 (i.e. $0 < k < 1$). In these cases, the image will be smaller than the object. Though smaller, the image is still called an enlargement.
2. The centre of enlargement can be a vertex on the object figure, inside it or outside.

To find the centre of enlargement, do the following.

1. Choose two points on the image and their corresponding points on the original figure.
2. From each of these points on the larger figure, draw a line to the corresponding point on the smaller figure.
3. Produce these lines until they intersect at the point that is the centre of enlargement.

EXAMPLE 1

Triangle *PQR* is the image of triangle *ABC* under an enlargement. $|AB| = 8$ and $|PR| = 24$. The scale factor of enlargement is 1·5.

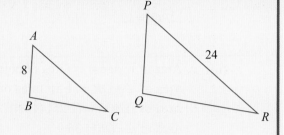

(i) Copy the diagram and show how to find the centre of enlargement, *O*.

(ii) Find: **(a)** $|PQ|$ **(b)** $|AC|$

(iii) If the area of $\triangle ABC$ is 16·4 square units, calculate the area of $\triangle PQR$.

Solution:

(i) Join *P* to *A* and continue beyond.
Join *R* to *C* and continue beyond.
Continue these lines until they meet.
This is the centre of enlargement, *O*.

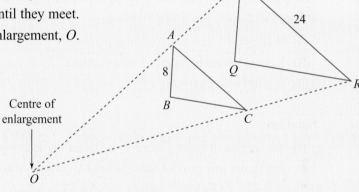

Centre of enlargement

(ii)

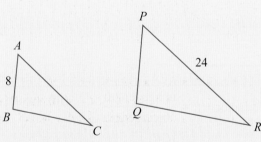

Image length = *k* (object length)

(a) $|PQ| = k|AB|$
$\quad |PQ| = 1\cdot5(8)$
$\quad |PQ| = 12$

(b) $|PR| = k|AC|$
$\quad 24 = 1\cdot5\,|AC|$
$\quad 16 = |AC|$

(divide both sides by $1\cdot5$)

(iii) $\therefore$ Area of image $= k^2$ (area of object)
Area of $\triangle PQR = (1\cdot5)^2$ (area of $\triangle ABC$)
Area of $\triangle PQR = (2\cdot25)\,(16\cdot4)$
Area of $\triangle PQR = 36\cdot9$

EXAMPLE 2

The triangle ORS is the image of the triangle OPQ under an enlargement. $|OP| = 6$ and $|PR| = 7\cdot5$.

  (i) Write down the centre of enlargement.

  (ii) Find k, the scale factor of enlargement.

  (iii) If $|OQ| = 8$, find $|QS|$.

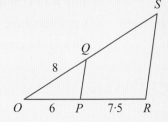

Solution:

  (i) The centre of enlargement is the point O (as O is common to both triangles). Divide the figure into two separate similar triangles. Mark in known lengths.

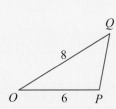
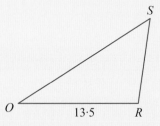

(ii) Scale factor $= k = \dfrac{\text{image length}}{\text{object length}}$

$\qquad = \dfrac{|OR|}{|OP|}$

$\qquad = \dfrac{13\cdot5}{6} = 2\cdot25$

(iii) Image length $= k(\text{object length})$
$\qquad |OS| = k|OQ|$
$\qquad\quad\; = 2\cdot25(8) = 18$
$\qquad |QS| = |OS| - |OQ| = 18 - 8 = 10$

EXAMPLE 3

The rectangle $PQRS$ is the image of the rectangle $ABCD$ under an enlargement, centre O. If the area of $PQRS$ is 121 cm^2 and the area of $ABCD$ is 25 cm^2, find the scale factor of enlargement, k.

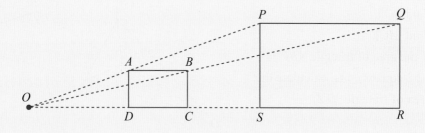

Solution:

$$(\text{Area of image}) = k^2(\text{area of object})$$
$$\therefore \text{Area of rectangle } PQRS = k^2(\text{area of rectangle } ABCD)$$

$$121 = k^2(25) \qquad \text{(put in known values)}$$
$$4{\cdot}84 = k^2 \qquad \text{(divide both sides by 25)}$$
$$\sqrt{4{\cdot}84} = k \qquad \text{(take the square root of both sides)}$$
$$2{\cdot}2 = k$$

Thus, the scale factor of enlargement is 2·2.

Exercise 6.10

1. Triangle PQR is the image of triangle ABC under an enlargement.
   $|PR| = 8, |AC| = 4, |AB| = 3$ and $|QR| = 4$.

   (i) Write down the centre of enlargement.

   (ii) Find the scale factor of enlargement, k.

   (iii) Find: (a) $|PQ|$ (b) $|BC|$

   (iv) If the area of triangle ABC is 3 square units, find the area of triangle PQR.

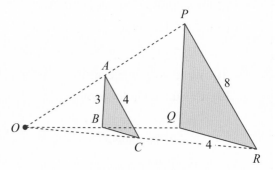

2. Triangle *XYZ* is the image of triangle *ABC* under the enlargement, centre *O*, with $|AB| = 4$ and $|XZ| = 12$. The scale factor of the enlargement is 1·5.

   (i) Find $|XY|$.
   (ii) Find $|AC|$.
   (iii) If the area of triangle *ABC* is 12·2 square units, calculate the area of triangle *XYZ*.

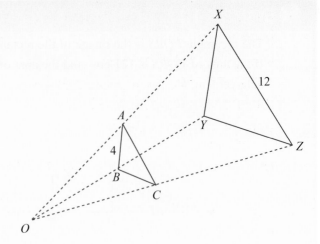

3. The right-angled triangle *A'B'C'* is the image of the right-angled triangle *ABC* under an enlargement with centre *O*. The scale factor is 2·5.

   (i) Find the length of [*AC*].
   (ii) Find the length of [*A'B'*].
   (iii) Find the area of triangle *ABC*.
   (iv) Find the area of triangle *A'B'C'*.

4. The diagram shows a rectangle, *a*, and its enlargement, *b*.

   (i) Write down the centre of enlargement.
   (ii) Calculate the following.
      (a) The scale factor of enlargement
      (b) $|OT|$
      (c) $\dfrac{\text{Area of } a}{\text{Area of } b}$

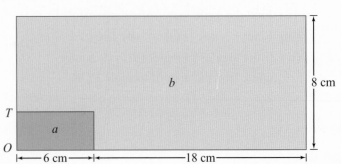

5. Triangle *ORS* is the image of triangle *OTU*
   under an enlargement, centre *O*.
   $|RS| = 10$ cm and $|TU| = 5$ cm.

   (i) Find the scale factor of the enlargement.

   (ii) If $|OR| = 12$ cm, find $|OT|$.

   (iii) If the area of triangle *ORS* is 60 cm^2,
   find the area of triangle *OTU*.

   (iv) Write down the area of the region *RSUT*.

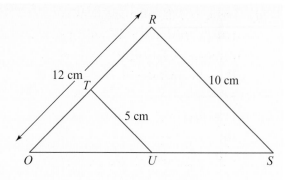

6. Triangle *OCD* is the image of triangle *OAB* under an
   enlargement, centre *O*, with $|OA| = 2$ and $|AC| = 3$.

   (i) Find the scale factor of the enlargement.

   (ii) If $|OB| = 1.8$, find $|BD|$.

   (iii) Calculate $|AB| : |CD|$.

   (iv) If the area of triangle *OCD* is 12·5 square units, find the
   area of triangle *OAB*.

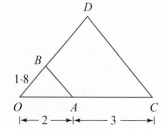

7. Triangle *OAB* is the image of triangle *OXY* under the
   enlargement, centre *O*, with $|XY| = 8$, $|OX| = 10$
   and $|AB| = 18$.

   (i) Find the scale factor of the enlargement.

   (ii) Find $|XA|$.

   (iii) The area of triangle *OAB* is 101·25 square units.
   Find the area of triangle *OXY*.

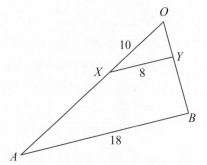

8. Triangle *ODC* is the image of triangle *OAB* under
   an enlargement, centre *O*.
   $|DC| = 9$ and $|AB| = 15$.

   (i) Find the scale factor of the enlargement.

   (ii) If the area of triangle *OAB* is 87·5 square units,
   find the area of triangle *ODC*.

   (iii) Write down the area of the region *ABCD*.

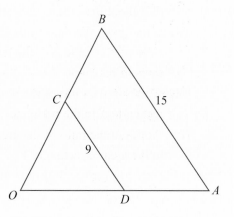

9.

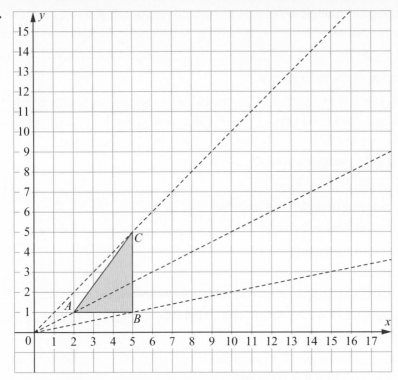

(i) Write down the coordinates of the points A, B and C.

(ii) Triangle PQR is the image of triangle ABC by a scale factor of 3 from the centre of enlargement $0(0, 0)$. Using the rays, or otherwise, find the coordinates of P, Q and R.

(iii) Calculate: (a) $|AC|$ (b) $|PR|$ (c) $|AC| : |PR|$

(iv) Calculate the ratio of the area of $\triangle PQR$: area of $\triangle ABC$.

10. (i) Enlarge the rectangle X by a scale factor of $\frac{2}{3}$ about the origin. Label the image Y.

(ii) Write down the ratio of the lengths of the sides of rectangle X to the lengths of the sides of rectangle Y.

(iii) Work out the ratio of the perimeter of rectangle X to the perimeter of rectangle Y.

(iv) Work out the ratio of the area of rectangle X to the area of rectangle Y.

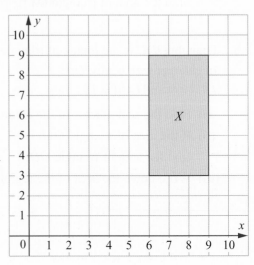

11. A woman spent €400 on a carpet for a bedroom. The cost is proportional to the area of the floor. She wants to carpet the living room in the house. Both the bedroom and the living room floors have the same shape. Each length of the living room is 1·6 times larger than the corresponding length in the bedroom. Calculate how much it will cost to carpet the living room.

12. Kenny painted two similar rooms with the same paint. One tin of paint can cover roughly 10 m². The smaller of the two rooms needed exactly two tins of paint. Each length in the larger room is 1·8 times larger than the corresponding length in the smaller room. How many tins of paint did Kenny need to paint the larger room?

13. The sauce bottles are similar, with heights as shown. The smaller bottle has a label of area 50 cm². What is the area of the label on the larger bottle? Show your work.

24 cm

20 cm

14. Vase *A* and vase *B* are similar.
Vase *A* is 8 cm in height.
The total surface of vase *A* is 60 cm².
The total surface of vase *B* is 375 cm².
Find the height of vase *B*.

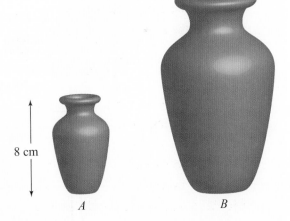

8 cm

A

B

15. The enlargement reading on a photocopier is 100% when the copy is to be the same size as the original. When the reading is 110%, then each length is increased by 10%.

    (i) What enlargement reading do you use if you want:

        (a) Each length decreased by 30%

        (b) An 8 cm line increased to 12 cm

        (c) A 15 cm line reduced to 9 cm

(ii) A shaded area on the original is 50 cm². What is the shaded area on the copy when the enlargement reading is: **(a)** 120%   **(b)** 60%

(iii) The ratio 120 : 60 is equal to 2 : 1. Explain why the answers in part **(ii)** are not in the ratio 2 : 1.

(iv) What percentage, correct to the nearest whole number, would you use on the photocopier to double the size of a document? Justify your answer.

(v) To exactly double the size of a document, the scale factor of enlargement is $\sqrt{k}$. What is the value of k? Justify your answer in conjunction with the answer in part **(iv)**.

16. Triangle *XYZ* is the image of triangle *ABC* under an enlargement.

   (i) Show how to find the centre of enlargement.
   (ii) If the area of triangle *ABC* is 81 cm² and the area of triangle *XYZ* is 36 cm², find the scale factor of enlargement, k.
   (iii) If $|BC| = 6$ cm, find $|YZ|$.

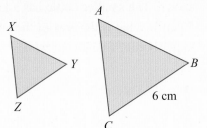

17. The ray method was used to enlarge a design for a Valentine card. The original is labelled *A* and the image is labelled *B*.

   (i) Find the centre of enlargement.
   (ii) Find the scale factor of the enlargement (use your ruler). Show your work.
   (iii) Calculate the ratio $\dfrac{\text{Area of drawing } B}{\text{Area of drawing } A}$.

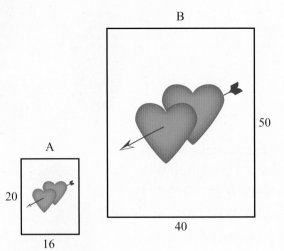

18. (i)   Draw a square *OPQR* with sides 8 cm.
    (ii) Draw the image of this square under the enlargement with centre *O* and scale
          factor 0·25.
    (iii) Calculate the area of this image square.
    (iv) Under another enlargement, the area of the image of the square *OPQR* is 92·16 cm^2.
          What is the scale factor of this enlargement?

Constructions

Any work involving accurate constructions requires a good pencil, a compass, a ruler and a protractor.
It is important not to rub out any construction lines or marks you make at any stage during a
construction. All construction lines or marks should **always** be left on the diagram.

Notes:

- A straight edge is like a ruler without any numbers or markings.
- A ruler is a straight edge but has numbers and markings on it.
- When a question requires a straight edge, you can use your ruler but not the numbers or markings
  on it.

Locus

A locus is a set of points that obey a certain rule. For example:

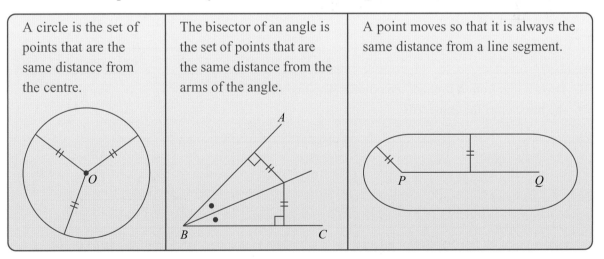

| A circle is the set of points that are the same distance from the centre. | The bisector of an angle is the set of points that are the same distance from the arms of the angle. | A point moves so that it is always the same distance from a line segment. |

Bisector of an angle

Given the angle *ABC*.

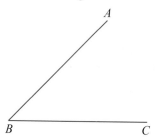

Steps to bisect any angle *ABC* (using only a compass and straight edge)

1. Set your compass to a sensible radius (not too large).
    Place the compass point on the vertex, *B*. Draw two
    arcs to intersect the arms at *X* and *Y*.

    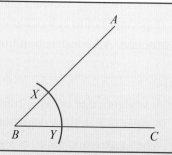

2. Place the compass point on *X* and draw an arc.
    Keep the same radius.
    Place the compass point on *Y* and draw an arc.
    Where the arcs intersect, label the point *Z*.

    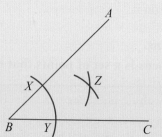

3. Draw a line from *B* through the point *Z*. The line *BZ* is
    the bisector of the angle *ABC*.

    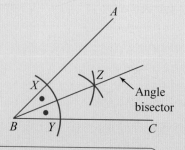

Any point on the bisector of an angle is equidistant (same distance) from the arms of the
angle. The bisector of an acute or obtuse angle also bisects its related reflex angle.

Perpendicular bisector of a given line segment

Given a line segment [AB].

A ——————————————— B

Steps to bisect any line segment [AB] (using only a compass and straight edge)

1. Set the compass to a radius of about three-quarters of the length of the line segment [AB].
   (Any radius above half the length of the line segment will do.)
   Place the compass point on A and draw arcs above and below the line segment.

   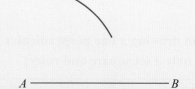

2. Keep the same radius as in step 1. Place the compass point on B and draw arcs above and below the line segment to intersect the other arcs. Where the arcs intersect, label the points X and Y.

3. Draw the line through X and Y.
   The line XY is the perpendicular bisector of the line segment [AB].

   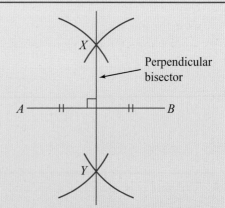

   Perpendicular bisector

Any point on the perpendicular bisector of a line segment [AB] is equidistant (same distance) from the points A and B. The perpendicular bisector of the line segment [AB] is always at right angles to the line segment.

Line perpendicular to a given line *l*, passing through a given point not on *l*

Given a line *l* with a point *A* not on *l*.

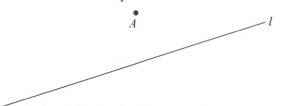

Steps in drawing a line perpendicular to a given line *l*, passing through a given point not on *l* (using only a set square and ruler)

1. Place one of the **shorter** edges of the 45° set square on the line *l*. Place the ruler under the set square.	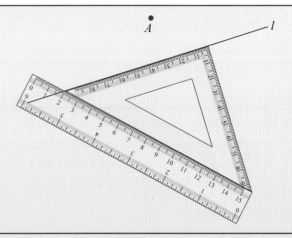
2. Keeping pressure on the ruler, slide the set square along the ruler until the edge meets the point *A*. Draw a line through the point *A* to meet the line *l*.	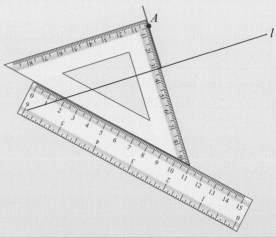
3. This line is perpendicular to *l* and passes through the point *A*.	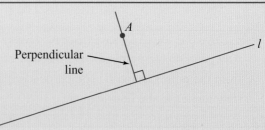

Line perpendicular to a given line *l*, passing through a point on *l*

Given line *l* and a point *A* on *l*.

Steps in drawing a line perpendicular to a given line *l*, passing through a point on *l*.
Method 1 (using a ruler and set square)

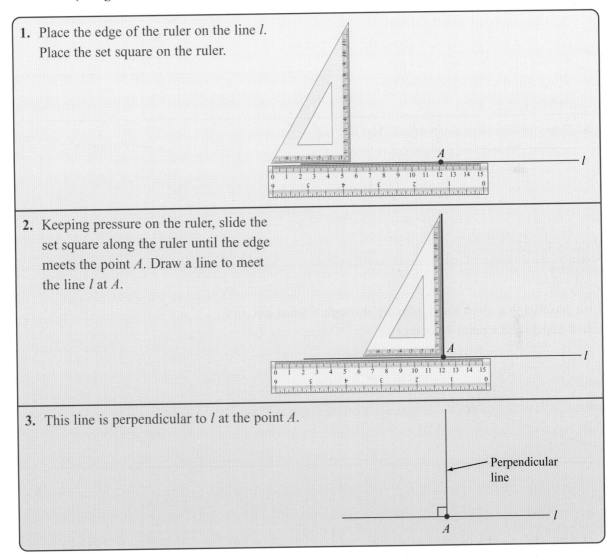

1. Place the edge of the ruler on the line *l*.
   Place the set square on the ruler.

2. Keeping pressure on the ruler, slide the set square along the ruler until the edge meets the point *A*. Draw a line to meet the line *l* at *A*.

3. This line is perpendicular to *l* at the point *A*.

Perpendicular line

Note: Method 1 is very useful when constructing rectangles and right-angled triangles.

Method 2 (using a compass and straight edge)

1. With *A* as the centre and using the same radius, draw two arcs to intersect the line *l* at *X* and *Y*.	
2. Place the compass point on *X* and draw an arc above the point *A*. Keep the same radius. Place the compass point on *Y* and draw an arc above the point *A* to intersect the other arc. Where the arcs intersect, label the point *Z*.	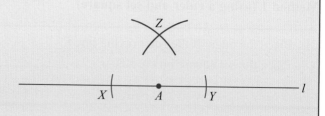
3. Draw the line from *A* through *Z*. The line *AZ* is perpendicular to *l* at the point *A*.	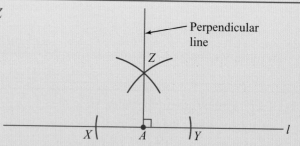

Line parallel to a given line *l*, passing through a point not on *l*

Given a line *l* and a point *A* not on *l*.

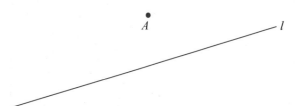

Steps in drawing a line parallel to a given line *l*, passing through a point *A* not on *l* (using only a ruler and set square)

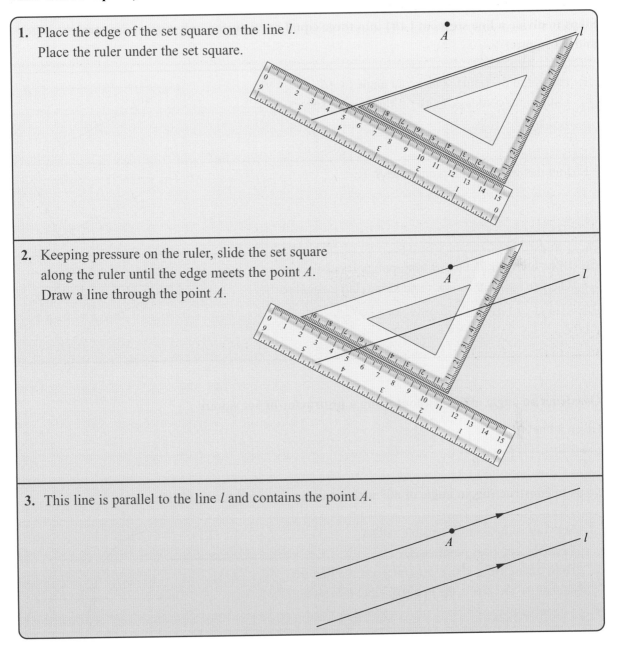

1. Place the edge of the set square on the line *l*.
   Place the ruler under the set square.

2. Keeping pressure on the ruler, slide the set square along the ruler until the edge meets the point *A*.
   Draw a line through the point *A*.

3. This line is parallel to the line *l* and contains the point *A*.

Division of a line segment into any number of equal parts (segments)

Note: This example shows how to divide a line segment into three equal parts. However, the method can also be used to divide a line segment into any number of equal parts. On your course, you can be asked to divide a line segment into any number of equal parts.

Given a line segment [AB].

A ——————————— B

Steps to divide a line segment [AB] into three equal parts (using only a compass, straight edge and set square)

1. From *A*, draw a line at an acute angle to *AB*. Using your compass, mark off three equal spaces, 1, 2 and 3.	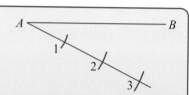
2. Join the last division, point 3, to *B*.	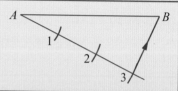
3. Draw lines parallel to 3*B* from points 2 and 1. The line segment is now divided into three equal parts.	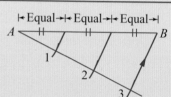

Construct an angle of 60° without using a protractor or set square

Given a line *AB*.

A ——————————— B

Steps in constructing an angle of 60° without using a protractor or set square

1. Set your compass to a sensible radius. Place the compass point on *A*. Draw an arc from above *A* to intersect the line *AB*. Where the arc meets the line *AB*, label this point *C*.	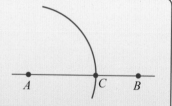
2. Keep the same radius as in step 1. Place the compass point on *C*. Draw an arc to meet the other arc. Where these arcs meet, label this point *D*.	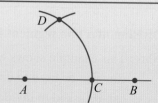

3. Using your ruler, draw the line *AD*.
$|\angle DAC| = 60°$.

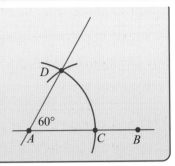

Tangent to a circle at a given point on the circle

A **tangent to a circle** is a line that touches a circle at one point only.

A tangent is perpendicular to the radius at the point of contact.

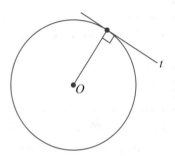

Given a circle, centre *O*, and a point *P* on the circumference.
(We need to construct a line through *P* perpendicular to *OP*.)

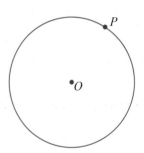

Steps to construct a tangent to a circle at a given point on the circle

Method 1:

1. Draw the line *OP*.

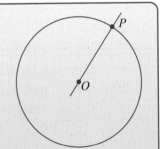

2. Place one of the **shorter** edges of the 45° set square on the line *OP* with the 90° vertex on point *P*. Draw a line towards *P*.

Note: You can also use the 30°/60° set square.

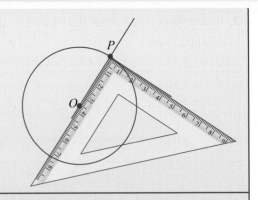

3. Using your ruler or set square, continue the line through *P*. This line is a tangent to the circle at the point *P*.

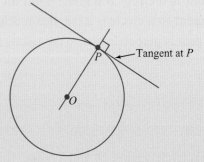

Tangent at *P*

Method 2:

1. Draw the line *OP.*

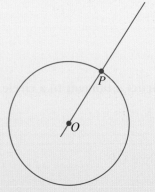

2. Set the compass to a sensible radius (usually a little less than *OP*). Place the compass point on *P*. Draw two arcs to intersect the line *OP* at *X* and *Y*.

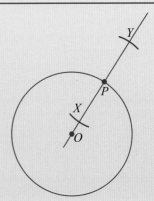

3. Place the compass point on *X*. Draw an arc. Keep the same radius. Place the compass point on *Y* and draw an arc to intersect the other arc.

Where the arcs intersect, label the point *Z*.

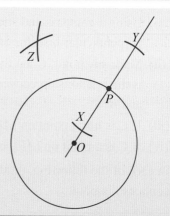

4. Draw the line *ZP*. The line *ZP* is a tangent to the circle at the point *P*.

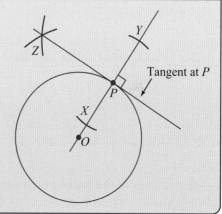

Tangent at *P*

Exercise 6.11

1. Using only a compass and straight edge, construct the angle bisector of each of the following angles, showing all your construction lines. In each case, use your protractor to check your work.

   (i)   **(ii)**   **(iii)**

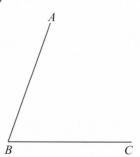 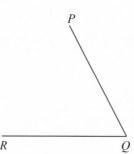 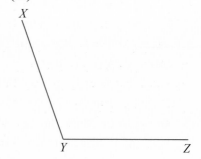

2. Construct each of the following line segments exactly. Using only a compass and straight edge, construct the perpendicular bisector of each line segment, showing all your construction lines. In each case, use your ruler to check your work.

   (i) $|AB| = 8$ cm   **(ii)** $|PQ| = 7$ cm   **(iii)** $|XY| = 64$ mm   **(iv)** $|RS| = 85$ mm

3. (i) Using a compass and straight edge only, construct the perpendicular bisector of the line segment [AB].

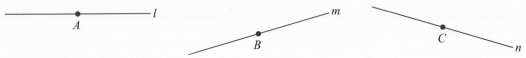

(ii) Mark any point, C, on the perpendicular bisector. What is the relationship between the point C and the points A and B?

(iii) If C is **not** a point on [AB], what type of triangle is △ABC?

(iv) If C is a point on [AB], complete the following: $|AC| + |CB| = |\quad|$.

4. In each of the following, draw a line through the given point, perpendicular to the line that contains the point.

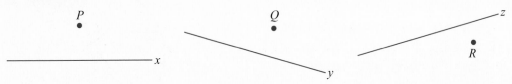

5. In each of the following, draw a line through the given point, not on the line, perpendicular to the line.

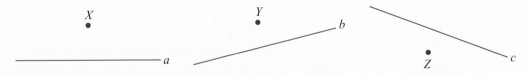

6. In each of the following, draw a line through the given point, not on the line, parallel to the line.

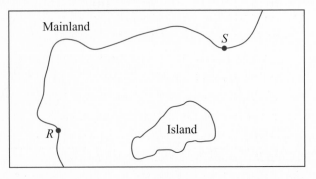

7. Using only a compass and straight edge, construct an angle of 60°.

8. A boat sails from a harbour, H, on the mainland to a harbour, G, on an island. Throughout the journey the boat sails a course that remains at equal distances from the lighthouses R and S. Using only a compass and straight edge, draw the path of the boat and indicate on the diagram the locations of the harbours H and G.

9. The diagram shows two fences that border a park that contains a circular garden, as shown. There is an entrance to the park where the two fences meet. A path is laid so that it is equidistant from each fence. Locate the point X on the circumference of the garden where that path meets the garden.

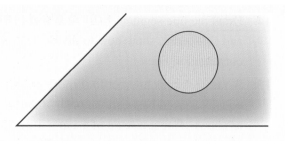

10. The diagram shows an island. There is treasure buried at the point T. T is equidistant from A and B and is also equidistant from C and D. Using only a compass and straight edge, locate the point T.

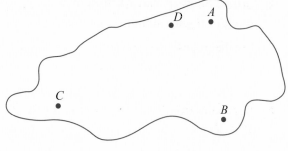

11. The diagram shows two straight roads connecting three towns A, B and C. A gas pipe was laid that is equidistant from towns B and C. Using a scale of 1 cm to 1 km, copy the diagram.

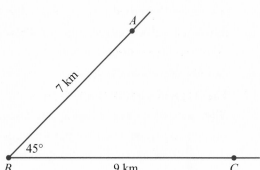

   (i) On your diagram, construct the path of the gas pipe.
   (ii) A new gas pipe is to be laid from town B that is to be equidistant from towns A and C. This new gas pipe is to connect to the older gas pipe at the point X. On your diagram, construct the path of the new gas pipeline and indicate the point X.

12. An electrical firm is asked to fit an outdoor spotlight in a rectangular garden measuring 16 m by 10 m. The light must be the same distance from the two corners, P and Q, of the back wall of the house, but also has to be the same distance from the fence RS at the end of the garden and the side of the garden, PS. Using a scale of 1 cm to 2 m, draw a scale drawing of the garden and find the position of the spotlight. Mark its position T.

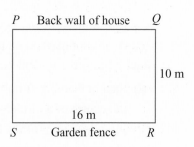

13. Construct each of the following line segments exactly. Using only a compass, straight edge and set square, show how to divide each of the line segments into three equal parts, showing all your construction lines. In each case, use your ruler to check your work.

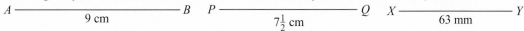

14. Draw the line segment [*AB*] such that |*AB*| = 10 cm. Using only a compass, straight edge and set square, show how to divide [*AB*] into four equal parts, showing all your construction lines.

15. A farmer wants to erect four more posts equally spaced between the posts *A* and *B*, as shown. Using a scale of 1 cm = 1 m, construct an accurate diagram for the farmer. Show all construction lines, using only a compass, straight edge and set square.

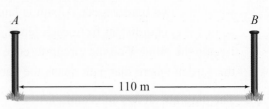

16. The diagram shows a rectangular garden, *PQRS*. Copy the diagram using a scale of 1 cm to 1 m.

    A concrete path is to be laid. The centre of the path runs diagonally from *P* to *R*. The width of the concrete path is to be 1 m. On your diagram, shade in the concrete path.

    A circular flowerbed is to be planted in this garden. The flowerbed will cover the area of the garden that lies within 3 m from the point *Q*. On your diagram, shade in the region that the flowerbed occupies.

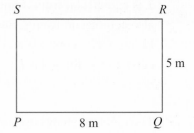

17. The diagram shows a circle with centre *O* and two chords, [*PQ*] and [*RS*]. Copy the diagram. Using only a compass and straight edge, construct the perpendicular bisectors of both chords. Show all your construction lines clearly. Comment on the point of intersection of the two chords.

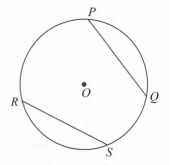

18. A part of a machine uses cylindrical cams (wheels). However, the centres are not marked on them. The exact centre of each wheel is required in order to drill holes in them.

    (i) State a theorem from your course that could be used to locate the centre of a circle with geometrical instruments.

    (ii) Find the centre of the circle on the right by applying the theorem you mentioned above. Show all your construction lines clearly.

    (iii) Describe another method that could be used to locate the centre of the circle.

Constructing triangles and quadrilaterals

Triangles

The method used for drawing a triangle depends on the information you are given. We will look at four cases. A triangle can be drawn if you are given:

> 1. The length of the three sides (SSS).
>
> 2. The length of two sides and the angle between them (SAS).
>
> 3. The length of one side and two angles (ASA).
>
> 4. A right angle, the length of the hypotenuse and one other side (RHS).
>
> In each case, make a rough sketch at the beginning.

Note: If you know two angles in a triangle, it is possible to calculate the third angle. The four cases above are related to the **four cases of congruence**.

1. Given the length of the three sides (SSS)

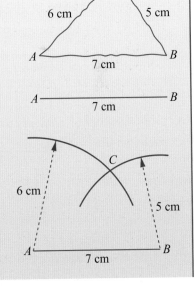

Construct triangle ABC with $|AB| = 7$ cm, $|AC| = 6$ cm and $|BC| = 5$ cm.

Solution:

1. A rough sketch with the given information is shown on the right.

2. Using a ruler, draw a horizontal line segment 7 cm in length. Label the end points A and B.

3. Set your compass to a radius of 6 cm.
   Place the compass point on the point A.
   Draw an arc above the line segment.
   Set your compass to a radius of 5 cm.
   Place the compass point on the point B.
   Draw an arc above the line segment to meet the other arc.
   Label the point where the arcs meet C.

4. Using your ruler, join A to C and B to C.
The triangle ABC is now drawn as required.

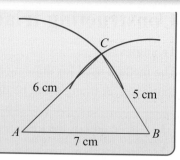

2. Given the length of two sides and the measure of the angle between them (SAS)

Construct triangle PQR with $|PQ| = 6$ cm, $|PR| = 5$ cm and
$|\angle QPR| = 55°$.

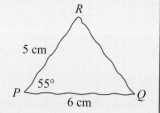

Solution:

1. A rough sketch with the given information is shown on the right.

2. Using a ruler, draw a horizontal line segment 6 cm
in length. Label the end points P and Q.

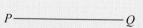

3. Place your protractor on the point P.
Draw an angle of 55°.

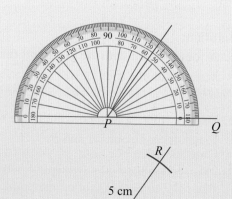

4. Use your ruler or compass to mark the point R
such that $|PR| = 5$ cm.

5. Using your ruler, join Q to R.
Triangle PQR is now drawn as required.

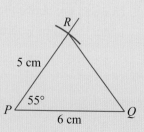

3. Given the length of one side and the measure of two angles (ASA)

Construct the triangle XYZ with $|XY| = 5$ cm, $|\angle YXZ| = 40°$ and $|\angle XYZ| = 70°$.

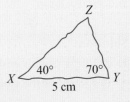

Solution:

1. A rough sketch with the given information is shown on the right.

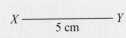

2. Using a ruler, draw a horizontal line segment 5 cm in length. Label the end points X and Y.

3. Place your protractor on the point X. Draw an angle of 40°.

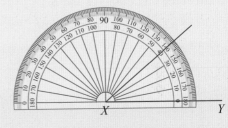

4. Place your protractor on the point Y. Draw an angle of 70°.

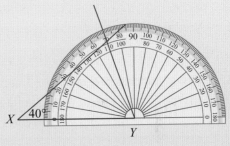

5. Where these two lines meet, label the point Z. The triangle XYZ is now drawn as required.

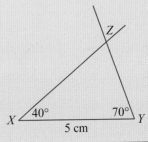

4. **Given a right angle, length of the hypotenuse and the length of one other side (RHS)**

Construct triangle ABC with $|\angle BAC| = 90°$, $|AB| = 7$ cm and $|BC| = 8$ cm.

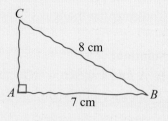

Solution:

1. A rough sketch with the given information is shown on the right.

2. Using a ruler, draw a horizontal line segment 7 cm in length. Label the end points A and B.

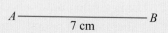

3. Using a set square or protractor, draw an angle of 90° at A.

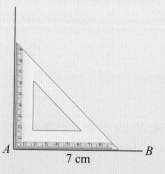

4. Set your compass to a radius of 8 cm. Place the compass point on the point B. Draw an arc to meet the vertical line. Label this point C.

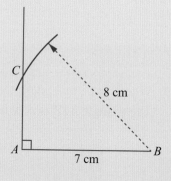

5. Using your ruler, join B to C. Triangle ABC is now drawn as required.

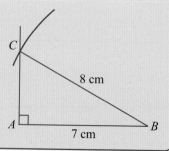

Quadrilaterals

As with triangles, always make a rough sketch at the beginning.

Parallelogram

Construct parallelogram $ABCD$ such that $|AB| = 8$ cm, $|BC| = 5$ cm and $|\angle BAD| = 70°$.

1. A rough sketch with the given information is shown on the right.

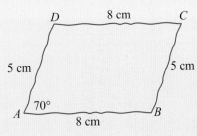

2. Using a ruler, draw a horizontal line segment 8 cm in length. Label the end points A and B.

3. Place your protractor on the point A. Draw an angle of $70°$.

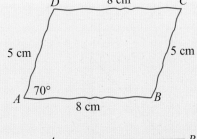

4. Place your protractor on the point B. Draw an angle of $70°$.

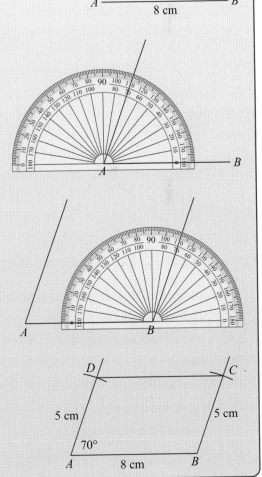

5. Use your ruler or compass to mark the points D and C such that $|AD| = 5$ cm and $|BC| = 5$ cm. Join D to C. Parallelogram $ABCD$ is now drawn.

Exercise 6.12

Accurately construct each of the triangles in questions 1–20, with all dimensions in centimetres (the diagrams are not drawn to scale).

1.

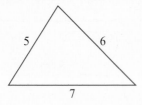

2.

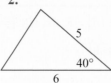

3.

4.

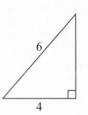

5.

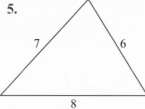

6.

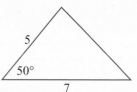

7.

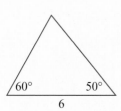

8.

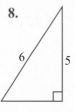

9.

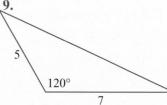

10.

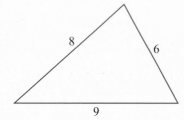

11.

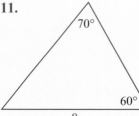

12.

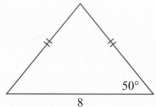

In questions 13–20, it is good practice to draw a rough sketch first and to draw one side as a horizontal base at the beginning.

13. Construct triangle ABC with $|AB| = 9$ cm, $|AC| = 8$ cm and $|BC| = 7$ cm.

14. Construct triangle PQR with $|PQ| = 8$ cm, $|QR| = 6$ cm and $|\angle PQR| = 30°$.

15. Construct triangle PQR with $|PQ| = 5$ cm, $|\angle RPQ| = 60°$ and $|\angle RQP| = 45°$.

16. **(i)** Construct triangle XYZ with $|XY| = 8$ cm, $|XZ| = 6$ cm and $|\angle YXZ| = 90°$. **(ii)** Hence or otherwise, write down $|YZ|$.

17. Construct triangle ABC with $|AB| = 6$ cm, $|AC| = 5$ cm and $|BC| = 4$ cm.

18. Construct triangle PQR with $|PQ| = 7$ cm, $|\angle RPQ| = 80°$ and $|PR| = 6$ cm.

19. Construct triangle XYZ with $|\angle YXZ| = 90°$, $|XZ| = 6$ cm and $|\angle XYZ| = 35°$.

20. Construct triangle ABC with $|AB| = 8$ cm, $|\angle BAC| = 30°$ and $|\angle ABC| = 110°$.

21. Construct the following parallelograms.

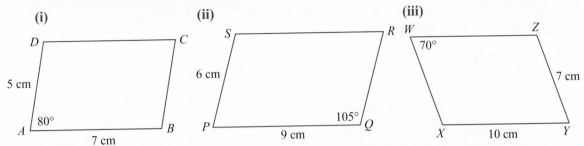

(i)   **(ii)**   **(iii)**

In questions 22–25, it is good practice to draw a rough sketch first and to draw one side as a horizontal base at the beginning.

22. Construct parallelogram $ABCD$ such that $|AB| = 6$ cm, $|\angle BAD| = 50°$ and $|AD| = 4$ cm.

23. Construct parallelogram $PQRS$ such that $|SR| = 8$ cm, $|\angle QPS| = 75°$ and $|QR| = 6$ cm.

24. Construct parallelogram $XYZW$ such that $|XY| = 9$ cm, $|YZ| = 7$ cm, $|\angle YXZ| = 30°$ and $|\angle XZY| = 35°$.

25. Construct parallelogram $PQRS$ such that $|PQ| = 12$ cm, $|QR| = 5$ cm and $|\angle PQR| = 90°$.

    (i) What type of parallelogram is $PQRS$?

    (ii) Using your ruler, find $|PR|$.

    (iii) Verify your answer by using Pythagoras' theorem.

26. In parallelogram $ABCD$, $|\angle BAD| = (3x + 5)°$ and $|\angle BCD| = (x + 45)°$.

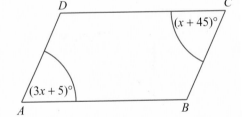

    (i) Complete the statement:

        Opposite angles in a parallelogram are _____ in measure.

    (ii) Write down an equation in x.

    (iii) Solve your equation for x and calculate $|\angle BAD|$.

    (iv) $|AB| = 9$ cm and $|BC| = \frac{2}{3}|AB|$.

        Construct the parallelogram $ABCD$.

27. Construct the following quadrilaterals.

(i)   **(ii)**

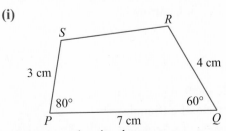

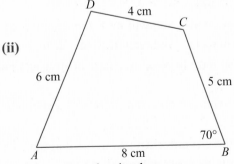

Measure and write down:

    (a) $|RS|$ **(b)** $|\angle QRS|$

Measure and write down:

    (a) $|\angle ADC|$ **(b)** $|\angle BCD|$

28. The diagram shows a rectangular lawn, 11 m by 6 m, containing a circular flowerbed of radius 2 m. A rose bush is to be planted in the garden. The rose bush is to be at least 1 m from the edge of the garden and at least 2 m from the flowerbed. On the diagram, shade in the region where the rose bush can be planted.

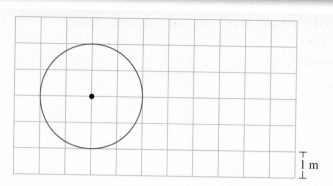

1 m

29. The diagram shows a rectangular garden, 24 m by 18 m. A tree is to be planted in the garden. The tree must be 12 m from P and the tree must be the same distance from SR and RQ. Copy the diagram using a scale of 1 cm to 3 m. Using only a compass and straight edge, construct the position of the tree.

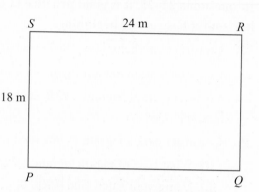

30. In a garden, a dog is on a lead that is 3 m in length. The lead is connected with a metal loop to a 10 m metal rail fixed horizontally to the ground so that the lead can slide easily along its length, as shown. Using a scale of 1 cm to 1 m, draw a diagram of the rail and shade the area of the garden that the dog can play on.

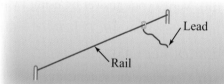

Centres of a triangle

On your course, you will meet three centres of a triangle:
1. Circumcentre and circumcircle **2.** Incentre and incircle **3.** Centroid
You also have to construct these centres and circles.

Circumcentre and circumcircle of a triangle
The three perpendicular bisectors of the sides of a triangle meet at one point called the **circumcentre**, K, in the diagram. The **circumcircle** of a triangle is a circle that passes through the three vertices of the triangle. The radius of the circumcircle is $r = |KA|$. ($|KB|$ or $|KC|$ could also be used as a radius.)

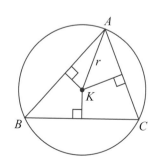

If the triangle has an obtuse angle, then the circumcentre is **outside** the triangle. If the triangle is a right-angled triangle, then the circumcentre is the **midpoint of the hypotenuse**.

Steps to construct the circumcentre and circumcircle of triangle *ABC*

1. Construct the perpendicular bisector of [*AB*].

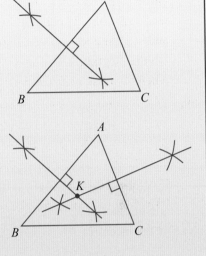

2. Construct the perpendicular bisector of [*AC*] to meet the other perpendicular bisector at *K*. *K* is the circumcentre.

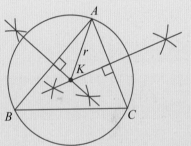

3. With *K* as the centre and radius $r = |KA|$, draw a circle. This circle will pass through the three vertices of the triangle.
   The circle drawn is the circumcircle.
   ($|KB|$ or $|KC|$ could also be used as a radius.)

Note: The perpendicular bisector of [*BC*] would also contain *K*.

Incentre and incircle of a triangle
The three angle bisectors of a triangle meet at one point called the **incentre**, *K*, in the diagram. The **incircle** of a triangle is a circle that touches the three sides of a triangle. *r* is the radius of the incircle.

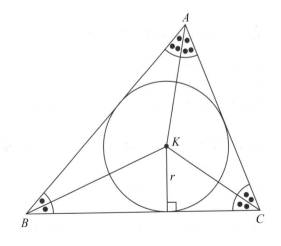

Steps to construct the incentre and incircle of triangle *ABC*

1. Construct the bisector of ∠*ABC*.

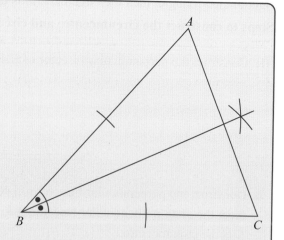

2. Construct the bisector of ∠*ACB* to meet the other
   angle bisector at *K*.
   K is the incentre.

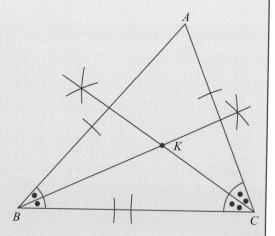

3. With *K* as the centre and radius *r*, draw a circle.
   This circle will touch the three sides of the
   triangle.
   The circle drawn is the incircle.

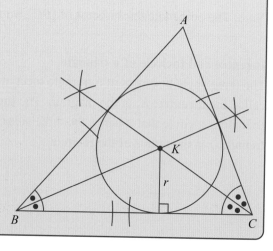

Note: The bisector of ∠*BAC* would also contain *K*.

Centroid of a triangle

A line drawn from a vertex of a triangle to the midpoint of the opposite side is called a **median**. The three medians of a triangle meet at one point called the **centroid**, K in the diagram. The centroid divides each median in the ratio $2 : 1$. K is also the centre of gravity of the triangle.

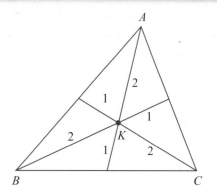

Steps in constructing the centroid of triangle ABC

1. Construct the perpendicular bisector of $[AB]$. Label the midpoint S.
   Join S to C (median).

2. Construct the perpendicular bisector of $[AC]$.
   Label the midpoint T.
   Join T to B (median).
   The two medians intersect at K.
   K is the centroid of the triangle.

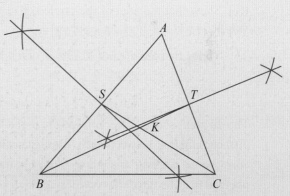

Note: The third median from A to the midpoint of $[BC]$ would also contain K.

Exercise 6.13

1. (i) Construct a triangle of sides 8 cm, 7 cm and 6 cm.
   (ii) Construct the **(a)** circumcentre and **(b)** circumcircle of the triangle.

2. (i) Construct a triangle of sides 11 cm, 8 cm and 6 cm.
   (ii) Construct the **(a)** incentre and **(b)** incircle of the triangle.

3. (i) Construct a triangle of sides 10 cm, 9 cm and 7 cm.

    (ii) Construct the centroid of the triangle.

4. In a certain area, there are two mobile phone transmitters, C and D, where $|CD| = 8$ km. Signals from transmitter C can reach 6 km and signals from transmitter D can reach 4 km. Using a scale of 1 cm = 1 km, indicate, by shading, the region in which signals can be reached from both transmitters.

5. P, Q and R represent three radio masts, where $|PQ| = 225$ km, $|PR| = 200$ km and $|QR| = 175$ km. Using a scale of 1 cm = 25 km, represent the situation on an accurate diagram. Signals from mast P can be received 125 km away, from mast Q 150 km away and from mast R 175 km away. Shade in the region in which signals can be received from all three masts.

    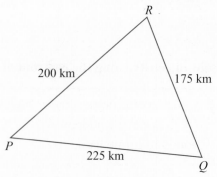

6. (i) Construct a triangle XYZ in which $|XY| = 10$ cm, $|YZ| = 8$ cm and $|XZ| = 6$ cm. Is the triangle a right-angled triangle? Justify your answer.

    (ii) Construct the circumcircle of the triangle, showing all your construction lines clearly. Explain why the centre of the circumcircle is the midpoint of $[XY]$.

    (iii) Calculate the area of the triangle using $\frac{1}{2}$ base $\times$ height.

    (iv) Show that the area of the circle is greater than three times the area of the triangle.

    (v) Let $|XY| = a$, $|YZ| = b$ and $|XZ| = c$.

    Verify that the area of $\triangle XYZ$ is given by $A = \sqrt{s(s - a)(s - b)(s - c)}$ cm^2,

    where $s = \dfrac{a + b + c}{2}$.

7. The diagram shows three villages, A, B and C, and the road distances, in km, between each. Using a scale of 1 cm = 1 km, construct an accurate triangle to represent the three towns. It is planned that the three towns will pool their resources to build a recreation centre. A vote was taken and it was decided to build the recreation centre in a place such that it is equidistant from each of the three villages. Using a compass and straight edge, construct on your diagram the position where the recreation centre should be built.

    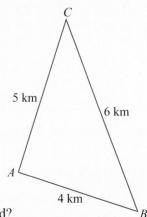

    (i) In geometry, what is the position of the recreation centre called?

    (ii) Is the position of the recreation centre fair to all three towns? Justify your answer.

    (iii) If the triangular road connecting the towns was a right-angled triangle or an obtuse triangle, would this make any difference? Discuss.

Exercise 1.1

1. $4i$ **2.** $3i$ **3.** $2i$ **4.** $5i$ **5.** $8i$ **6.** $10i$ **7.** $7i$ **8.** $12i$

Exercise 1.2

1. $R = 5, I = 3$ **2.** $R = 2, I = 5$ **3.** $R = 6, I = 7$ **4.** $R = 5, I = 4$

5. $R = 2, I = -7$ **6.** $R = -4, I = 6$ **7.** $R = -3, I = -5$ **8.** $R = -9, I = 8$

9. $R = 2, I = 1$ **10.** $R = 3, I = -1$ **11.** $R = -5, I = 1$ **12.** $R = -1, I = -1$

13. $R = 6, I = 0$ **14.** $R = 0, I = 2$ **15.** $R = -2, I = 0$ **16.** $R = 0, I = -5$

Exercise 1.3

1. $6 + 5i$ **2.** $3 + 4i$ **3.** $6 + 7i$ **4.** $-2 + 3i$ **5.** $2 + 4i$ **6.** $-3 + 6i$

7. $14 + 5i$ **8.** $17 + 16i$ **9.** $0 - 3i$ **10.** $15 + 0i$ **11.** $5 - i$ **12.** $3 + 2i$

13. $4 - i$ **14.** $2 + 0i$ **15.** $3 + 0i$ **16.** $4 - 2i$ **17.** $5 + 3i$ **18.** $5 + 0i$

19. $0 + 7i$ **20.** $3 - 2i$ **21.** $5 - 5i$ **22.** $2 + 5i$ **23.** $5 + i$ **24.** $8 + 4i$

25. $-4 - 32i$

Exercise 1.4

1. $4 + 6i$ **2.** $-6 + 12i$ **3.** $-2 - i$ **4.** $4 + 3i$ **5.** $1 + 2i$ **6.** $3 - i$ **7.** $5 + 14i$

8. $5 + 5i$ **9.** $16 - 11i$ **10.** $21 - 22i$ **11.** $-10 - 5i$ **12.** $13 + 0i$ **13.** $3 + 4i$

14. $5 - 12i$ **15.** $21 + 20i$ **16.** $5 + i$ **17.** $-5 + 12i$ **18.** $-24 - 10i$

19. $-2 + 0i$ **20.** $-3 + i$ **21.** $-8 + i$ **22.** $-1 + 5i$ **23.** $-2 + 0i$

Exercise 1.5

1. $3 - 2i$ **2.** $4 + 3i$ **3.** $-2 - 6i$ **4.** $-3 + 7i$ **5.** $1 + 5i$ **6.** $-1 - 3i$

7. $-4 + 5i$ **8.** $-2 - 3i$ **9.** $7 - 3i$ **10.** $3 - i$ **11.** $-8 - 6i$ **12.** (i) 8 (ii) $10i$

(iii) 41 **13.** (i) 6 (ii) $-4i$ (iii) 13 **14.** (i) -8 (ii) $4i$ (iii) 20 **15.** (i) -2

(ii) $-2i$ (iii) 2 **16.** 2 **17.** 6 **18.** 17 **21.** $\sqrt{10}$

Exercise 1.6

1. $2 + 2i$ **2.** $2 + 3i$ **3.** $2 + i$ **4.** $-2 + i$ **5.** $5 + 2i$ **6.** $3 - 4i$ **7.** $3 - 5i$

8. $2 - 3i$ **9.** $4 + 0i$ **10.** $0 - i$ **11.** $\frac{1}{2} + \frac{3}{2}i$ **12.** $\frac{6}{5} - \frac{8}{5}i$ **13.** $5 + i$ **14.** $3 - 5i$

15. (i) $2 + i$ (ii) $3 + i$ **16.** (i) $4 + 0i$ (ii) 6 **17.** -1 **18.** (i) yes   (ii) $3 + 4i$; 5

19. real $= 2$ and imaginary $= 3$

Exercise 1.7

1. $x = 5, y = 3$ **2.** $x = 6, y = -3$ **3.** $x = 2, y = 1$ **4.** $x = 3, y = 5$ **5.** $x = 2, y = 3$

6. $x = 1, y = 4$ **7.** $x = 2, y = -1$ **8.** $x = -4, y = 3$ **9.** $x = -2, y = 5$

10. $x = 5, y = -2$ **11.** $k = 3, l = 2$ **12.** $p = 4, q = -1$ **13.** $k = 2, t = 2$

14. $k = 12$ **15.** $k = -1, t = -5$ **16.** $p = 1, q = 2$ **17.** (i) $3 - 4i$ (ii) $k = -1, t = 2$

18. (ii) $k = -1, t = -3$ **19.** (ii) $p = 3, q = -1$ **20.** (i) $2 + 2i$ (ii) $a = 1, b = -4$

21. $s = 36, t = 2$ **22.** $x = 1, y = 3$ **23.** (i) $\frac{11 + 10i}{17}$ (ii) $p = 11, q = 5$ **24.** $a = 3, b = 1$

Exercise 1.8

1. $3 \pm 2i$ **2.** $1 \pm 3i$ **3.** $-2 \pm i$ **4.** $5 \pm 3i$ **5.** $-2 \pm 3i$ **6.** $5 \pm 4i$ **7.** $-1 \pm i$

8. $1 \pm 2i$ **9.** $-4 \pm i$ **10.** $\pm 2i$ **11.** $\pm 5i$ **12.** $\pm 3i$ **13.** $\frac{1}{2} \pm \frac{1}{2}i$ **14.** $\frac{3}{2} \pm \frac{1}{2}i$

15. $1 \pm \frac{1}{2}i$ **16.** $1 + 2i$ **17.** $2 + 5i$ **18.** $4 + 3i$ **19.** $-1 + 2i$ **20.** $-6 + i$

21. (i) $p = 2, k = 3$ (ii) yes   **22.** (i) $-2 + i$ (ii) $-2 - i$ **23.** $3 + 5i$ **24.** $x^2 + 4x + 5 = 0$

25. $x^2 - 2x + 2 = 0$ **26.** $x^2 + 2x + 10 = 0$ **27.** $x^2 - 6x + 34 = 0$ **28.** $x^2 + 16 = 0$

29. $x^2 + 1 = 0$ **30.** $p = -6, q = 34$ **31.** $a = -14, b = 50$ **32.** $m = 6, n = 18$

33. $k = 26$

Exercise 1.9

1. $x = 2 \pm 3i$ or $b^2 - 4ac = -36 < 0$ **2.** $x = -3 \pm 4i$ or $y = -2 \pm 4i$ or $b^2 - 4ac = -64 < 0$

3. $x = 1 \pm 2i$ or $y = -2 \pm 2i$ or $b^2 - 4ac = -16 < 0$ **4.** $x = 4 \pm 5i$ or $b^2 - 4ac = -100 < 0$

5. $x = \pm 3i$ or $b^2 - 4ac = -36 < 0$ **6.** $x = \pm 2i$ or $b^2 - 4ac = -16 < 0$

7. $x = -2 \pm 5i$ or $y = 2 \pm 5i$ or $b^2 - 4ac = -100 < 0$ **8.** $x = 3 \pm 5i$ or $y = 3 \pm 5i$ or $b^2 - 4ac = -100 < 0$

9. $x = 1 \pm i$ or $y = 1 \pm i$ or $b^2 - 4ac = -4 < 0$ **10.** $x = 1 \pm 4i$ or $y = \pm 4i$ or $b^2 - 4ac = -64 < 0$

11. $x = -2 \pm i$ or $y = 2 \pm i$ or $b^2 - 4ac = -4 < 0$ **12.** $x = -3 \pm i$ or $y = 3 \pm i$ or $b^2 - 4ac = -4 < 0$

13. $x = 4 \pm i$ or $y = 4 \pm i$ or $b^2 - 4ac = -4 < 0$ **14.** $x = 5 \pm 2i$ or $y = 5 \pm 2i$ or $b^2 - 4ac = -16 < 0$

15. (i) $x = -2 \pm 5i$ or $y = 1 \pm 5i$ or $b^2 - 4ac = -100 < 0$

16. (ii)

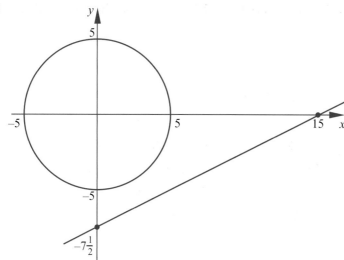

(iii) $x = -6 \pm 2i$ or $b^2 - 4ac = -16 < 0$ **17.** $x = 2 + 3i$ and $y = 2 - 3i$ or $x = 2 - 3i$ and $y = 2 + 3i$

18. $a = 5 + 2i$ and $b = 5 - 2i$ or $a = 5 - 2i$ and $b = 5 + 2i$

Exercise 1.10

1.

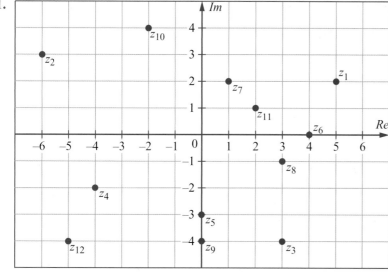

3. (i) -6 **(ii)** 2

Exercise 1.11

1. 5 **2.** 10 **3.** 13 **4.** 17 **5.** 26 **6.** 25 **7.** 29 **8.** 41 **9.** 3 **10.** $\sqrt{5}$

11. $\sqrt{61}$ **12.** 13 **13.** 10 **14.** 1 **15.** $\sqrt{2}$ **16.** $\sqrt{13}$ **18.** $\sqrt{10}$

20. $1 + i$; 2 **21.** no   **22.** yes   **23.** no   **24. (i)** $5 - 5i$ **25. (i)** $-21 + 20i$

26. (i) $22 + 4i$; $-2 + i$ **27.** $\frac{13}{10}$ or 1.3 **28. (i)** 5 **(ii)** $p = 3, q = 2$ **(iii)** $s = \frac{3}{25}, t = -\frac{4}{25}$

29. w, as $\sqrt{164} < 13$ **30. (i)** $x = 4$, $y = 3$ **31. (i)** $3 - 4i$ **(iii)** $h = 2$, $k = -\frac{2}{5}$

32. $a = 1$, $b = -2$ **34. (ii)** ± 4 **35.** ± 6 **36.** ± 2 **37.** ± 5 **38.** ± 4

Exercise 1.12

1. -1 **2.** $-i$ **3.** 1 **4.** i **5.** -1 **6.** $-i$ **7.** 1 **8.** -1 **9.** i **10.** 1

11. -1 **12.** $-i$ **13.** 2 **14.** $-3i$ **15. (i)** $-1 - 5i$ **(ii)** $-2 + 3i$ **(iii)** $6 - 2i$

18. (i) -1 **(ii)** $-i$ **(iii)** 1 **(iv)** -1 **19. (i)** -1 **(ii)** $-i$ **(iii)** 1 **(iv)** 1

Exercise 1.13

1. yes, both the same distance, 5, from the origin **2. (ii)** same as z **(iii)** central symmetry
    in the origin, $O(0, 0)$ **(iv)** z **(v)** rotation of $90°$ and $450°$ about the origin, $O(0, 0)$, maps
    (moves) a point to the position **(vi)** rotate by $90°$ and double its distance from the origin
    (in a straight line from the origin) or vice versa **(vii)** $5 > \sqrt{5}$

3. **(i)** $u = 4 + 2i$, $v = 2 + i$ **(ii)** $k = 2$ **(iii)** $l = \frac{1}{2}$ **(iv)** on the same straight through the origin
    with $2i^3 v$ twice as far as $-iv$ from the origin, $O(0, 0)$; $(2 - 4i = 2(1 - 2i))$

4. **(ii)** rotation of $360°$ about the origin maps (moves) a point to it original position **(iii)** yes; rotation
    of $180° =$ rotation of $-180°$ about the origin, $O(0, 0)$ **(iv)** rotate by $90°$ and treble its distance
    from the origin (in a straight line from the origin) or vice versa

5. **(iii)** no; $iz_1 = -4 + 2i$, $z_2 = 2 - 4i$ **(iv)** axial symmetry in the real axis **(v)** yes

6. **(iv)** circle; centre $= (2, 1)$ and radius $= 5$ **(v)** yes **(vi)** $5 + 5i$ **7. (i)** $1 + 2i$

8. **(i)** $z_1 = 2 + i$; $z_2 = -1 + 2i$; $z_3 = 4 + 2i$; $z_4 = 3 + 4i$ **(ii)** $k = 2$

9. **(i)** $z^2 = 0 + 2i$, $z^3 = -2 + 2i$ **(iii)**

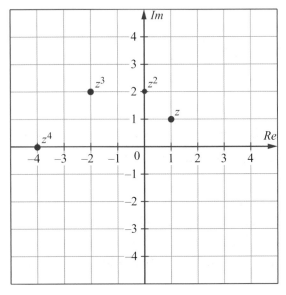

(iv) Each time z is multiplied by itself it
rotates by $45°$ about the origin and it also
moves further away from the origin by
$\sqrt{2}$ each time. If we keep multiplying z
by itself and join the points the curve will
look like a spiral.

(v) $z^8 = 16$, $z^{12} = -64$, $z^{16} = 256$

(vi) $z^{40} = (z^4)^{10} = (-4)^{10} = 1,048,572$ positive
number. Alternatively, (-4) to an even
exponent (power) will always be positive.

(vii) $z^{40} = (-2)^{20}$

(viii) $z^{41} = 1,048,576(1 + i)$ or $1,048,576 +$
$1,048,576i$

(ix) $(\sqrt{2})^{41}$ or $2^{20}\sqrt{2}$ or $1,048,576 \sqrt{2}$ or
$1,482,910.4$

Exercise 2.1

1. $\frac{1}{6}$; $16\frac{2}{3}\%$ 2. (i) $\frac{1}{10}$ (ii) €120

3. (i) (a) e: $\frac{1}{6}$ or $16\frac{2}{3}\%$; a: $\frac{1}{18}$ or $5\frac{5}{9}\%$; t: $\frac{1}{9}$ or $11\frac{1}{9}\%$ (b) e: more; a: less; t: more

   (ii) (a) e: $\frac{7}{66}$ or 10·6%; a: $\frac{4}{66}$ or 6·06%; t: $\frac{7}{66}$ or 10·6%   (b) e: less; a: less; t: more

4. (i) $\frac{5}{8}$ (ii) 144,000   5. €550   6. 27·2 km

Exercise 2.2

1. (i) €56; €24   (ii) 250 g; 200 g   2. (i) €120; €160; €200   (ii) €1,000; €1,600; €1,400
3. (i) 119 g; 34 g; 85 g   (ii) 72 cm; 54 cm; 36 cm   4. (i) €126; €168; €210
   (ii) 48 cm; 120 cm; 168 cm   5. (i) €102; €119; €153   (ii) 960 g; 120 g; 480 g   6. 3 : 4
7. 1 : 3   8. 2 : 1 : 4   9. 3 : 2 : 4   10. (i) €28; €14   (ii) 56 g; 224 g   11. (i) €60; €120; €30
   (ii) 39 cm; 156 cm; 390 cm   12. (i) 252 g; 168 g; 126 g   (ii) €240; €320; €360
13. Team A received €15,750; Team B received €12,250   14. €178,800
15. (i) 5 : 9 : 6   (ii) David €125, Eric €225, Fred €150   16. €120   17. 100 cm   18. 162 cm
19. (i) €30   (ii) €165   20. €10,160   21. 35 cm   22. €9,500   23. $k = 5$
24. (i) Roy: €320, Sam €120   (ii) 5 : 3

Exercise 2.3

1. (i) €9·60   (ii) €25·92   (iii) €26·04   2. €4,573·80   3. (i) €288   (ii) (a) €244·80   (b) 2%
4. 20%   5. 60%   6. €82   7. €10·08   8. (i) €1,200   (ii) €1,452   9. €72·80
10. €3,267   11. 700   12. 160   13. €14,000   14. €232,000   15. €1,560
16. €350,000   17. 2·8 litres   18. (i) 400   (ii) 700   19. €20   20. (i) €1,533   (ii) 18
21. (i) €260   (ii) €82·80   (iii) 42%   22. no   23. better offer   24. €6·35; €8·25; €15·88
25. less than

Exercise 2.4

1. 2; $\frac{1}{6}$; 16·7%   2. 3; $\frac{3}{43}$; 7·0%   3. 4; $\frac{1}{34}$; 2·9%   4. 0·2; $\frac{1}{24}$; 4·2%   5. 0·3; $\frac{1}{19}$; 5·3%
6. 10; $\frac{1}{39}$; 2·6%   7. (i) 0·15 m   (ii) 9·1%   8. (i) 2·5 kg   (ii) 3·7%   9. (i) 5 km
   (ii) $\frac{5}{105}$ or $\frac{1}{21}$ (iii) 4·8%   10. 5%   11. 5·44%   12. 2·3%   13. (i) $\frac{1}{10}$
   (ii) 1·64%   14. (i) 1,584 cm^3 (ii) 4·5%   15. 10·3%   16. (i) 4%   (ii) 0·8%
17. (i) 1%   (ii) 6,187·5 kg   (iii) 12,375 tins   (iv) €62·50

Exercise 2.5

1. 10; 14   2. 115; 125   3. 75%; 85%   4. 3·995 m; 4·005 m   5. €2,750; €3,650
6. −2; 8   7. 150 ± 3 sweets   8. (i) 0·2 m or 20 cm
9. (i) 30,000 cm^3 (ii) 29,601 cm^3; 30,401 cm^3 (iii) 6·4 kg

Exercise 2.6

1. (i) $257·50 (ii) €600   2. €50   3. (i) ¥72,960 (ii) €380   4. South Africa; €30

5. (i) R11,000 (ii) R750   6. (i) €8·10 (ii) $1\frac{1}{2}$%   7. €3,587·50   8. (i) €48 (ii) 2%

9. $2\frac{1}{2}$%   10. $880   11. €140   12. (i) 30% (ii) 24·8%

Exercise 2.7

1. €1,996·80   2. €2,173·50   3. €2,837·25   4. €6,492·80   5. €248·25

6. €306·04   7. €1,664·39   8. €6,151·25   9. €368   10. €1,755·52   11. €8,234·85

Exercise 2.8

1. €24,812·48   2. €26,981·76   3. €12,624·60   4. 3%   5. 4%   6. $3\frac{1}{2}$%

7. $2\frac{1}{2}$%   8. (i) 5% (ii) $4\frac{1}{2}$%   9. (i) €62,400 (ii) 3%   10. (i) €43,056 (ii) $2\frac{1}{2}$%

11. (i) €22,950 (ii) 3%   12. (i) €10,868 (ii) 3%   13. (i) €68,500 (ii) $3\frac{1}{2}$%

14. (i) €33,075 (ii) €8,075   15. €7,120   16. w = €5,600   17. w = €4,450

Exercise 2.9

1. €18,423·75   2. €36,085·50   3. (i) €74,290 (ii) €25,710

4. (i)

Years after purchase	0	1	2	3	4
Value of car (€)	50,000	40,000	32,000	25,600	20,480

(ii)

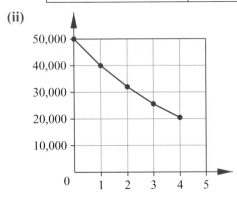

5. (i) 8% (ii) €17,910

Exercise 2.10

1. €29,549·11   2. €19,661·94   3. €45,551·48   4. €29,255·87 5. €5,955·08

6. €15,315·38   7. €7,813·56   8. €4,415·25   9. (i) (a) €20 (b) €20·50

(ii) 10%; 10·25% (iii) €20·76   10. (i) €110 (ii) €112·36 (iii) €112·62

(iv) 10%; 12·36%; 12·62%   11. (i) €1,195·62 (ii) 19·6%

12. (i) $P = \dfrac{F}{(1+i)^t}$ (ii) €50,000   13. €200,000   14. (i) 1·046% (ii) €1,882·32   16. 1·02%

Exercise 2.11

1. (i) 30 mins (ii) 36 mins (iii) 6 mins (iv) 42 mins (v) 24 mins

2. (i) 1 hr 12 mins (ii) 2 hrs 45 mins (iii) 3 hrs 21 mins (iv) 1 hr 20 mins (v) 2 hrs 27 mins

3. (i) $\frac{1}{4}$ hr or 0·25 hr (ii) $\frac{1}{3}$ hr or 0·$\dot{3}$ hr (iii) $1\frac{1}{2}$ hrs or 1·5 hrs (iv) $2\frac{3}{4}$ hrs or 2·75 hrs

   (v) $3\frac{2}{5}$ hrs or 3·4 hrs 4. 80 km/h 5. 1 hr 45 mins 6. 150 km 7. 15:29

8. (i) 1 hr 15 mins (ii) 12:30 (iii) €7·75 9. 64 km/h 10. 4 m/s 11. 18:30

12. (i) $4\frac{1}{4}$ hrs or 4·25 hrs (ii) 60 km/h 13. 72 km/h 14. 91 km 15. 08:35

16. (i) 18 m/s (ii) 64·8 km/h 17. 21 mins 18. 14·25 km or 14,250 m 19. 09:05

20. 200 m race 21. 32 km/h 22. 29·4 km 23. (i) 8·67 m/s; 8·82 m/s; 8·88 m/s; 8·92 m/s

    (ii) 8·82 m/s 24. 54 km/h 25. (i) 280 km (ii) 5 hrs (iii) 56 km/h

26. (i) 6 hrs (ii) 462 km (iii) 77 km/h 27. (i) 4 hrs (ii) 260 km (iii) 65 km/h

28. 90 km/h 29. (i) 504 km (ii) 8 hrs (iii) 63 km/h 30. (i) 55 km/h (ii) 66 km/h

    (iii) 11 hrs; 660 km (iv) 60 km/h

Exercise 2.12

1. €160 2. €350 3. €920 4. €260 5. €620 6. €0 7. €9,020 8. €5,420

9. €190 10. €150 11. €359·28 12. €1,278·80 13. €2,118·80 14. €5,618·80

15. €16,118·80 16. €80·20 17. (i) Alex: €4,000; Bruce: €4,550 (ii) Alex: €0; Bruce: €91

    (iv) €18

Exercise 2.13

1. (i) €11,100 (ii) €7,300 2. (i) €9,960 (ii) €7,470 3. (i) €9,370 (ii) €6,130

4. (i) €11,876·50 (ii) €8,726·50 5. 20% 6. 18% 7. (i) €19,000 (ii) €48,000

8. (i) €23,500 (ii) €52,000

Exercise 2.14

1. gross tax: €2,000; USC: €200; take-home pay: €9,300

2. gross tax: €11,600; USC: €2,120; take-home pay: €35,480

3. gross tax: €20,400; USC: €4,220; take-home pay: €55,380

4. gross tax: €41,600; USC: €6,620; take-home pay: €76,580

5. gross tax: €3,150; USC: €399·28; take-home pay: €14,600·72

6. gross tax: €9,980; USC: €1,978·80; take-home pay: €31,041·20

7. gross tax: €55,900; USC: €9,818·80; take-home pay: €90,381·20

8. gross tax: €117,400; USC: €20,318·80; take-home pay: €169,781·20

Exercise 2.15

1. 8×10^3 2. $5·4 \times 10^4$ 3. $3·47 \times 10^5$ 4. $4·7 \times 10^2$ 5. $2·9 \times 10^3$ 6. $3·4 \times 10^6$

7. $3·94 \times 10^2$ 8. $3·9 \times 10^1$ 9. 6×10^{-3} 10. 9×10^{-4} 11. $5·2 \times 10^{-2}$

12. 4.32×10^{-4} **13.** 4.2×10^3 **14.** 7.8×10^4 **15.** 3.2×10^{-2} **16.** 4.5×10^{-3}
17. $n = 3$ **18.** $n = 4$ **19.** $n = -2$

Exercise 2.16

1. 3.2×10^3 **2.** 2.8×10^6 **3.** 5.2×10^5 **4.** 2.3×10^4 **5.** 7.8×10^{-3}
6. 2.94×10^{-4} **7.** 7.2×10^7 **8.** 3.6×10^7 **9.** 7.48×10^5 **10.** 9.54×10^6
11. 2.3×10^3 **12.** 1.4×10^5 **13.** 2.4×10^3 **14.** 5.8×10^3 **15.** 1.5×10^5
16. 2.8×10^{-4} **17.** 3.51×10^6 **18.** 5.4×10^3 **19.** 3×10^3 **20.** 5×10^2
21. 1.52×10^2 **22.** 2.8×10^3 **23.** 0·078; less   **24.** 0·2; greater   **25.** $k = 20$

Exercise 2.17

1. (i) €25,872 (ii) €18,815   **2.** 1,398   **3.** (i) €574,349·12 (ii) €768,608·68
  (iii) 40 years   **5.** €186   **6.** (ii) €2,665·84 (iii) 2·8%
7. (i) $11\frac{1}{2}$ hours (ii) €86·25   **8.** (i) €390 (ii) 15–21 days before departure (iii) €1,260
9. (i) €48·40 (ii) €58·56   **10.** brand C   **11.** 2.8×10^{-6} mm²   **12.** (i) 1.5×10^{-2} m
  (ii) 5×10^{-11} seconds   **13.** 7.6×10^{-3} **14.** (i) 1.44×10^6 (ii) 3,550
15. (i) 1.44×10^8 km (ii) 2.19×10^{19} km (iii) 2.3×10^6 years   **16.** 8.8×10^6 tonnes
17. 2×10^5 **18.** 11 people per square km   **19.** (i) 1.2×10^{-2} cm (ii) 3.4992×10^9
  (iii) 420 km   **20.** 1.68×10^7 **21.** 320 times   **22.** 6.37×10^3 km   **23.** 2.05×10^7
24. 200 or 2×10^2 **25.** $k = 3 \times 10^4$ **26.** 3.64×10^{14} m²   **27.** 2.5×10^4 cm

Exercise 3.1

1. discrete   **3.** continuous   **5.** discrete   **9.** categorical   **12.** continuous   **15.** ordinal

Exercise 4.1

1. mean = 4; mode = 3; median = 3   **2.** mean = 6; mode = 4; median = 5
3. mean = 6·3; mode = no mode; median = 6·4   **4.** mean = 4·7; mode = no mode; median = 4·35
5. (i) (a) €5·06 (b) €5·15   **6.** 45   **7.** 9; 8   **8.** 2   **9.** 11   **10.** $3a + 5$
11. (i) 2 or 3 (ii) 3   **12.** median = 7 as it's the highest   **13.** (i) mean = €50; median = €40;
  mode = €34
14. (i) (a) mean = 21·9 (b) median = 21·5 (c) mode = 22

Exercise 4.2

1. (i) 2 (ii) 1 (iii) 2   **2.** (i) 3 (ii) 1 (iii) 3   **3.** (i) 8 (ii) 7 (iii) 7
4. (i) 14 (ii) 14 (iii) 14   **5.** (i) 3 (ii) 2 (iii) 2   **6.** (i) 12·75 (ii) 12 (iii) 12·5
7. (i) 3 (ii) 4 (iii) 3·25 (iv) 3·3   **8.** (ii) 4 (iii) 4 (iv) 5 (v) 40% (vi) 200 (vii) 6

9. (i)

No. of people	2	3	4	5	6	7	8
Frequency	14	24	20	10	8	4	2

(ii) 4 median, 3 mode   (iii) 322   (iv) 3·9

Exercise 4.3

1. 3; 2−4; 0−2   2. 10; 9−13; 5−9   3. 54; 40−60; 40−60   4. 10; 6−12; 12−20
5. 29; 15−35; 15−35   6. 22; 20−35; 20−35   7. 117; 60−120; 60−120
8. 20; 15−25; 15−25   10. (i) 36   (ii) 31   (iii) 90   (iv) 30−40   (v) 40−50

Exercise 4.4

1. 1·41   2. 3·06   3. 1·87   4. 1·63   5. 2·45   6. 4·24   7. 3·87   8. 2·65
9. 2·73   10. $k = 2$ 11. $\sqrt{5·2} = \sqrt{5·2}$ 14. 1·5   15. (i) 2·37; 4·90   (ii) X has a
smaller standard deviation, which means values deviate from each other and from the mean less.
16. (i) Q, R (ii) P (iii) P (iv) {4, 4, 4, 4, 4, 4, 4, 4, 4, 4, 4, 4}   (v) 4
17. (i) $\sigma = 0$ implies that each fish caught by Bren is equal to the mean = 2   (ii) agree – as Hailey
has the largest mean and standard deviation   (iii) 4·1   18. (i) 62   (ii) 74   (iii) 56   (iv) 44
19. 0·02125

Exercise 4.5

1. 3, 1·21, discrete   2. 8, 3·02, discrete   3. 11, 4·36, continuous   4. 35, 20·37, continuous
5. (i) 4−12, continuous   (iii) 13   (iv) 8·54   6. (i) 40, 14·8   (ii) 1   7. (i) 6−8
(ii) continuous   (iii) 6, 2·9   (iv) 95

Exercise 4.7

1. (ii) 170   (iii) 103   2. (i) 24, 16, 42, 40, 12   (ii) 40−60   (iii) 134 × €50,000 = €6,700,000
3. (ii) (a) 8   (b) 3·56   (iii) 68%   4. (ii) (a) mean = 24   (b) $\sigma = 12$ (iii) yes, impossible
(iv) €108 − €150

Exercise 4.8

1. (i) 5·9 minutes   (ii) 0·59 m   (iii) 0·059 g   3. (ii) modal grade B
4. (i) 35   (iii) (a) 48   (b) 22   (c) 10   (d) 29   (e) 19   (iv) 22
5. (ii) girls performed better on test   6. left-hand key missing; Physics/Maths?; missing two
   students on RHS; missing one student on LHS; scores 66 and 64 not ordered
7. (ii) (a) 71·5   (b) 100·5   (iii) (a) 63   (b) 76   (v) have similar statistics for non-factory workers

Exercise 4.9

1. (ii) (11, 65)   2. (iii) €115   3. (iii) Nora   (iv) 4 min. rate for Nora
4. $P \to B$, $Q \to A$, $R \to C$ 5. (iii) (a) 17°C   (b) 5°C

Exercise 4.10

1. (i) (e)   (ii) (d)   (iii) (b)   (iv) (c)   (v) (a)   2. (ii) positively skewed
3. (i) no   (ii) negatively skewed   (iii) bimodal   4. (i) positively skewed   (ii) unimodal
5. (i) positively skewed   (ii) unimodal   (iii) 12·5   (iv) 16   6. (ii) multimodal

Exercise 4.11

1. (ii) (c)   (iii) (c)   2. (ii) moderate correlation   (iii) (a) B (b) D (c) no obvious outliers
3. (iii) Trip B   4. (i) none   (ii) strong negative   (iii) moderate skewed positive

Exercise 4.12

3. hypothesis is false
5. (ii) mean = 170, standard deviation = 2; from 168−172 is 80%, so hypothesis is false

Exercise 4.13

1. (ii) (c)   (iv) 39   3. (i) 42 years   (ii) 9·3 g   (iv) negative

Exercise 4.14

1. 5   2. 2   3. (i) 8   (ii) 30   4. (i) 6   5. 2

Exercise 4.15

2. – Second bar is much wider than first.
   – Vertical scale does not begin at zero.
   – Vertical scale jumps from 600 to 800 instead of 650.
5. Yes. They have included the €180,000 salary in the statistics to increase the mean, even though the new employee will most likely only receive €40,000.

Exercise 5.1

1. (i) 64 cm   (ii) 240 cm^2 2. (i) 60 cm   (ii) 225 cm^2 3. (i) 24 cm   (ii) 24 cm^2
4. (i) 94·2 cm   (ii) 706·5 cm^2 5. (i) 35·7 cm   (ii) 78·5 cm^2 6. (i) 52·56 cm   (ii) 125·6 cm^2
7. (i) 56 cm   (ii) 144 cm^2 8. (i) 68 cm   (ii) 290 cm^2 9. (i) 80 cm   (ii) 280 cm^2
10. 24 m^2 11. 276 m^2 12. 60 cm^2 13. 3,000 cm^2 14. (i) $10\sqrt{3}$ (ii) 17·3 cm^2
15. (i) $16\sqrt{3}$ (ii) 27·7 cm^2 16. (i) $6\sqrt{5}$ (ii) 13·4 cm^2 17. 24 cm^2 18. 19·5 cm^2
19. 23·4 cm^2 20. 108 cm^2 21. 251·3 cm^2 22. 86 cm^2
23. (i) 16 cm   (ii) 128π cm^2 (iii) 50%   24. (i) 420 cm^2 (ii) 29 cm
25. (i) 72 cm   (ii) 324 cm^2 26. 513π cm^2 27. 71.5 cm   28. 19 cm   29. 400 m
30. (i) 100 m   (ii) D (iii) 7·3 m/sec   31. $540 - 80\pi$ cm^2

Exercise 5.2

1. (i) 23 cm   (ii) 483 cm^2 2. (i) 8 cm   (ii) 96 cm   3. (i) 81 cm^2 (ii) 20 cm
4. 8 cm   5. 15 m   6. 8 cm; 96 cm^2 7. 675 m^2 8. 16 m by 8 m

	π	Circumference	Area	Radius
9.	π	10π cm	25π cm^2	5 cm
10.	π	6π m	9π m^2	3 m
11.	π	5π cm	$6\cdot25\pi$ cm^2	2·5 cm
12.	$\frac{22}{7}$	264 cm	5,544 cm^2	42 cm
13.	$\frac{22}{7}$	88 m	616 m^2	14 m
14.	3·14	157 mm	1,962·5 mm^2	25 mm
15.	3·14	125·6 m	1,256 m^2	20 m
16.	π	11π cm	$30\cdot25\pi$ cm^2	5·5 cm
17.	$\frac{22}{7}$	66 m	346·5 m^2	10·5 m
18.	3·14	75·36 cm	452·16 cm^2	12 cm

19. 49 cm **20.** 21 cm **21.** (i) 41 cm (ii) 100 cm^2 **22.** 39π cm^2 **23.** 10 cm
24. 6 cm **25.** 6·5 cm **26.** 9 cm

Exercise 5.3

1. (i) 120 cm^3 (ii) 148 cm^2 **2.** (i) 576 m^3 (ii) 432 m^2 **3.** (i) 1,260 mm^3 (ii) 766 mm^2
4. (i) 5 cm (ii) 392 cm^2 **5.** 525 litres **6.** (i) 8 cm (ii) 860 cm^2 **7.** 576 **8.** 54 cm^2
9. 96 cm^2 **10.** 8 cm^3 **11.** 125 cm^3 **12.** 8 cm by 12 cm by 28 cm; 1,312 cm^2
13. (i) 9 cm (ii) 270 cm^3 **14.** (i) €12,000 (ii) 96 (iii) €25
15. (i) 1·5 cm (ii) 171 cm^2 (iii) 150

Exercise 5.4

1. 400 cm^3 **2.** 8,160 cm^3 **3.** 864 cm^3 **4.** 400 cm^3 **5.** 1,350 cm^3 **6.** 3,840 cm^3
7. 133·2 cm^3 **8.** 121 cm^3 **9.** 1,119 cm^3 **10.** (i) 240 cm^2 (ii) 96,000 cm^3
11. 1·44 m^3 **12.** (i) 3,480 m^3 (ii) 5 hours 48 minutes (iii) €41·76 **13.** (i) 6 cm^2 (ii) 20

Exercise 5.5

	π	Radius	Height	Volume	Curved surface area	Total surface area
1.	$\frac{22}{7}$	7 cm	12 cm	1,848 cm^3	528 cm^2	836 cm^2
2.	3·14	15 cm	40 cm	28,260 cm^3	3,768 cm^2	5,181 cm^2
3.	π	8 mm	11 mm	704π mm^3	176π mm^2	304π mm^2
4.	$\frac{22}{7}$	3·5 m	10 m	385 m^3	220 m^2	297 m^2
5.	3·14	12 cm	40 cm	18,086·4 cm^3	3,014·4 cm^2	3,918·72 cm^2
6.	π	13 mm	30 mm	$5,070\pi$ mm^3	780π mm^2	$1,118\pi$ mm^2

	π	Radius	Volume	Curved surface area
7.	$\frac{22}{7}$	21 cm	38,808 cm^3	5,544 cm^2
8.	3·14	9 m	3,052·08 m^3	1,017·36 m^2
9.	π	6 mm	288π mm^3	144π mm^2
10.	$\frac{22}{7}$	10·5 cm	4,851 cm^3	1,386 cm^2
11.	3·14	7·5 cm	1,766·25 cm^3	706·5 cm^2
12.	π	1·5 m	4·5π m^3	9π m^2

	π	Radius	Volume	Curved surface area	Total surface area
13.	π	15 mm	2,250π mm^3	450π mm^2	675π mm^2
14.	π	$1\frac{1}{2}$ cm	$\frac{9}{4}\pi$ cm^3	$\frac{9}{2}\pi$ cm^2	$\frac{27}{4}\pi$ cm^2
15.	$\frac{22}{7}$	42 cm	155,232 cm^3	11,088 cm^2	16,632 cm^2
16.	3·14	12 m	3,617·28 m^3	904·32 m^2	1,356·48 m^2

17. 24,492 cm^3 18. (i) 576 m^2 (ii) 2·4 m^2 (iii) 3·75%   19. 9
20. (i) 19,800 cm^3 (ii) 4,851 cm^3 (iii) 14,949 cm^3

Exercise 5.6

	π	Radius	Height	Slant height	Volume	Curved surface area
1.	π	8 cm	6 cm	10 cm	128π cm^3	80π cm^2
2.	$\frac{22}{7}$	21 mm	20 mm	29 mm	9,240 mm^3	1,914 mm^2
3.	3·14	3 cm	4 cm	5 cm	37·68 cm^3	47·1 cm^2
4.	π	1·5 m	2 m	2·5 m	1·5π m^3	3·75π m^2
5.	3·14	40 cm	9 cm	41 cm	15,072 cm^3	5,149·6 cm^2
6.	π	8 m	15 m	17 m	320π m^3	136π m^2
7.	$\frac{22}{7}$	2·8 cm	4·5 cm	5·3 cm	36·96 cm^3	46·64 cm^2
8.	π	4·8 mm	1·4 mm	5 mm	10·752π mm^3	24π mm^2
9.	π	12 m	35 m	37 m	1,680π m^3	444π m^2
10.	3·14	11 cm	60 cm	61 cm	7,598·8 cm^3	2,106·94 cm^2

11. (i) $123\frac{1}{5}$ cm^3 (ii) $316\frac{4}{5}$ cm^2 12. (i) 5,510·7 cm^3 (ii) 2,387·97 cm^2
13. (i) 720π cm^3 (ii) (a) 10 cm   (b) $213\frac{1}{3}\pi$ cm^3 (c) $506\frac{2}{3}\pi$ cm^3
14. (i) 4 cm   (ii) 234·5 cm^3 (iii) 135·6 cm^3
15. (i) 2·4 cm   (ii) 42·24 cm^3 (iii) 617·76 cm^3
16. (i) πx^3 cm^3 (ii) 2 : 1   17. (i) 32π cm^3 (ii) 6 minutes

Exercise 5.7

2. 36π cm^3 **3. (i)** 936π m^3 **(ii)** 360π m^2 **4.** $4\cdot1$, $1{,}944\pi$ cm^3; 549π cm^2

5. (i) $795\cdot048$ cm^3 **(ii)** $431\cdot436$ cm^2 **6. (i)** $9{,}800$ cm^2 **(iii)** $2{,}502{,}218$ cm^3

7. (iii) $5\cdot02$ cm^3 **(iv)** 265 **8. (i)** 180 litres **(ii)** 268 litres **(iii)** 88 litres

9. (i) 15 m^2 **(ii)** $123\cdot75$ m^3 **10. (i)** $38{,}676$ cm^3

11. (i) $350{,}000\pi$ m^3 **(ii)** $2{,}500\pi$ m^3 **(iii)** $\frac{5}{7}\%$

Exercise 5.8

1. (i) 20 cm **(ii)** 240π cm^2 **2. (i)** 6 cm **(ii)** 288π cm^3 **3.** 15 cm

4. (i) 3 cm **(ii)** 36π cm^2 **5. (i)** 4 cm **(ii)** 80π cm^2 **6. (i)** 20 cm **(ii)** $1{,}570$ cm^3

7. (i) $3\frac{1}{2}$ m **(ii)** 341 m^2 **8. (i)** 10 cm **(ii)** 96π cm^3 **9.** 10 cm

10. (i) 2 cm **(ii)** $35\cdot2$ cm^2 **11. (i)** 4 m **(ii)** $301\cdot44$ m^2 **12.** 45 cm

13. (i) $2\cdot1$ m **(ii)** $0\cdot81\pi$ m^3 **(iii)** $0\cdot096\pi$ m^3

14. (i) $\frac{250}{3}\pi$ cm^3 **(ii)** $\frac{25}{3}h\pi$ cm^3 **(iii)** 12 cm   **15. (i)** $\frac{3{,}087}{2}\pi$ cm^3 **(ii)** 42 cm

16. (i) $\frac{243}{4}\pi$ cm^3 **(ii)** 405π cm^3

Exercise 5.9

1. $h = 9$ cm   **2.** $r = 2$ cm   **3.** $r = 6$ cm   **4.** $h = 18$ cm   **5.** $r = 5$ cm   **6.** $h = 7\frac{1}{2}$ cm

7. 20 cm   **8. (i)** $30{,}375\pi$ cm^2 **(ii)** $22\cdot5$ cm   **9.** 8 cm   **10. (i)** $\frac{32}{3}\pi$ cm^3

  (ii) 150π cm^3 **(iii)** $0\cdot43$ cm   **11.** 400 **12. (i)** 3 cm **(iv)** 2 cm   **13. (i)** $121\cdot5\pi$ cm^3

  (ii) $3\cdot4$ cm   **14. (i)** $300{,}000\pi$ cm^3 **(ii)** $28{,}125$ **(iii)** 1 cm   **15. (i)** $l = 8$ m

  (ii) 32 minutes   **16.** 20 cm   **17. (i)** $4\cdot5\pi$ cm^3 **(ii) (a)** $1\cdot5$ cm, 12 cm **(b)** 27π cm^3

  (c) $\frac{2}{3}$ **18. (i)** 6 **(ii)** 972 cm^3 **(iii)** $1\cdot3$ g   **19. (i)** 509 mm^3 **(ii) (a)** 48 mm **(b)** 18 mm

  (c) 20 mm **(iii)** $17{,}280$ mm^3 **(iv)** $5{,}064$ mm^3 **20. (i)** 66 cm^3 **(ii)** 52 **21. (i)** $3{,}920\pi$ cm^3

  (ii) 144π cm^3 **(iii)** 9 cm **(iv)** 27 **22. (i)** $1\cdot75$ m **(iii)** approximately 9 m^3

Exercise 5.10

1. 228 m^2 **2.** 750 m^2 **3.** 416 m^2 **4.** 464 m^2 **5.** 195 m^2 **6.** $265\cdot5$ m^2 **7.** 5 m

8. 5 cm   **9.** $\frac{47}{3}$ **10.** $19\cdot76$; $79\cdot04$ m   **11. (i)** $3{,}600$ m^2 **(ii)** 50%

12. (i) 12 cm **(ii)** $(0, 5, 7, 4, 0)$; 48 cm^2 **13. (i)** 747 m^2 **(ii)** €$28{,}386$ **14. (i)** $74\cdot75$ cm^2

(ii) $78\cdot5$ cm^2 **(iii)** $3\cdot75$ cm^2 **(v)** 5% **(vi)** $76\cdot2$ cm^2 **15. (i)** $45\cdot6$ m^2 **(ii)** 285 m^2

16. (i) $27\cdot4$ m^2 **(ii) (a)** 822 m^3 **(b)** $822{,}000$ litres   **17. (ii)** $52\cdot5$ sq. units **(iii)** $1\cdot6\%$

18. (i) $x = 3$, $y = 4\frac{1}{2}$ **(ii) (a)** 47 cm^2 **(b)** 23 km^2

19. heights $\left\{7, 6\frac{1}{2}, 7\frac{1}{2}, 8, 5\frac{1}{2}, 0\right\}$, area approx 93 cm^2

Exercise 5.11

1. (2, E), (3, A), (4, F), (5, B), (6, D)

2. (i)   (ii) 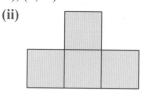   (iii)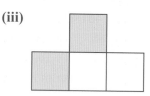

5. (i) five faces   (ii) six vertices   (iii) (a) 336 cm^2 (b) 288 cm^3 6. (i) pyramid
(ii) triangular prism   7. (ii) (a) 46,400 cm^2 (b) 4·64 m^2 8. (i) 26,400 cm^2
(ii) (a) 378,000 cm^3 (b) 0·378 m^3 (c) 378 litres   10. (i) (a) cuboid   (b) tetrahedron
(c) cylinder   (ii) (a) 160 cm^2 (b) 36√3 cm^2 (c) 1,188 cm^2 (iii) (a) 144 cm^3 (c) 3,080 cm^3
11. (i) cylinder   (ii) $h = 8$ cm, $x = 62·8$ cm   12. 4,060 cm^3

Exercise 6.1

1. $A = 110°$ 2. $B = 80°, C = 100°, D = 135°$ 3. $E = 65°$ 4. $x = 55°, y = 125°$
5. $a = 20°$ 6. $x = 120°$ 7. $X = 65°, Y = 65°$ 8. $A = 60°, Q = 50°, R = 50°, S = 70°$
9. $P = 90°$ 10. (i) 110°   (ii) 70°   (iii) 40°   11. (i) 50°   (ii) 50°   (iii) 85°   (iv) 45°
12. (i) 125°   (ii) 25°   (iii) 30°   (iv) 30°   13. (i) 66°   (ii) 24°   14. 40°
19. (i) 45°   (ii) 60°   (iii) 105°   23. (i) (a) 110°   (b) 70°

Exercise 6.2

2. $\angle PRQ$ 3. [AB]   4. [EF]   5. [PR]   19. [AB], [AD], [BD], [BC], [CD]
20. 10 cm   21. 9 cm   22. (i) $2 < k < 10$ (ii) $4 < k < 10$ (iii) $3 < k < 13$
23. $a = 2, b = 18$; min $= 3$, max $= 17$ 24. (i) $2 < x < 10$ (ii) $6 < d < 14$

Exercise 6.3

2. 5   3. 13   4. 8   5. 7   6. 20   7. 40   8. 34   9. 12   10. 11   11. 16
12. 5   13. 2   14. 4   15. 3   16. 2   17. 14   18. √13   19. √41   20. √24
21. √11   22. 2   23. 4   24. 5   25. 4   27. (i), (ii), (iv) and (v) are right-angled
28. (i) 4   (ii) 32   29. (i) 4 cm   (ii) 40 cm^2 30. (i) 12 cm   (ii) 180 cm^2
31. (i) 15 cm   (ii) 300 cm^2 32. $A = 20$ cm^2; $B = 9$ cm^2 33. 4·8 m
34. (i) 90°   (ii) 10 cm   35. $x = 15; y = 8$ 36. (i) 3 cm   (ii) 9 cm   (iii) 12 cm   (iv) 13 cm
37. 78 mm   38. 9·6 m   39. (i) 100 cm   (ii) 625 cm^2 40. 18 cm   41. (i) 54 m
(ii) perimeter; 10·5 seconds   42. (i) (a) 9·6 km   (b) 48 km   (ii) (a) 6,000 s   (b) 100 min
(c) $1\frac{2}{3}$ hrs   43. (i) 13 cm   (ii) 15 cm   (iii) 15·81 cm   44. 21 cm   45. 1
46. (i) 18 cm^2 (ii) 6 cm   49. (i) right angle   (ii) obtuse angle   (iii) acute angle

Exercise 6.4

1. 12 cm^2 2. 40 cm^2 3. 120 cm^2 4. 27 cm^2 5. 14 cm^2 6. 8·1 cm

7. 10 cm   8. 8 cm   9. 5 cm   10. (i) 22 cm   (ii) 24 cm^2 11. (i) 30 cm   (ii) 48 cm^2

12. (i) 34 cm   (ii) 50 cm^2 13. (i) 40 cm   (ii) 72 cm^2 14. (i) 44 cm   (ii) 88 cm^2

15. (i) 52 cm   (ii) 144 cm^2 16. 8 cm   17. 5 cm   18. 6 cm   19. (i) 8 cm   (ii) 80 cm^2

20. (i) 12 cm   (ii) 180 cm^2 21. (i) 40 cm   (ii) 2,000 cm^2 22. 12 m   23. (i) 23 cm

(ii) 483 cm^2 24. (i) 4   (ii) 32   (iii) 6·4   (iv) 26   25. 40 m^2 26. 8 cm

27. (ii) 75 sq. units   (iii) 5 units   28. 30   29. 204   30. 360   31. 43,200 m^2

32. (i) (a) 5   (b) $\dfrac{5}{13}$ (ii) (a) 30   (b) 30   (c) 30   33. (i) 10   (ii) 6   (iii) $\dfrac{6}{10}$ or $\dfrac{3}{5}$

(iv) (a) 48   (b) 48   (c) 48   34. (ii) 8 cm   (iii) (a) $\dfrac{8}{10}$ or $\dfrac{4}{5}$ (b) $\dfrac{8}{17}$ (v) 16·8 cm

Exercise 6.5

1. $x = 8, y = 7$ 2. $a = 5, b = 4$ 3. $x = 2, y = 11$ 4. $a = 4, b = 2$

5. (i) transversals   (ii) (a) 5   (b) 6   6. (i) 7 cm   (ii) 8 cm   (iii) 224 cm^2

7. (i) (a) 0·6 m   (b) 1 m   (ii) (b) 0·96 m^2 8. (iii) 10 cm   (iv) 12 cm   (v) 300 cm^2

(vi) 25 cm

Exercise 6.7

1. $a = 90°, b = 20°$ 2. $C = 35°, D = 125°$ 3. $x = 90°, y = 18°$ 4. $x = 50°$ 5. $x = 60°$

6. $x = 60°, y = 30°$ 7. $a = 65°, b = 90°, c = 25°$ 8. $x = 45°$ 9. $x = 20°$

10. (i) 70°   (ii) 50°   (iii) 50°   11. (i) 60°   (ii) 75°   12. 6 cm   13. 17 cm

14. 18 cm   15. 6 cm   16. (i) 15 cm   (ii) 17 cm   (iii) 120 cm^2 17. (i) 24 cm

(ii) 25 cm   (iii) 168 cm^2 18. (i) 9 cm   (iii) 609 cm^2 19. (i) 6·4 m   20. (i) 60 cm

(ii) 72 cm   (iii) 2,160 cm^2 (iv) 19·11%   21. (i) 15 cm   (ii) 9 cm   (iii) 12 cm

(iv) 648 cm^2 22. 24 cm   24. (i) 20 cm   (ii) 12 cm   25. (i) 13   (iii) 12   (iv) $\dfrac{5}{12}$; 23°

(v) (a) 67°   (b) 34°   26. (ii) (a) 180°   (b) 90°   (c) 90°   (iii) right angle

Exercise 6.8

14. (iii) (a) 2   (b) 3   (c) 9   15. $p = 8$ cm, $q = 10$ cm   16. $p = 7$ cm, $q = 6$ cm

17. $p = 12$ cm, $q = 6$ cm   18. $p = 25$ cm, $q = 16$ cm   19. $p = 8$ cm, $q = 15$ cm

20. $p = 6$ cm, $q = 10$ cm   21. $p = 20$ cm, $q = 9$ cm   22. $p = 8$ cm, $q = 6$ cm

23. $p = 12$ cm, $q = 6$ cm   24. $p = 6$ cm, $q = 15$ cm   25. (i) 75°   (ii) (a) 10 cm   (b) 18 cm

26. (ii) 9 cm   (iii) (a) 6 cm   (b) 4 cm   (c) 4 cm   27. (ii) 15 cm   (iii) (a) 22·5 cm

(b) 7·5 cm   (c) 20 cm   28. (ii) 8 cm   (iii) (a) 18 cm   (b) 6 cm   (iv) 9 cm

29. (i) 15 cm   (ii) 6 cm   (iii) 24 cm   (iv) 27 cm   30. (ii) (a) 2 cm   (b) 7·5 cm

33. (iii) (a) 5 m^2 (b) 15 m^2

Exercise 6.9

1. 16 m   2. 16 m   3. 15 m   4. 96 cm   5. (i) 18 m   6. (i) 32 m

7. (i) 14·4 m   (ii) (a) 9·6 m   (b) 1·4 m   8. 15 m

Exercise 6.10

1. (i) O (ii) 2   (iii) (a) 6   (b) 2   (iv) 12   2. (i) 6   (ii) 8   (iii) 27·45

3. (i) 3   (ii) 10   (iii) 6   (iv) 37·5   4. (i) O (ii) (a) 4   (b) 2   (c) $\dfrac{1}{16}$

5. (i) 2   (ii) 6 cm   (iii) 15 cm^2 (iv) 45 cm^2 6. (i) 2·5   (ii) 2·7   (iii) 2 : 5   (iv) 2

7. (i) 2·25   (ii) 12·5   (iii) 20   8. (i) $\dfrac{3}{5}$ (ii) 31·5   (iii) 56   9. (i) (2, 1), (5, 1), (5, 5)

(ii) $P(6, 3)$, $Q(15, 3)$, $R(15, 15)$ (iii) (a) 5   (b) 15   (c) 1 : 3   (iv) 9 : 1

10. (ii) 3 : 2   (iii) 3 : 2   (iv) 9 : 4   11. €1,024   12. 7   13. 72 cm^2 14. 20 cm

15. (i) (a) 70%   (b) 150%   (c) 60%   (ii) (a) 72 cm^2 (b) 18 cm^2 (iv) 141%   (v) 2

16. (ii) 1·5 or $\dfrac{3}{2}$ (iii) 4 cm   17. (ii) 2·5   (iii) $\dfrac{25}{4}$ 18. (iii) 2   (iv) 1·2